Reher-Morrison Championship Engine Assembly

Staff:

Subject Matter Experts.............. David Reher and the R-M Racing Engines Staff
Photography .... Don Cooper, Reher-Morrison Racing Engines
Writer/Editor.............................. Robert Colesworthy, IQ Learning Systems, Inc.

Fifth Edition: April, 2010

ISBN: 978-0-9723432-8-2

Important Notice to Reader:

Race car engine assembly, machining, adjustment, and operation are inherently hazardous. Although every effort has been made to ensure the accuracy of the information contained in this book, Reher-Morrison Racing Engines, Inc. and IQ Learning Systems, Inc., their agents and representatives do not assume, and expressly disclaim, any liability for loss, damages, expenses, failures, or injury that may result from the use of the information, parts, tools, equipment, materials, or procedures contained herein.

The reader is expressly warned to work only under supervision and adopt any and all safety precautions recommended by the parts, tools, materials, and equipment manufacturers as well as those of your sanctioning organization. The reader willingly assumes all risks in connection with race car engine assembly, machining, adjustment, and operation.

1120 Enterprise Place
Arlington, TX 76001
www.rehermorrison.com
(817) 467-7171

1833 Scherer Parkway
St. Charles, MO 63303
www.iqlearningsystems.com

Foreword

I wish that I had a book like this 40 years ago. Like most racers, I started out with a lot more enthusiasm than experience, more eagerness than equipment, and more optimism than money. I discovered drag racing when I was a student at the University of Texas, but most of my real education came at the School of Hard Knocks.

I learned how to build engines the hard way—by trial and error. Fortunately, I had friends and fellow racers who helped me through some of the rough spots. Not everyone who becomes involved in motorsports is so lucky. That's why we wrote this book—to provide practical, accurate information on how to build racing engines.

We wanted this book to be like a conversation with a champion engine builder—a teacher who explains the *why* as well as the *how*. We've included basic theory along with hands-on instructions to help you understand how a racing engine really works. We've also pointed out some of the common myths and misconceptions about high performance motors.

I use the term "we" because this book is a collective effort. It distills the knowledge of dozens of people at Reher-Morrison Racing Engines. Our staff includes skillful machinists, head porters, engine assemblers, and dyno operators. Many of them are racers who know first-hand what it takes to win. We worked together, literally sitting around a table for hours, to make sure that what we wrote is accurate and we racked our brains to make sure that we didn't overlook anything essential.

There are three people I must mention who are directly responsible for the success of Reher-Morrison Racing Engines and indirectly responsible for creating this book: Buddy Morrison, Lee Shepherd, and Bruce Allen.

Buddy Morrison and I started our engine building business in the back of an auto parts store in Mansfield, Texas in 1971. Buddy was truly an outstanding person, and I am proud that he was my friend and partner for 30 years. Buddy died of cancer in 1998, but his amazing generosity, intelligence, and humor are still with us.

In the early days, Buddy and I raced against Lee Shepherd at hole-in-the-wall tracks from Arkansas to Oklahoma. When we needed a driver, we knew where to look. Lee was a self-taught cylinder head porter who was as good with a grinder as he was with a 4-speed. Lee, Buddy, and I won Modified Eliminator at the '74 NHRA Winternationals with a Chevy-powered Maverick, and we were on our way.

In 1976, we took the giant step to Pro Stock with a Monza. We had a pretty rough initiation to professional racing. Lee crashed in Englishtown, and we couldn't get the trick cylinder head castings we needed to be competitive. It wasn't until we built a long-wheelbase Camaro that we started to win consistently. In ten NHRA national events in 1980, that red, white, and blue Z28 racked up six wins and three runners-up.

The following season, we developed a small-displacement big block that won six more times and powered Lee to his first of four straight NHRA championships. In the five years from 1980 to 1984, a Reher-Morrison car reached the finals in 44 out of 56 NHRA national events. In 1983 and 1984, Lee swept the NHRA and IHRA Pro Stock titles. He won every race on the NHRA tour at least once, and compiled a 173-47 win-loss record.

Bruce Allen joined our team after Lee's death in a testing accident in 1985. I got to know Bruce Allen when he was building turbocharged Indy car engines on weekdays and winning races with his stunning Corvette on weekends. Bruce continued the record of success at Reher-Morrison Racing Engines, capturing another IHRA championship and winning 16 NHRA races in 38 final round appearances. He finished third in the NHRA standings three consecutive seasons, was runner-up to Bob Glidden in the 1989 NHRA championship, and went to the final round of the Pro Stock Challenge six times. Bruce is an accomplished machinist, an outstanding race car driver, a natural athlete, and a true friend.

The racing world has changed dramatically since Buddy and I bolted together our first small block at Mansfield Auto Supply. We scoured the junkyards for blocks, cranks, and cylinder heads. Now we can buy factory and aftermarket parts that are light-years ahead of anything we imagined back then. Engine dynamometers, flow benches, and computers have triggered an information explosion in motorsports.

What hasn't changed is the importance of doing the job right—selecting the best parts, preparing them properly, and assembling them correctly. That's what this book is about. I sincerely hope that these words help you to achieve your goals in racing.

David Reher

Championship Engine Assembly

Unit III - Short Block Component Selection & Preparation

Unit IV - Upper End Component Selection

Unit V - Upper End Measurements & Preparation

Unit VI - Short Block Pre-Assembly Measurements

Unit VII - Short Block Assembly Procedures

Unit VIII - Final Engine Assembly

Reher-Morrison RACING • ENGINES

Racing Engine School

Join us at Reher-Morrison racing engines in Arlington, Texas to find out first-hand what goes into building and testing high horsepower racing engines! Accelerate your learning curve, and get answers to all those questions you have been dying to ask! Scheduled appearances and Q&A sessions by David Reher and Bruce Allen.

- ***Cylinder Head Theory and Practice -*** Darin Morgan is heavily involved in the cylinder head R&D at Reher-Morrison. He'll share his vast knowledge and show you the important details of head porting. You'll watch as Darin tests the heads on the flowbench and shows you what makes horsepower. Bring one of your own heads for Darin to critique!*
  *(Call first for details)
- ***Precision Measurement -*** Learn what to measure, how to measure it and what the results mean in the engine building process. Includes the use of micrometers, calipers, bore gages and dial indicators. You'll also "cc" a combustion chamber and determine the dome volumes on pistons, a critical step in figuring your static compression ratio.
- ***Component Selection -*** Find out what block, cam, lifters, intake and cylinder heads are best for your application. Avoid wasting money on parts you don't need.
- ***Question & Answer Sessions -*** David Reher & Bruce Allen answer your questions based on their years of experience. Find out from the people who've won eight World Championships what it takes to do it right.
- ***Engine Assembly -*** Learn about all of the considerations for final engine assembly, including what to check and how to check it. Learn by doing as you assemble a short block.
- ***Dyno Session -*** Hearing an engine roar to life on the dyno gets everyone's attention. Witness a dyno session of one of our crate engines and learn how it's done as well as what all the numbers on the dyno sheet mean.

This 2-day, 16 hour seminar takes place on weekends. Contact us for the next class date and current pricing. Call (817) 467-7171 or email us at info@rehermorrison.com

www.rehermorrison.com

Championship Engine Assembly

Automobile racing is the fastest growing sport in America, and this trend shows no signs of reversing. Each weekend, thousands of people from "weekend warriors" to seasoned professionals build and test race cars, boats, and engines—all in pursuit of that race day victory. As the number of racing participants increases, so do the money and time required to gain and maintain a competitive advantage.

Racers spend thousands of dollars constructing, tuning, testing, and maintaining their engines. Speed costs money, so the first question you must answer is "how fast can you afford to go?" It's important to realize that all racers wind up spending more than they initially planned.

Racing is an expensive endeavor, but if money could really buy performance, races would be unnecessary. Officials could simply examine each participant's bank balance and declare the winner. However, the event winner is not usually the one who spent the most money, but rather the one who used his funds most wisely. Why do so many racers waste money in an attempt to build the ultimate performance engine? The answer is that they lack the most important tool for building a racing engine—knowledge. A better saying might be "knowledge is power; how much power would you like?"

For more than two decades, we have been building championship racing engines for a variety of racing applications. This book includes our best information, presented in easy step-by-step lessons. You'll learn how to select the right parts, and then build the engine for your needs without wasting your money or time.

Reher-Morrison
speedco
SG-440
TWINLAB
Lee College
www.lee.edu

Championship Engine Assembly

Unit I - Basic Engine Operation

Around 1860, German engineer Nicholas Otto built and tested the first four-stroke cycle internal combustion engine. It is amazing to consider that, other than some refinements to individual components, his engine has remained virtually unchanged in design and operation.

Over the years, many determined attempts have been made to replace Dr. Otto's basic design with another, such as the turbine engine, Wankel® (rotary) engine, and the electric motor. Despite these challenges, the basic efficiency, reliability, and high power to weight ratio of the four-stroke cycle engine make it the odds-on favorite to remain the primary power source in automobiles and race cars for many years to come.

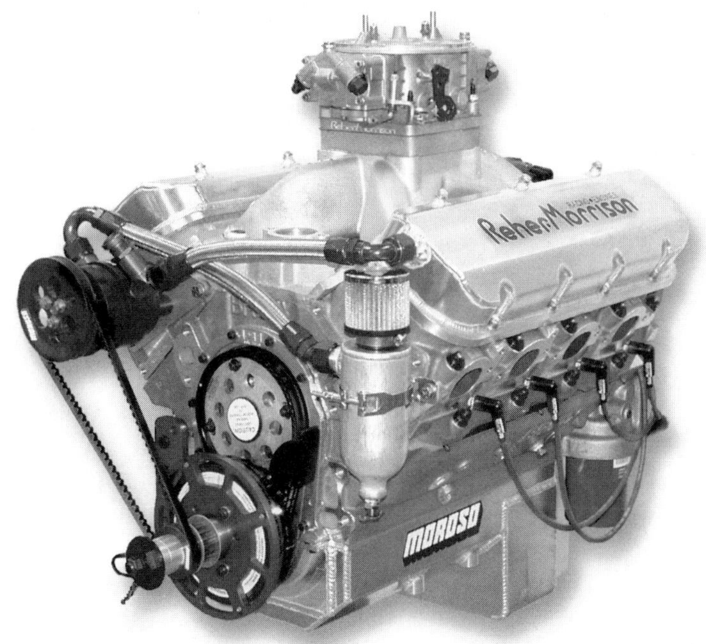

Building a great racing engine begins with a thorough understanding of the underlying principles of operation.

Basic Engine Components

Lower Engine Assembly:

These are some of the basic components that make up the lower engine assembly in a V-type engine:

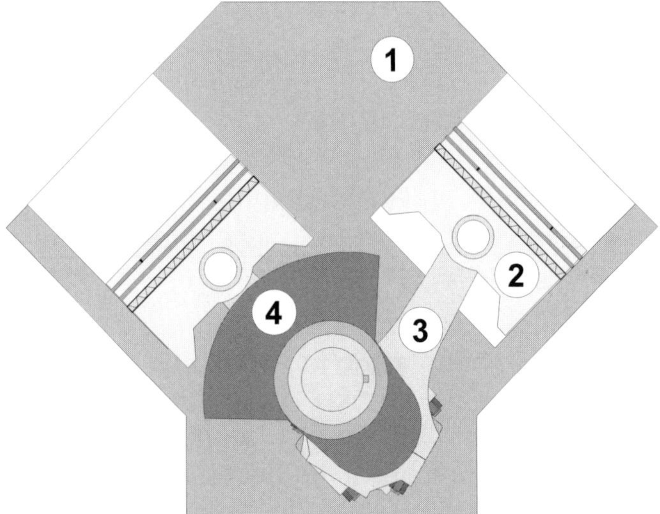

1. *Block*
2. *Piston*
3. *Rod*
4. *Crankshaft*

The block has cylinder bores for the pistons. The pistons are connected to the crankshaft by connecting rods. The crankshaft and rods convert the *reciprocating motion* (moving up and down) of the pistons to *rotary motion* (spinning). In all passenger car and most racing engines, the crankshaft rotates in a clockwise direction when viewed from the front.

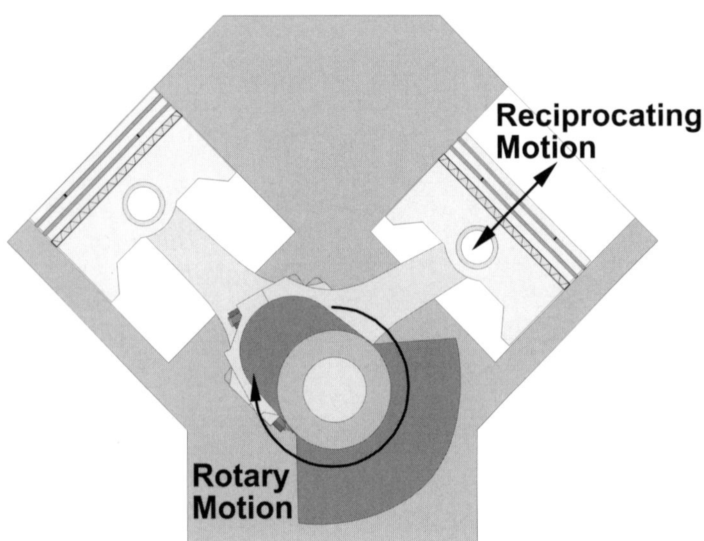

Nearly all racing engines have a clockwise crankshaft rotation.

The lower engine assembly also includes the camshaft, crank sprocket, cam sprocket, and timing chain. These are parts of the *valve train*.

NOTE: If you're installing a belt-drive system, the sprockets are cogged pulleys.

The camshaft has lobes that operate the valves. There is one lobe for each valve in the engine.

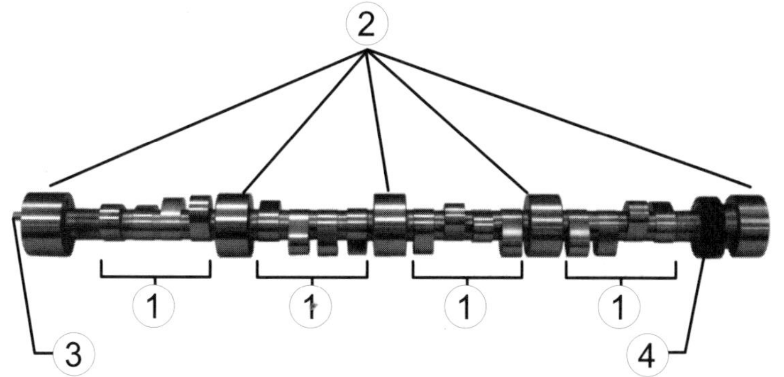

1. *Lobes*
2. *Bearing Journals*
3. *Alignment Pin*
4. *Distributor Drive Gear*

The camshaft fits into a bore in the engine block and is driven by a belt, chain, or gears.

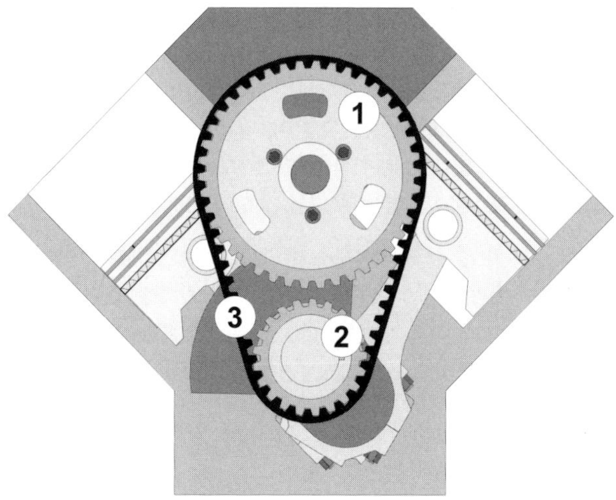

1. *Cam Pulley (or Sprocket)*
2. *Crank Pulley (or Sprocket)*
3. *Timing Belt (or Chain)*

The lower engine assembly is sometimes called the *short block*. Depending on the engine builder, the short block may have some additional parts.

Upper Engine Assembly:

These are some of the basic components that make up the upper engine assembly in a typical 4-stroke racing engine:

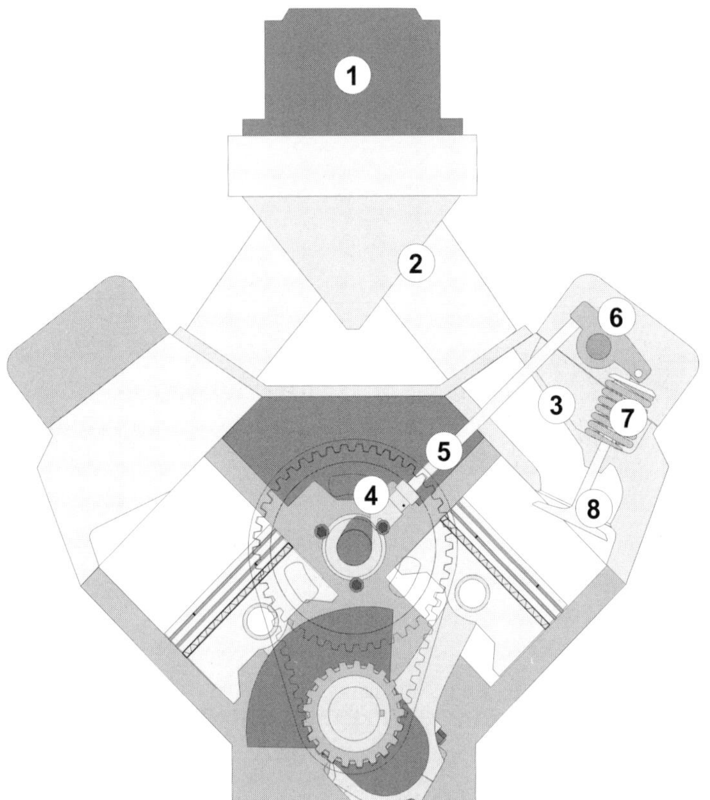

1. *Carburetor*
2. *Intake Manifold*
3. *Cylinder Head*
4. *Lifter*
5. *Pushrod*
6. *Rocker Arm*
7. *Valve Spring*
8. *Valve*

When the cylinder heads and valve train have been added to the lower assembly, the engine is sometimes called a "long block". A long block engine will require a number of other components to make it ready to run including the carburetor, intake manifold, exhaust headers, water pump, starter motor, and ignition system.

When projecting the total cost of building your engine, don't forget all the other "little" items that you will need such as a can or two of engine paint, motor mounts, belts, hoses, clamps, oil, oil filter, air filter, and engine coolant. Individually, these may not be very costly, but they often add up to a hundred dollars or more by the time your engine is installed in the vehicle and ready to start.

The 4-Stroke Cycle

The process of building more horsepower begins with a complete understanding of the 4-stroke cycle. In most race car categories, you are restricted from building more power by simply building a bigger engine or using a more powerful fuel. While you may find some small gains by reducing frictional losses, the best way to make large increases in engine power is to improve the efficiency of each stroke in the 4-stroke cycle.

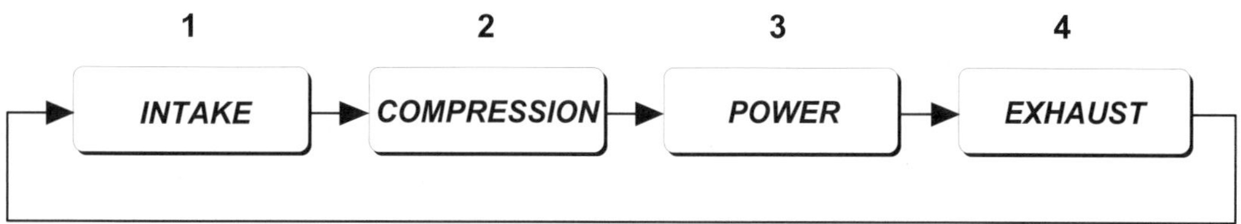

The 4-stroke cycle is intake, compression, power, exhaust.

This cycle repeats endlessly as the engine runs. Remember that an intake stroke always follows the exhaust stroke as the cycle begins again.

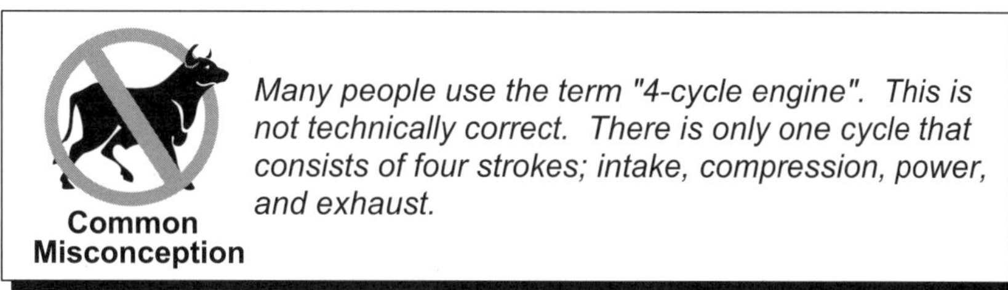

Many people use the term "4-cycle engine". This is not technically correct. There is only one cycle that consists of four strokes; intake, compression, power, and exhaust.

Before you build this sportsman racing engine or a 1400+horsepower Pro Stock engine, it will help you to have a thorough understanding of what's really going on in the 4-stroke engine cycle.

Intake Stroke:

The first step is to get the air/fuel mixture into the cylinder. The air/fuel mixture is supplied by the carburetor or fuel injectors. The intake manifold distributes this mixture to ports in the cylinder head. This is how the intake stroke works:

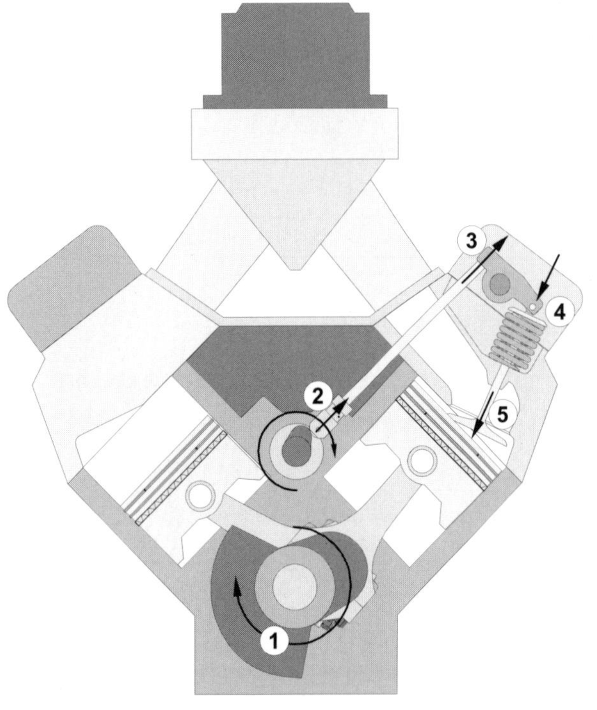

1. *The crankshaft is rotating.*
2. *The intake cam lobe begins to push the lifter up just before the piston reaches the top and starts to move down.*
3. *The pushrod pushes on the rocker arm.*
4. *The rocker arm pushes down on the valve stem.*
5. *The valve opens against spring pressure.*

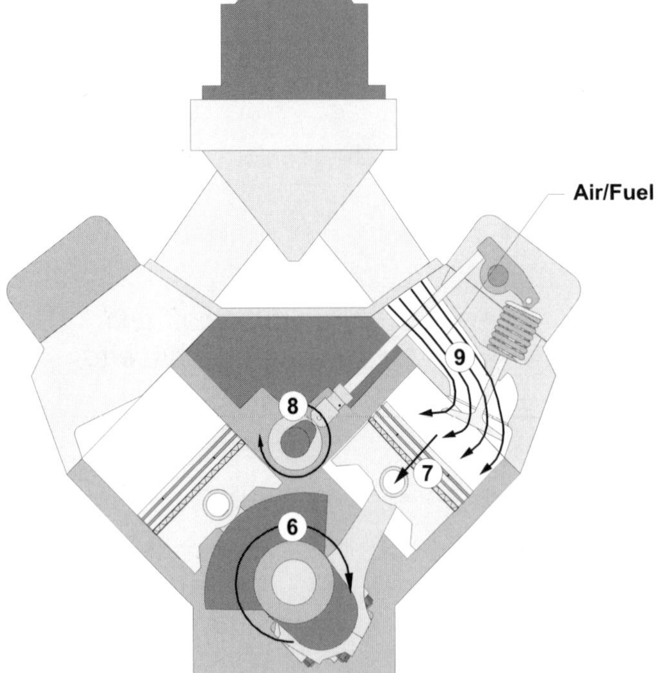

6. *The crankshaft continues to rotate.*
7. *The piston moves down, lowering the pressure in the cylinder.*
8. *The camshaft continues to push the valve open.*
9. *The air/fuel mixture flows into the low pressure in the cylinder.*

NOTE: Although it is common practice to say that "vacuum in the cylinder draws in the air/fuel mixture", this is not technically correct. Vacuum is not something that exists, but rather is the *absence* of pressure. The higher pressure air outside the engine pushes through the carburetor, manifold, and port to fill the area of low pressure created in the cylinder as the piston moves down. With that understanding of what really happens, we will adhere to the common description of vacuum "drawing in" air & fuel throughout this book.

Compression Stroke:

The air fuel mixture is compressed on this stroke so that it will burn faster. This is how the compression stroke works:

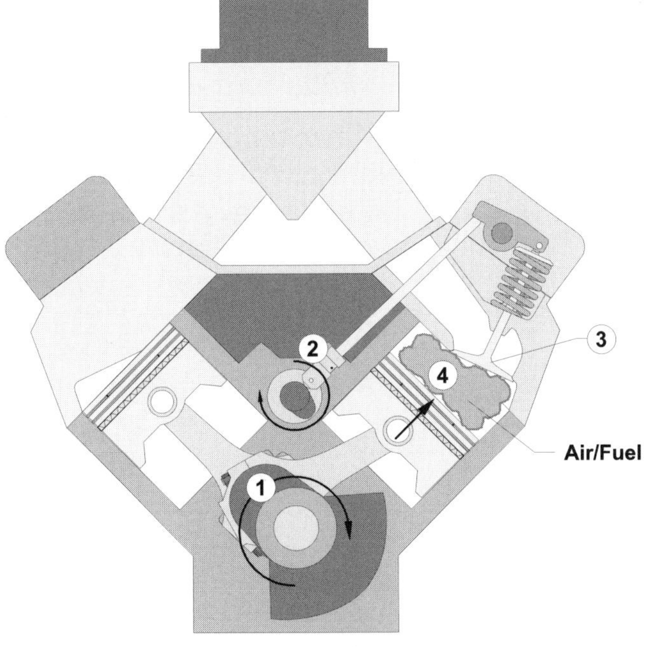

1. *The crankshaft continues to rotate.*
2. *The cam lobe turns until the lifter is back down.*
3. *The intake valve closes.*
4. *The air fuel mixture is trapped in the cylinder.*

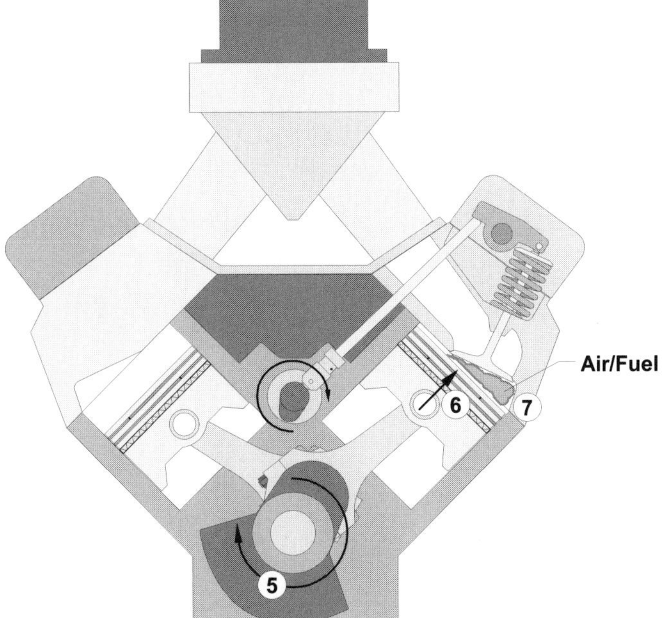

5. *The crankshaft and camshaft continue to rotate.*
6. *The piston moves toward the top of the cylinder.*
7. *The air/fuel mixture is compressed into the combustion chamber.*

Power Stroke:

Up to this point, the piston has moved down and up, but no power has yet been created. In fact, of the four strokes, the power stroke is the only one that contributes to the rotation of the crankshaft. Here's what happens:

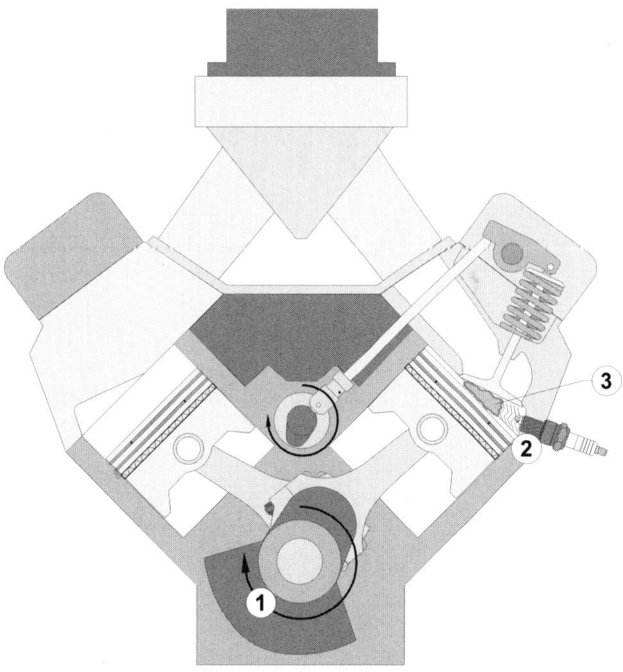

1. *The crankshaft and camshaft continue to rotate.*
2. *An electric arc at the tip of the spark plug ignites the air/fuel mixture.*
3. *A flame front travels across the combustion chamber. The air/fuel mixture is consumed rapidly, releasing a great deal of heat and pressure.*

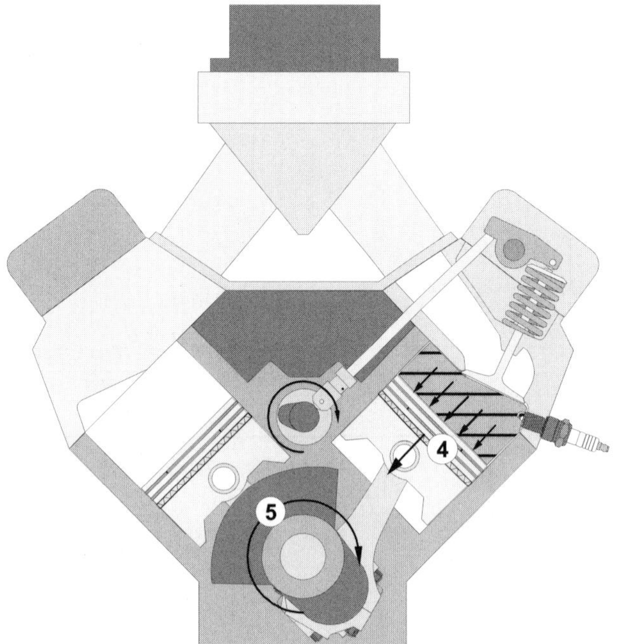

4. *The hot, high pressure gases push the piston down.*
5. *A powerful rotational force is applied to the crankshaft through the connecting rod.*

Common Misconception

Some books say that an "explosion" pushes the piston down on the power stroke. If the air/fuel mixture were to burn explosively, the resulting "detonation" would cause serious damage to the piston, spark plug, or engine bearings. The average burn time is about .0015 seconds - very fast indeed, but not explosive.

Exhaust Stroke:

Although the piston has not yet moved to the bottom, the pressure in the cylinder has dropped significantly, and the rod is no longer at a favorable angle to push on the crankshaft. It's time to open the exhaust valve and clear the cylinder of the waste gases. This is how the exhaust stroke works:

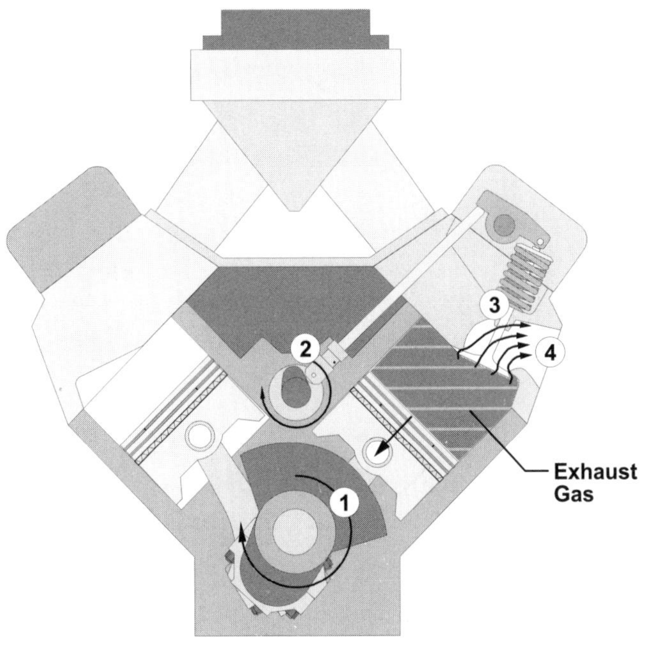

1. *The crankshaft continues to turn.*
2. *The cam lobe begins to push up on the exhaust lifter.*
3. *The exhaust valve begins to open against cylinder and spring pressure.*
4. *A burst of high velocity exhaust enters the exhaust port.*

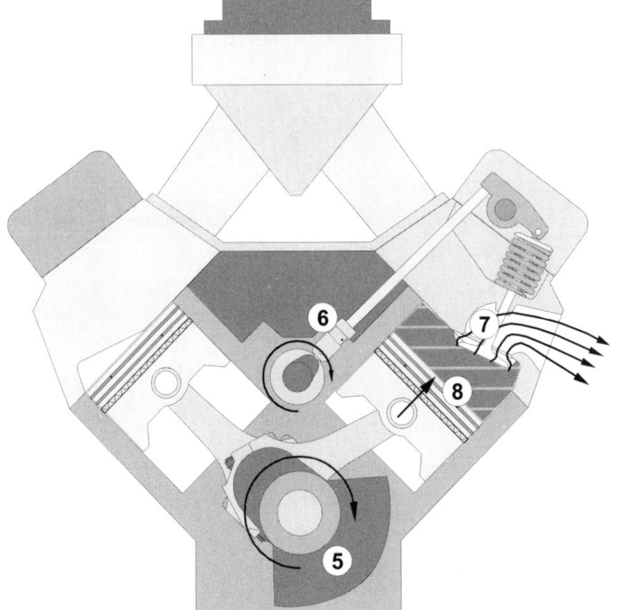

5. *The crankshaft turns.*
6. *The cam pushes the lifter higher.*
7. *The exhaust valve is now wide open.*
8. *The piston helps push the exhaust gases out of the cylinder.*

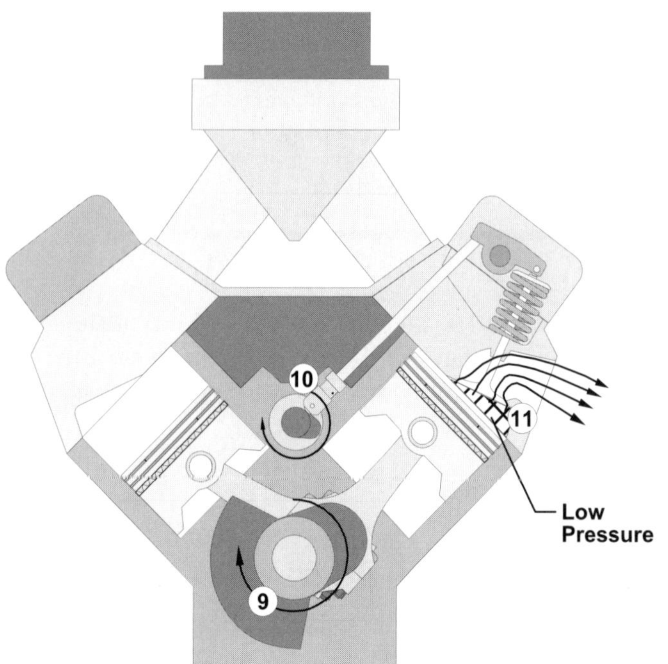

9. *The crankshaft turns, and the piston begins to move down.*
10. *The cam rotates, and the exhaust valve is nearly closed.*
11. *High exhaust velocity scavenges (draws out) exhaust gases until the exhaust valve closes. This leaves relatively low pressure in the cylinder.*

Overlap:

Before the exhaust valve closes, the intake valve has already started to open. For about 45° of crankshaft rotation, both valves are actually open at the same time. This is called valve *overlap*.

Why would the engine need both valves open at the same time? The high velocity exhaust gases scavenge low pressure in the combustion chamber at the end of the exhaust stroke. Valve overlap takes advantage of this pressure differential to pull in additional intake gases.

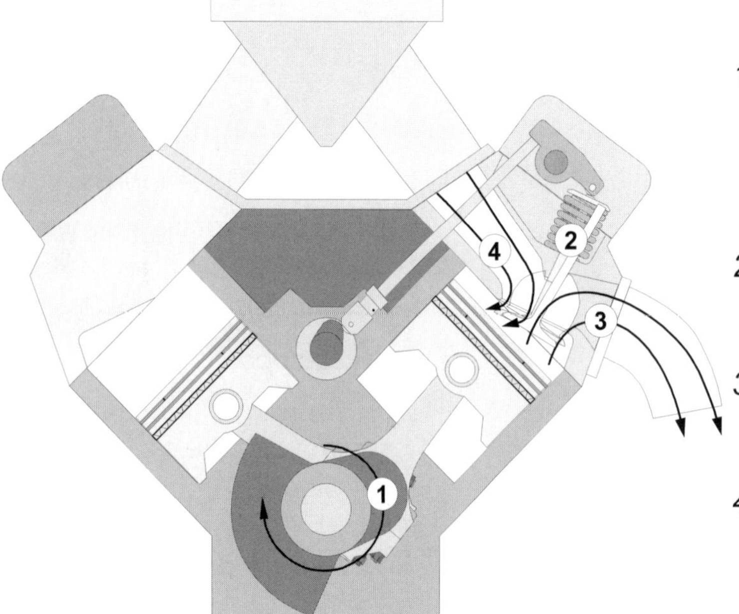

1. *The crankshaft continues to rotate through the end of the exhaust and beginning of the intake strokes.*
2. *The intake and exhaust valves are partially open at the same time.*
3. *High velocity exhaust gases scavenge low pressure in the cylinder.*
4. *The air/fuel mixture begins to move into the vacuum in the cylinder.*

Multiple Cylinder Engines:

Of the two full revolutions necessary to complete the 4-stroke cycle, the crankshaft is only accelerated on power strokes. The crankshaft slows until another power stroke comes along and is accelerated once again. This constant acceleration/deceleration produces *torsional* (twisting) vibrations in the crankshaft that can lead to breakage.

One of the best ways to smooth crankshaft rotation (and build a bigger engine at the same time) is to add more cylinders. This shortens the time interval between power strokes and reduces vibration problems. There are a number of different multiple cylinder configurations for racing engines.

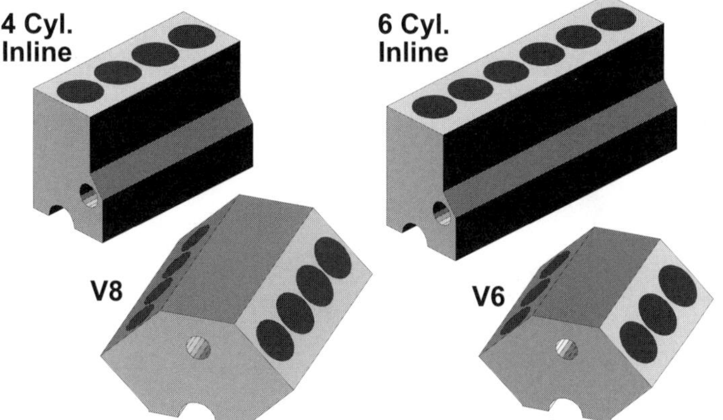

All of these multiple cylinder configurations can be found in racing.

The V-design makes the engine block profile lower when compared to an upright in-line type engine. This allows it to fit under the sleek, low hood lines of modern cars. Another important advantage of a V-design is that the crankshaft is much shorter. A short crankshaft from a V-engine will not twist nearly as much as one from an in-line engine with the same number of cylinders.

One cylinder bank must be offset ahead of the other so that the rods can be paired together on the same crank journal. Most engines are laid out so that the forward offset bank is the one containing #1 cylinder. This is the typical cylinder layout for Chevrolet/GM V8 racing engines:

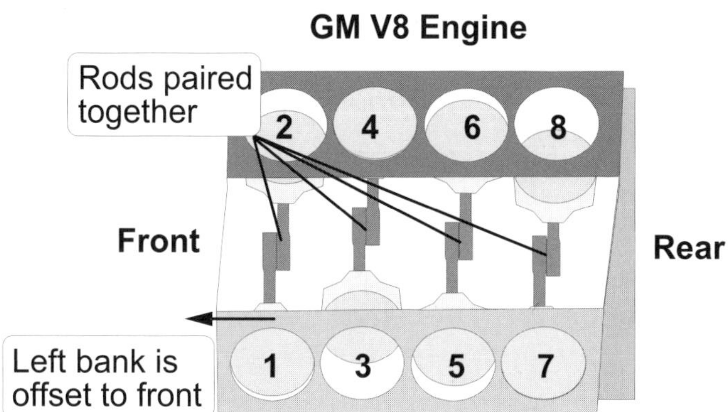

The left (driver's side) cylinder bank is offset on most GM V-type engines to allow the rods to be paired together on the crank journals.

Crank Journal Layout

Crankshaft journals are precision machined surfaces for the main and rod bearings. The crankshaft spins on main journals that are all on the same centerline. Rod journals are offset from the main journals on the *throws* (cranks) of the crankshaft. The photo below shows the location of the main and rod journals on a V8 crankshaft.

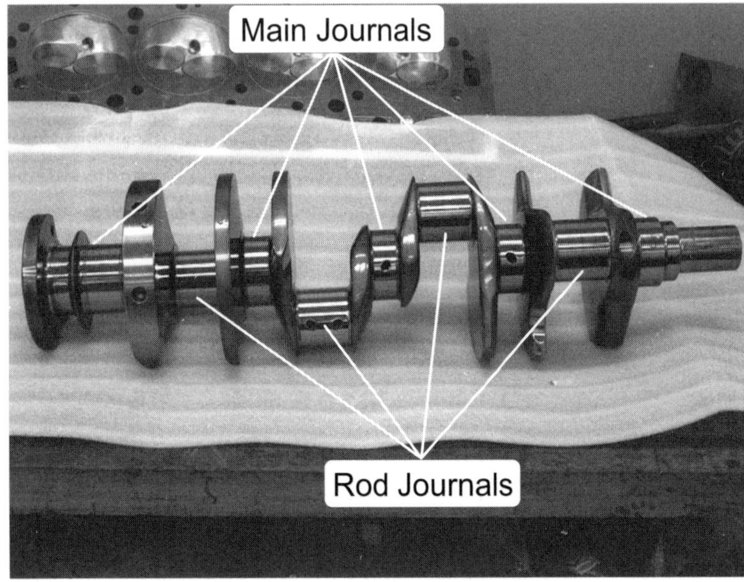

Most V8 crankshafts have five main journals and four rod journals.

The smoothest turning action results when the degrees of crankshaft rotation between cylinder firings are equal. Two full crank revolutions, or 720° rotation, are required to complete the 4-stroke cycle. The ideal angle of crankshaft rotation between cylinder firings can be easily calculated by dividing 720° by the number of cylinders:

$$\textbf{angle of rotation between cylinder firings} = \frac{\textbf{720}^\circ}{\textbf{\# of cylinders}}$$

This is the formula to determine the ideal angle between cylinder firings.

Let's calculate the ideal angle of rotation between cylinder firings for a V8 engine. Apply the formula and divide 720° by 8.

$$\textbf{angle of rotation between cylinder firings} = \frac{\textbf{720}^\circ}{\textbf{\# of cylinders}} = \frac{\textbf{720}^\circ}{\textbf{8}} = \textbf{90}^\circ$$

A V8 engine should have 90° between each cylinder firing.

To achieve 90° of crankshaft rotation between cylinder firings, the crankshaft throws are placed at 90° intervals, and the cylinder banks in the block are bored at 90°.

Firing Order

The *firing order* is the sequence of cylinder power strokes in the engine. Although some stock 2.8 Liter GM V6 engines fire in numerical order (1-2-3-4-5-6), most engines do not. This is the firing order pattern for a typical GM V8 racing engine:

GM Corporate V8 Engine

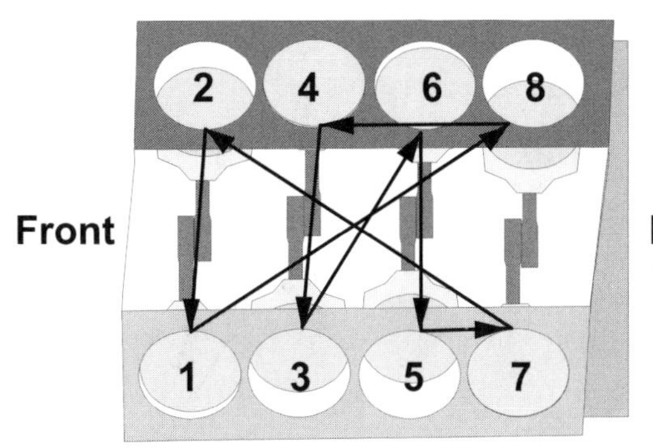

Front **Rear**

This is the standard cylinder numbering system and firing order for GM V8 racing engines. The arrows indicate the pattern of cylinder firings created by this sequence.

1-8-4-3-6-5-7-2

Firing Order

The figure below represents the cylinder firings in an eight cylinder engine graphically. Notice that four cylinders (#'s 1, 8, 4, & 3) fire on the first crankshaft revolution, and the remaining four (#'s 6, 5, 7, & 2) fire on the second revolution. Each cylinder is separated by an interval of 90° of crankshaft rotation.

Firing Order = 1-8-4-3-6-5-7-2

1st Crankshaft Revolution (#'s 1, 8, 4, & 3)

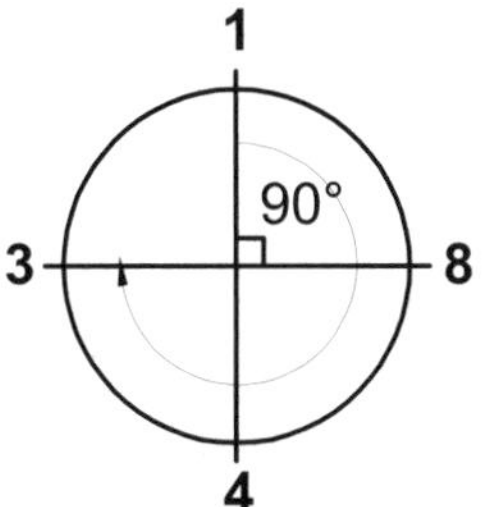

2nd Crankshaft Revolution (#'s 6, 5, 7, & 2)

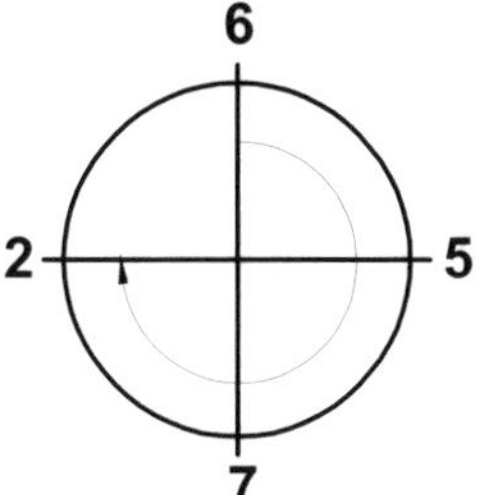

The cylinders fire 90° apart in an 8 cylinder engine.

Ninety degrees (¼ turn) after the last cylinder has fired, two full crankshaft revolutions have been completed (720°) and the 4-stroke cycle starts again with the firing of #1 cylinder.

Companion Cylinders:

You may wonder why the standard GM V8 firing order is not a simple numerical sequence like 1-2-3-4-5-6-7-8. This is because a cylinder can only fire when the piston nears the top on a compression stroke.

The rods in a V8 engine are paired together on the crankshaft throws, so a different pair of pistons comes to the top every 90° of crankshaft rotation. These pairs are called *companion cylinders.*

Companion Cylinders, GM V8 Racing Engine

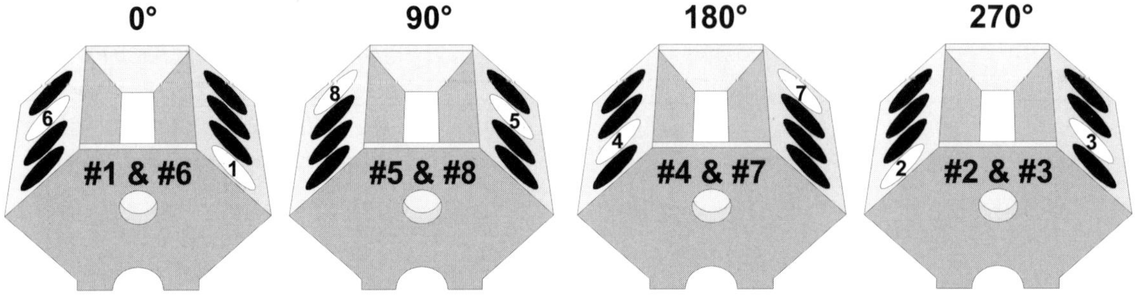

0°	90°	180°	270°
#1 & #6	#5 & #8	#4 & #7	#2 & #3

These are the companion cylinders in a typical GM V8 racing engine.

The lobes on the camshaft are arranged so that they are on opposite strokes. While one cylinder is on a power stroke, its companion cylinder is in valve overlap.

After firing #1 cylinder, the next cylinder firing choice is either cylinder #5 or cylinder #8. If you choose to fire #5 cylinder (power stroke), its companion cylinder #8 must be starting an intake stroke.

The pattern of companion cylinders limits the firing orders that can work. In an effort to improve breathing characteristics or distribute cylinder heat better, we have tested nearly every engine firing order. Here is a list of all possible firing orders when using the crankshaft/block layout for a GM V8 racing engine:

1-8-4-3-6-5-7-2 (standard)
1-8-4-2-6-5-7-3
1-8-7-2-6-5-4-3
1-8-7-3-6-5-4-2 (4-7 switch)
1-5-4-3-6-8-7-2
1-5-7-3-6-8-4-2
1-5-7-2-6-8-4-3
1-5-4-2-6-8-7-3

The order that we call the *"4-7 switch"* (1-8-7-3-6-5-4-2) has produced 5-8 more horsepower in our Pro Stock engines and was a well-kept secret by racing teams for years. Although any gain is good, it is only about .5% of the total engine power output and requires a more expensive custom-ground camshaft with repositioned lobes for the two switched cylinders.

If your resources are limited, you must decide if a half percent is really worth the extra money. However, at Reher-Morrison Racing Engines, we buy a lot of camshafts and are able to make the 4-7 switch part of our *Super Series* engines at very little additional cost.

Engine Compression

There are two types of engine compression; *static and dynamic*. Static means "standing still". Static compression can be measured during engine assembly. Dynamic means "moving". Dynamic compression is the maximum pressure in the cylinder during the compression stroke.

Dynamic Compression:

The degree to which the air/fuel mixture is compressed has a lot to do with engine performance. Racing engines are high compression engines. High dynamic compression causes the air/fuel mixture to burn faster and creates more pressure on the pistons. While raising engine compression generally helps, serious detonation problems result if you compress the air/fuel mixture too much.

The goal for racing engine builders is to create as much dynamic compression as possible without causing detonation. Very efficient cooling systems and high octane fuels will help discourage detonation, but only to a point. There are practical limits as to how fast you can remove heat or squeeze the air and racing gasoline mixture before detonation occurs. Dynamic engine compression is influenced by several factors including:

- Engine Breathing Efficiency
- Camshaft Profile
- Ring Seal
- Weather Conditions

Engine Breathing Efficiency - If the engine "breathes" better, more air and fuel enters the cylinders and more dynamic compression is created. This is why racing engine builders spend so much time modifying and testing cylinder heads, intake manifolds, carburetors, and air inlet systems.

Camshaft Profile - *Camshaft profile* is a measurement of how long and far the valves open. This has a lot to do with how much air/fuel mixture comes in and how much exhaust gets out.

Ring Seal - All rings leak at least some compression. This has a direct effect on dynamic compression. The total amount of ring leakage depends on several factors including the type and quality of rings, cylinder wall finish, clearances, and engine rpm's. Wear is also a factor. As the rings "seat" during the break-in period, ring seal usually improves. With engine wear, the rings leak more and more, reducing dynamic compression.

Weather Conditions - Most racers have *naturally aspirated* engines. These engines must breathe in whatever air is available on race day. *Air density* fluctuates with altitude and temperature and has a significant effect on horsepower output. When we race in Denver at 6000 ft. altitude, the naturally aspirated Pro Stock cars lose about a half second in the quarter mile. Humidity also plays an important role. The more water that is contained in air, the less room there is for oxygen to burn the fuel.

The amount of pressure that a given fuel can take without detonating could be calculated rather easily. However, this information would have little value because there is no easy way to measure cylinder pressures while the engine is running. In addition, it would not be possible to duplicate the varying conditions under which the racing engine may operate. The best that we can do is measure the static compression ratio and adjust it to what experience has shown us to be the optimal ratio for a particular application.

Static Compression Ratio:

To achieve the right dynamic engine compression, most naturally-aspirated racing engines have a *static compression ratio* between 13:1 and 16.5:1. Static compression ratio is found by dividing the volume when the piston is all the way down by the volume left when the piston is at the top.

Compression Ratio = 15:1

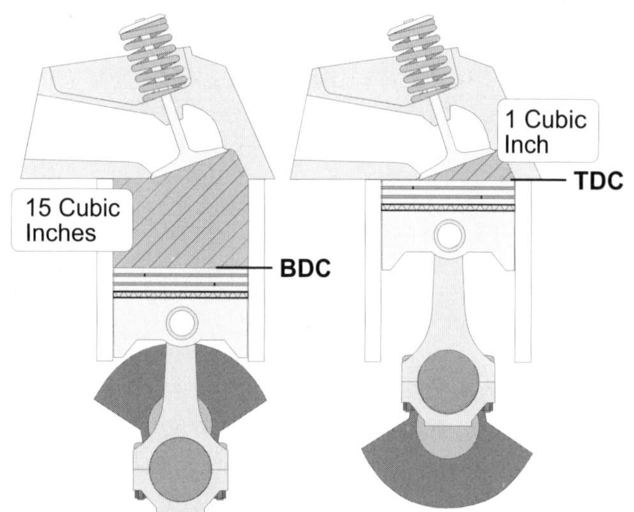

To determine the static compression ratio, divide the volume when the piston is at BDC by the volume left when it is at TDC. This engine has a static compression ratio of 15:1.

Piston Compression Domes:

Older cylinder head designs have rather large combustion chambers. In order to achieve a high static compression ratio for racing, the piston must have a *compression dome*. A compression dome is a raised area that is contoured to fit the shape of the combustion chamber on the cylinder head. The dome squeezes the air/fuel mixture into a smaller space.

Compression Dome

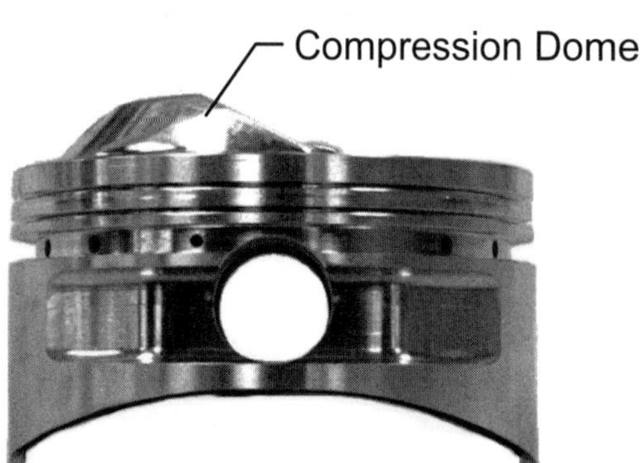

A big compression dome is required to increase the static compression ratio when using heads that have large combustion chamber volumes.

Camshaft Profile

These are three important camshaft profile measurements:

Valve Lift
Duration
Lobe Separation

Valve Lift:

Valve lift is a measurement of how far the valves are opened by the camshaft and rocker arms. *Lobe lift* is the distance from the base circle (lifter is all the way down) to the highest point on the cam lobe called the *nose* or *toe* (lifter is all the way up).

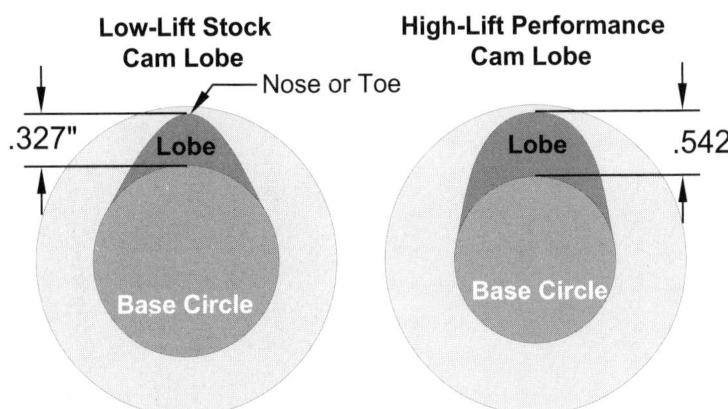

Lobe lift is the difference between the height of the base circle of the cam and the nose. High performance cams have greater lobe lift than do stock cams.

Rocker arms are a simple lever system. The closer the pushrod cup is to the pivot point, the greater is the rocker arm ratio. *Gross valve lift* is the cam lobe height multiplied by the rocker arm ratio. The *net valve lift* (actual valve lift) is less than the gross lift by about .040" because of valve *lash* (looseness) and component flex.

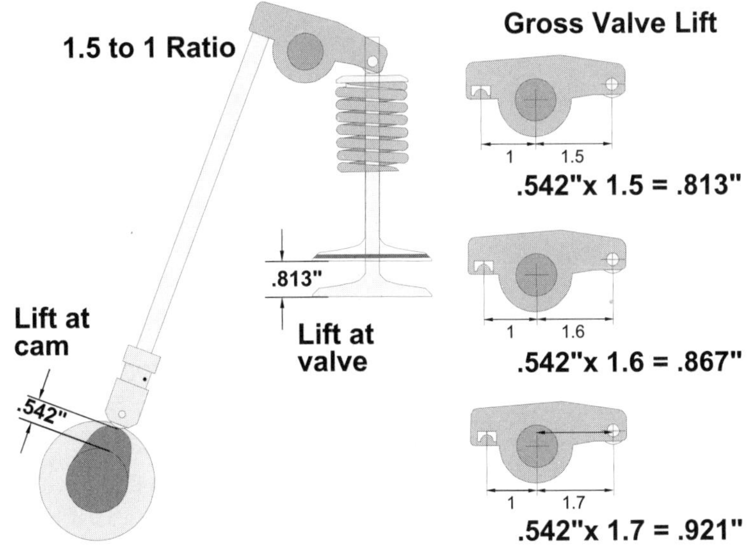

Gross valve lift at the cam is multiplied by the rocker arm ratio. With the same cam lift of .542", lift at the valve seat can be as high as .921" with 1.7 to 1 rocker arms.

The net valve lift is usually about .040" less than the gross lift. About half of the lost lift is due to valve lash settings, the other half to component flex.

Duration:

Duration is how long, measured in degrees of crankshaft rotation, that the valves remain open. When an engine runs at high rpm's, high intake velocities are created. The incoming stream of air/fuel mixture has considerable inertia and will continue to pack into the cylinder if the valves remain open longer (more duration).

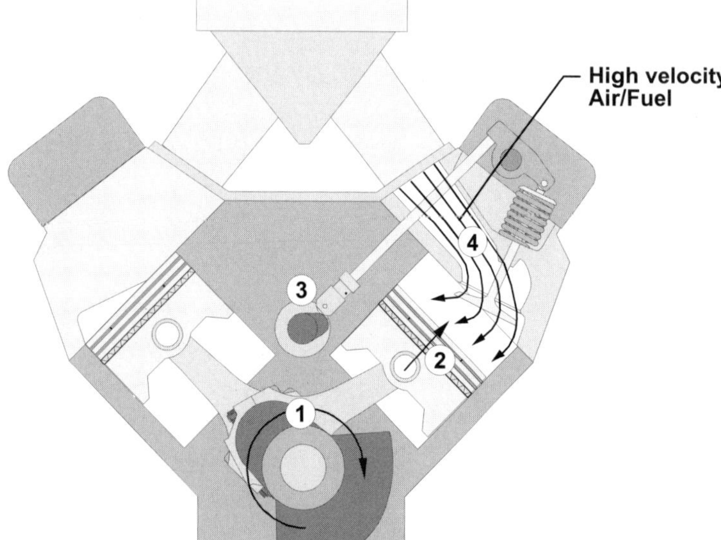

1. *The crankshaft is rotating at high rpm's.*
2. *The piston begins to move up in the cylinder.*
3. *The high-duration cam still has the intake valve partly open.*
4. *The high velocity air/fuel mixture has enough inertia to overcome the moving piston and continues to pack into the cylinder.*

The specifications for duration are always expressed in degrees of crankshaft rotation. Because the crankshaft turns at twice camshaft speed, the listed duration is double that of the camshaft lobe angle.

Short-Duration Stock Cam Lobe

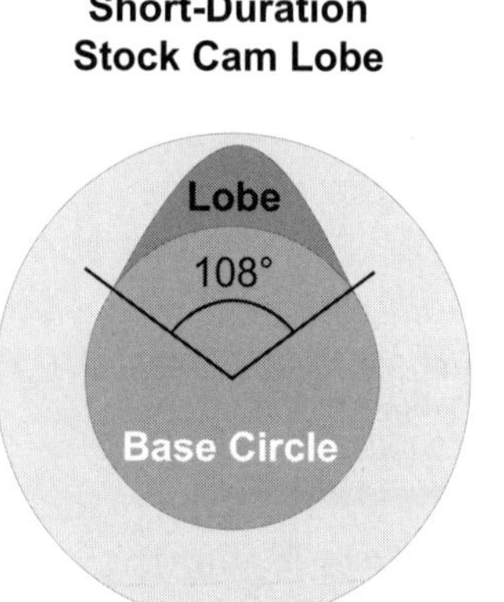

Listed Duration 108° x 2 = 216°

Long-Duration Performance Cam Lobe

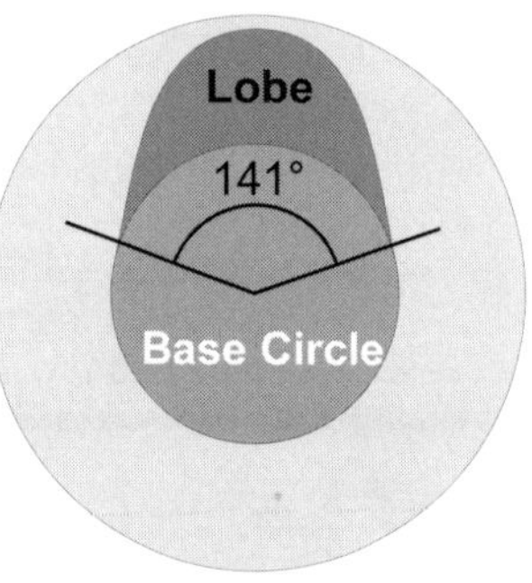

Listed Duration 141° x 2 = 282°

High performance camshafts have longer duration when compared to stock profiles. The duration is listed in crankshaft degrees—double that of camshaft degrees.

> ***NOTE:*** Because it is very hard to determine the precise location at which a lifter begins to rise off the base circle, high performance cam companies list the duration for their camshafts at standard *checking heights*. Checking height is the amount of lifter rise off the base circle, measured in thousandths of an inch. When you are looking at the duration specs of different camshafts, be sure that you are comparing them at the same checking height (usually .050" or .020").

In a high horsepower racing engine, the camshaft keeps the intake valve open until the piston is nearly half way up in the cylinder on the compression stroke. Velocity is key to keeping the incoming stream of gases moving into the cylinder.

At low rpm's and cranking, there is insufficient velocity to maintain the inflow of the air/fuel mixture into the cylinder. Some of the intake gases are pushed back into the intake manifold.

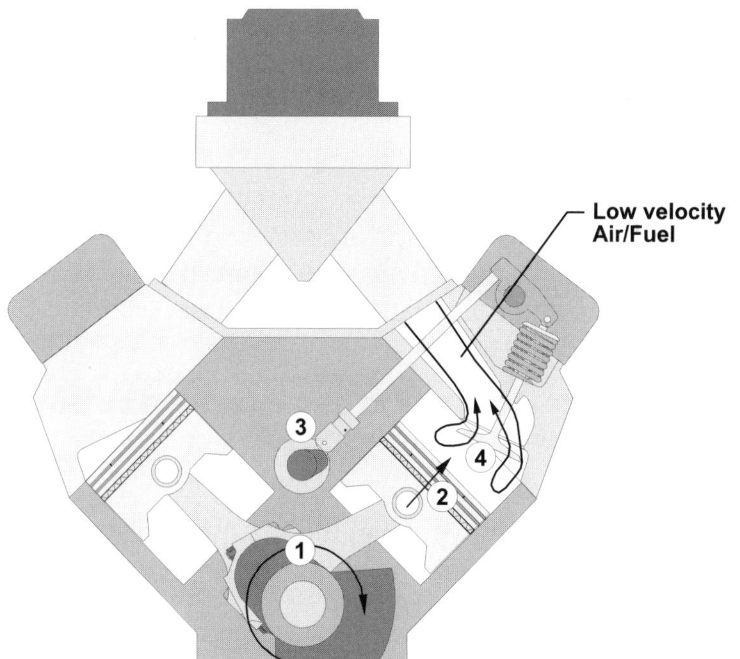

1. *The crankshaft is rotating at low rpm's.*
2. *The piston begins to move up in the cylinder.*
3. *The high-duration cam still has the intake valve partly open.*
4. *The low velocity air/fuel mixture does not have enough inertia to overcome the moving piston. It reverses direction and returns to the intake port.*

Common Misconception

Some racers become concerned with measurements of cranking compression and wrongly believe it directly relates to engine dyamic compression and power. In fact, racing camshaft profiles tend to cause lower cranking compression readings because the velocites at cranking rpm's are too low to keep incoming intake gasses from reverting back into the intake manifold.

Long duration camshafts cause very low intake manifold vacuum at low rpm's and the characteristic "loping" sound of a high performance engine.

Lobe Separation:

Lobe separation is the angle between the centerlines of the intake and exhaust cam lobes on a given cylinder.

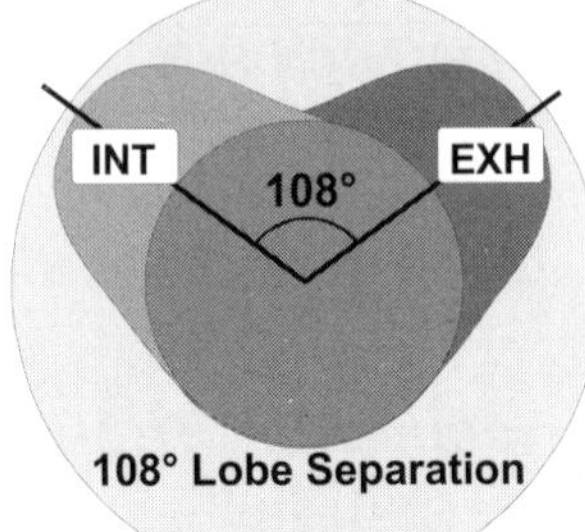

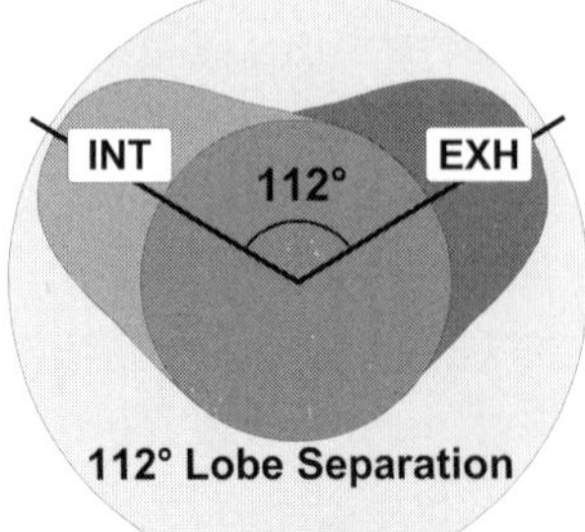

This is a comparison between a small block cam with 108° lobe separation and one with 112° lobe separation.

Lobe separation affects the amount of valve overlap. The amount of lobe separation that works best in a particular racing engine is related to the operating rpm range and breathing characteristics of the cylinder heads. Low rpm engines usually require a tighter (smaller) separation angle. High rpm engines usually work best with a greater separation angle.

NOTE: Long cam overlap intervals allow some raw fuel to escape into the exhaust stream as a *hydrocarbon* (raw fuel) emission. Check the state and federal laws before you install a racing cam in a street driven vehicle.

Camshaft *phasing* affects how the engine will run. Phasing means the position of the camshaft relative to the location of the crankshaft and pistons. The camshaft can be rotated slightly to achieve the desired phasing. If both the intake and exhaust centerlines are the same distance from TDC (Top Dead Center), the cam is installed "straight up".

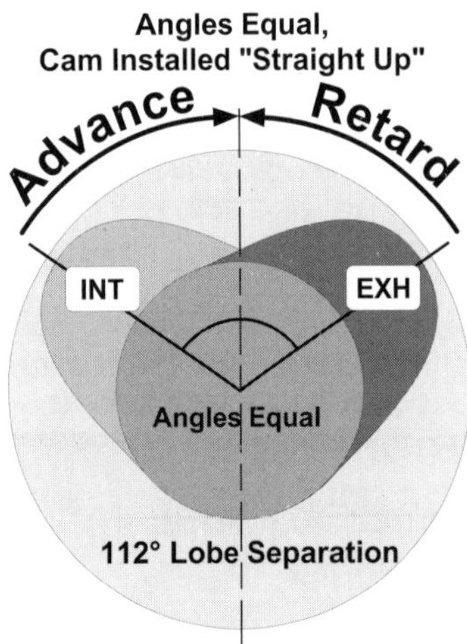

When both cam lobes are the same distance from TDC, the cam in installed "straight up". If the intake centerline is moved clockwise toward TDC (smaller intake centerline angle), the cam is advanced. If the intake centerline is moved farther from TDC (larger intake centerline angle), the cam is retarded.

Cam phasing is checked with a degree wheel that is mounted on the crankshaft snout. Because the crankshaft turns at twice camshaft speed, the distance from TDC is also doubled. This means that the degree wheel will read the same as the lobe separation angle when the cam is installed "straight up".

NOTE: For more information about camshaft phasing, see *Unit VI, Short Block Pre-Assembly Measurements, Degreeing-In the Camshaft.*

Review Questions

1. Identify the basic lower engine assembly components in the figure below:

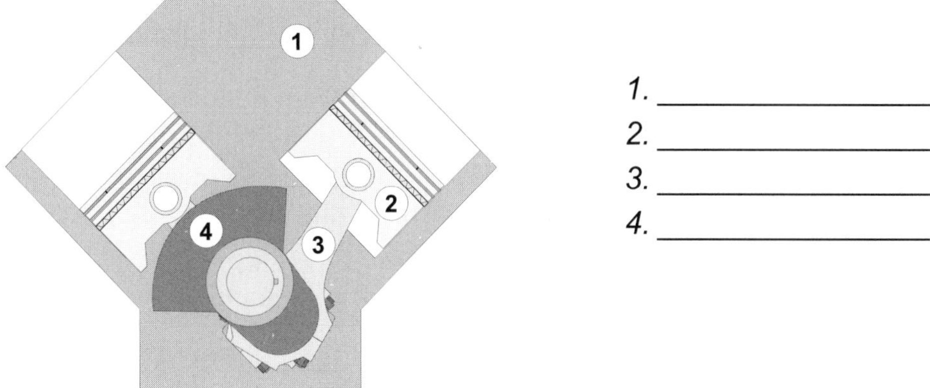

2. Describe how the basic lower engine assembly components are connected.

3. How is reciprocating motion converted to rotary motion in the lower engine assembly?

4. What main function does the camshaft serve? How many lobes are there on the camshaft in a typical two valves per cylinder V8 racing engine?

5. Identify the cam drive components in the figure below:

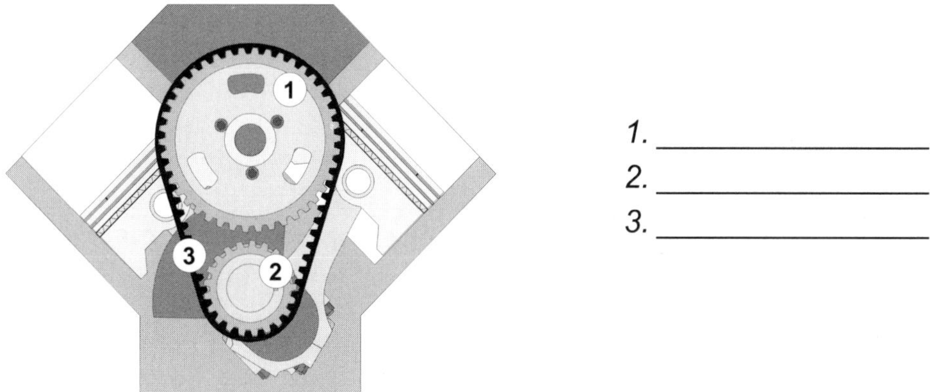

6. What is a "short block"? What accessory components may need to be purchased for your short block to complete the lower engine assembly?

7. Viewed from the front, what is the normal direction of crankshaft rotation for most stock and racing engines?

8. Identify the basic upper engine assembly components in the figure below:

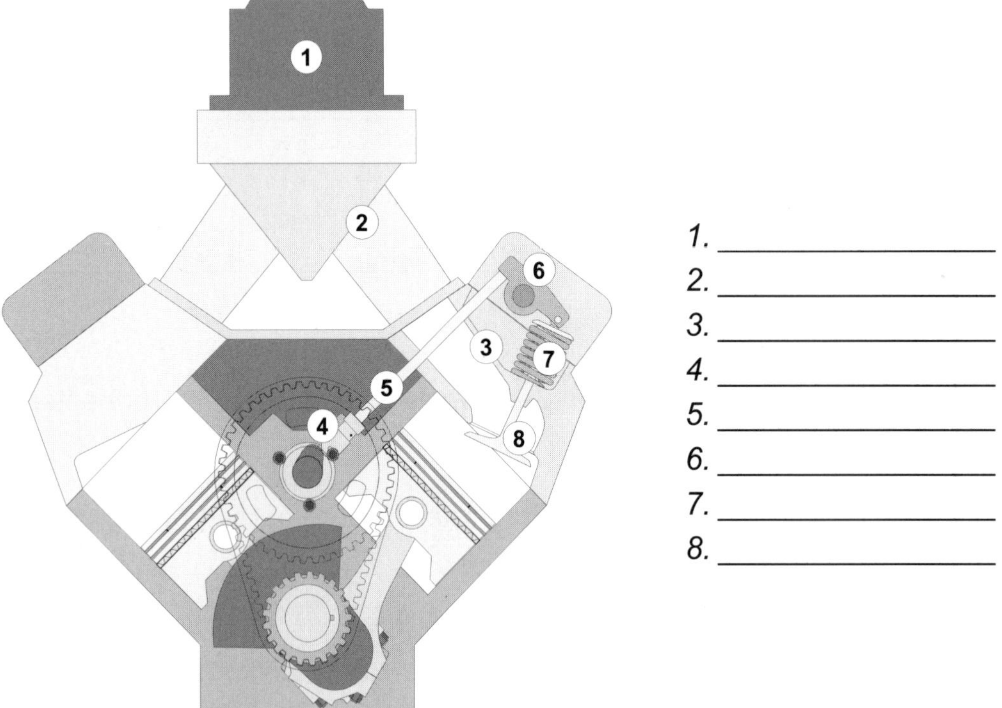

1. ____________________
2. ____________________
3. ____________________
4. ____________________
5. ____________________
6. ____________________
7. ____________________
8. ____________________

9. What accessory components may need to be purchased for your "complete engine" before it can be run?

10. What is the difference between a stroke and a cycle?

11. Name the strokes in a 4-stroke cycle engine.

12. Describe what takes place on the intake stroke.

13. Describe what takes place on the compression stroke.

14. Describe what takes place on the power stroke.

15. Describe what takes place on the exhaust stroke.

16. What are some advantages of the V6 and V8 engines over in-line designs?

17. Why is one cylinder bank of a V-type engine located ahead of the other? Which bank is usually offset to the front? Number the cylinders in the figure below, as they would be in a typical GM V8 racing engine.

GM V8 Engine

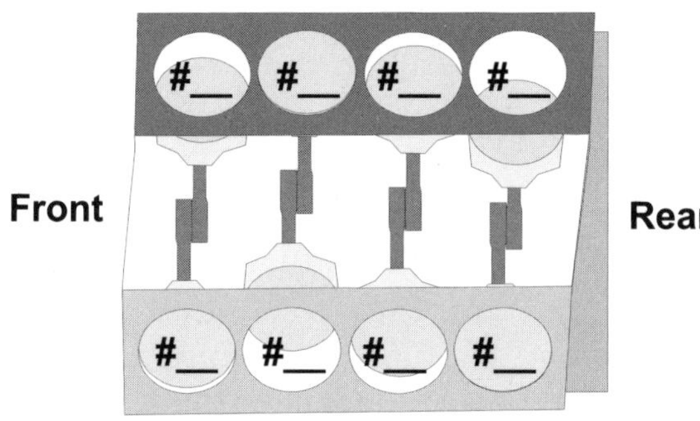

18. What is the angle between the throws of a V8 crankshaft? How can you determine the correct intervals for any engine?

19. What are companion cylinders?

20. What is static compression? What is dynamic engine compression? Why do racing engines have high dynamic compression?

21. How does engine breathing efficiency affect dynamic engine compression?

22. How does camshaft profile efficiency affect dynamic engine compression? What are lift, duration, and lobe separation?

23. How does ring seal affect dynamic engine compression? How does air density affect dynamic engine compression? What is a naturally aspirated engine?

24. How is static compression ratio calculated? What is the purpose of a piston compression dome?

25. What is valve lift and what factors affect the amount of valve lift in a running engine? What is the difference between gross valve lift and net valve lift? Why do racing camshafts have more valve lift than stock ones?

26. How is camshaft duration measured? Explain how long duration cam profiles create more power at high rpm's. Why is the air/fuel velocity so important to a racing engine? Describe the effect that long duration cam profiles have at low rpm engine operation.

27. What is valve overlap and when does it occur? Describe how valve overlap allows more air/fuel mixture to come into the cylinder at high rpm's.

28. What is lobe separation? What is the relationship between engine rpm range and the amount of lobe separation that works best?

29. What is camshaft phasing? Where are the intake and exhaust lobes positioned relative to TDC when the camshaft is installed "straight up"? How is the intake centerline changed to advance the camshaft phasing?

Championship Engine Assembly

Unit II - Building Horsepower

Building more horsepower in the engine is the goal for nearly every racer. All other things being equal, the person with the most horsepower is most likely to win races and championships. Unfortunately, many racers take the wrong approach to building power and waste a lot of time and money in doing so. In this unit, you will learn what horsepower really is and how engine components must work together to minimize losses. This is the best approach to getting the most out of your racing engine.

This 780 cubic inch 3-stage nitrous engine makes over 2200 horsepower on carburetors and racing gasoline. Learn the underlying principles of engine operation that make this possible in this unit.

What is Horsepower?

Often, inexperienced racers look at racing engine components as "bolt-on" horsepower. They tend to believe everything they read about the power each part "adds" to the engine. Feelings of confusion and disappointment usually set in when the real-world power output of the engine falls far short of expectations.

Common Misconception

Many people believe that racing engine parts somehow "make horsepower". In fact, all moving parts lose power - all have frictional losses and inefficiencies. The best parts minimize these losses and maximize the use of the energy that's in the real source of power - the fuel.

Do high lift, long duration camshafts make horsepower? A pair of 1300 cfm carburetors or a really radical racing camshaft may *increase* or *decrease* horsepower—it depends on the size, efficiency, and operating rpm range of your engine.

Our best 500 CID Pro Stock engines can put out over 1350 horsepower with a camshaft that has 280° intake duration, 300° exhaust duration, and over an inch of valve lift. But slip a camshaft with specifications even close to that into your street-driven 396 V8 and you'll be lucky if it has enough power to start and run!

The best approach to building horsepower is to learn as much as you can about how a racing engine works, the function of each part, and how all the parts work together efficiently to produce winning horsepower.

Horsepower Formula:

In 1765, an English instrument maker named James Watt thought of a way to build a practical steam engine. By 1785, his steam engines were rapidly replacing the horse as a source of power. Watt realized that he needed to describe the power of his engines in a way that people of the time would understand—*horsepower.*

Horsepower is just a way to express the amount of *work* the engine can do. In scientific terms, work is the ability to move or accelerate something. It is calculated by this simple formula:

Work = Force x Distance

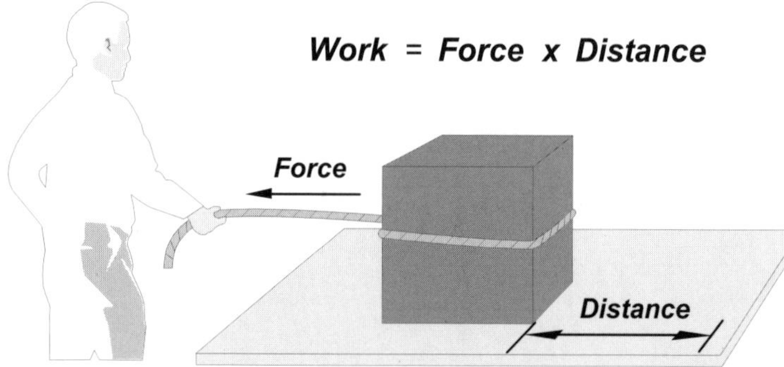

Work is the applied force times the distance traveled. This worker expended some fractional horsepower when pulling the box across the table.

The work formula tells us something very important about engine power—it's not enough just to have a *force*—some *distance* must also be covered. Take a look at the formula devised by Watt to calculate the horsepower of his engines:

$$\textbf{Horsepower} = \frac{\textbf{Torque} \times \textbf{RPM's}}{\textbf{5252}}$$

Notice the similarity between this horsepower formula and the formula for work. In the horsepower formula, force is expressed as *torque*. Torque is a twisting force that the crankshaft can apply to the rest of the driveline. The distance traveled by the crankshaft is expressed as *rpm's*, or revolutions per minute. The number on the bottom (5252) turns the answer into units of horsepower.

Engine torque is measured with a *dynamometer*. A computer terminal connected to a load sensor at the rear of the engine saves torque data as the engine sweeps through the test rpm range. It then applies the formula to convert torque and rpm's into horsepower data and a curve. Dyno testing lets the racer know if all the effort and money expended in building the engine achieved the desired result. It's also a great tool for tuning valve timing, ignition timing, and carburetion.

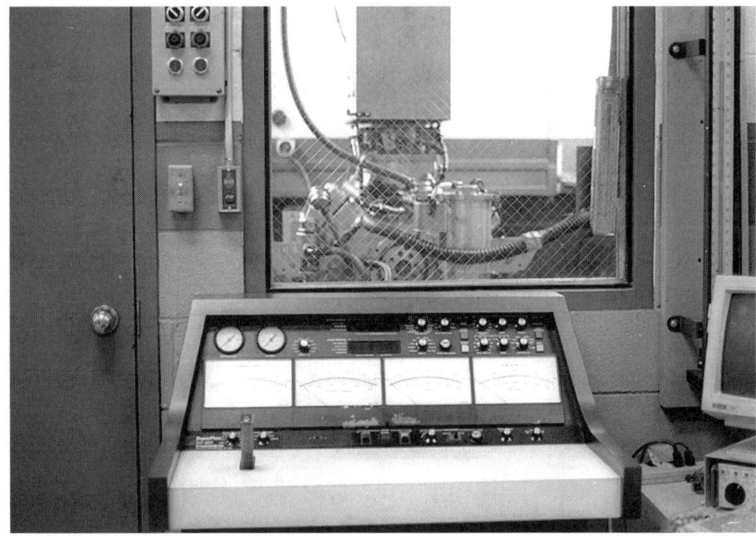

Dyno testing is the best way to measure horsepower and predict the performance potential of an engine prior to racing.

What does the formula tell us about building horsepower? Horsepower may be increased in an engine by creating more torque or more rpm's, or both.

How to Increase Engine Torque:

Torque is created when the pistons push on the crankshaft through the connecting rods. Here are three basic ways to increase engine torque.

- Increase engine displacement
- Increase cylinder pressures
- Reduce parasitic losses

Increasing Engine Displacement

Perhaps the most straightforward means of making more torque is to build a bigger engine. When the pistons move through the 4-stroke cycle, they pump, or *displace*, a certain volume. *Engine displacement* is the way we express the size of an engine. This is the formula for calculating engine displacement:

Engine Displacement =
$bore^2$ x stroke x .7854 x # of cyl.

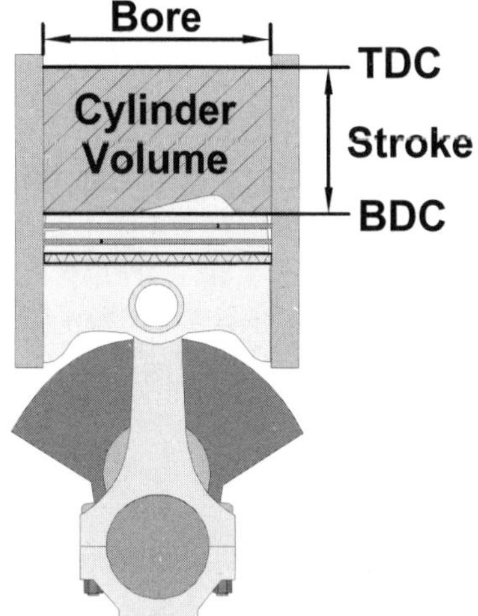

Engine displacement is equal to the bore squared (times itself) times the stroke times .7854 times the number of cylinders.

If you increase the bore, stroke, or number of cylinders, the engine will have a greater displacement. A greater displacement usually, but not always, results in greater engine horsepower.

Remember that rpm's are as important as torque in the horsepower formula. The high stresses created by large pistons and long strokes may limit the maximum rpm's at which the engine can safely or efficiently operate. This can offset any gains made in engine torque output.

Changes in size affect nearly every engine system and characteristic, so you must treat it as a completely new assembly. If you use the same cylinder heads on an engine with larger cylinders, the breathing efficiency usually suffers (see the *Improving Volumetric Efficiency* section in this unit). Changes to engine displacement also affect static and dynamic compression ratios. A larger engine will have unique tuning requirements and the race car may require different gearing or other driveline and chassis modifications.

To a point, bigger can be better, but building 800+ cubic inch monster engines is a rather specialized field and is best left to professional engine builders who are familiar with these problems and have found component combinations that work.

Increasing Cylinder Pressures

The pressure created by the hot, expanding gases of combustion is what pushes the pistons down on power strokes. When more pressure is applied to the pistons, more torque is applied to the crankshaft. There are several ways to increase cylinder pressure including:

- Finding a more energetic fuel
- Burning the air/fuel mixture more efficiently
- Improving the volumetric efficiency
- Sealing the cylinder pressure better

Finding a More Energetic Fuel:

It is important to remember that racing engines are *heat* engines. The heat released during the combustion of the fuel causes gases in the cylinder to expand with extreme pressure, sometimes exceeding 2500 psi.

Combustion, also known as *burning* or *oxidation,* is a chemical reaction in which fuel molecules combine with oxygen. Most racing fuels are hydrocarbon chemicals. This means that the fuel molecules contain hydrogen and carbon atoms. Any time hydrogen and carbon atoms combust (oxidize), new molecules are formed and a great deal of heat energy is released.

More heat energy means greater pressure on the pistons. If you burn a more energetic fuel efficiently, more horsepower will be produced. Some common racing fuels are nitromethane, methanol, and gasoline.

Often, the type of fuel that you can use is dictated by your race sanctioning organization. Nitromethane and methanol can develop a lot more cylinder pressure and power in a racing engine, but the rules for most race car classes require the use of gasoline or racing gasoline as the motor fuel.

NOTE: This course is limited to the development of horsepower in engines that burn racing gasoline. Some classes like Super Gas now allow fuels like E-85 (up to 85% ethanol). Check your rulebook carefully before building your engine to run a particular fuel.

Burning the Air/Fuel Mixture More Efficiently:

There are limits as to how much air and fuel a naturally aspirated racing engine can "breathe" into the cylinders. One of the best ways to produce maximum horsepower is to burn what air and fuel the engine does bring in as completely and efficiently as possible.

Stoichiometric - If there is too little fuel for the volume of air in the cylinder, the air/fuel mixture is *lean*. If there is too much fuel, the mixture is *rich*. The chemically perfect air/fuel ratio for a fuel is called the *stoichiometric*.

Air/fuel ratios are always expressed by weight, not volume. A typical air/fuel ratio for a gasoline powered racing engine may be 13/1. In terms of volume, that's about 7325 cubic feet of air for every cubic foot of fuel that enters the engine.

During the combustion process, fuel molecules break up into individual hydrogen and carbon atoms. Pairs of hydrogen atoms join with just one oxygen atom to form a water molecule (H_2O). Carbon atoms are much more greedy with regard to oxygen needs. One carbon atom needs two oxygen atoms to be fully burned into *carbon dioxide* (CO_2).

If the mixture is too lean, the fuel is burned completely into water and carbon dioxide, but more could have been burned to make power. When the mixture is right, there is just enough oxygen to burn fuel efficiently and produce the most heat and power. If the mixture is too rich, there isn't enough oxygen to allow complete combustion. Carbon atoms may "find" only one oxygen atom each and become *carbon monoxide* (CO). Some carbon atoms won't find any oxygen atoms at all and become black carbon soot.

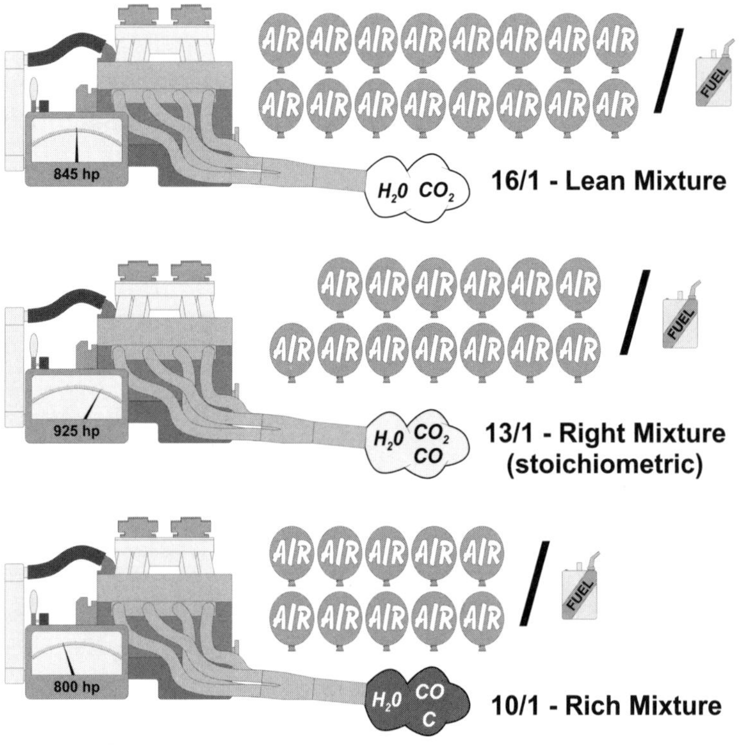

16/1 - Lean Mixture:

This engine burns less fuel and makes less heat & power. The exhaust is mostly water vapor (H_2O) and carbon dioxide (CO_2).

13/1 - Stoichiometric Mixture:

This engine has the right amount of air to burn the fuel efficiently for the highest power output. The exhaust contains water vapor (H_2O), carbon dioxide (CO_2) and some carbon monoxide (CO).

10/1 - Rich Mixture:

This engine burns fuel incompletely and makes less heat & power. The exhaust contains water vapor (H_2O) and high levels of carbon monoxide (CO) & carbon (C).

Racing gasoline is usually a mixture of several different hydrocarbon chemicals. Each hydrocarbon molecule has a unique ratio of hydrogen and carbon atoms and has a slightly different stoichiometric.

Other factors like engine compression and temperature also affect the stoichiometric. An engine under power is creating much more heat and pressure. Additional fuel is required to burn efficiently and also to help cool the combustion chamber.

These are some common fuels and the approximate stoichiometric air/fuel ratios (by weight) for maximum horsepower:

Fuel	****Power Stoichiometric Air/Fuel** (by wt.)*
Gasoline	12.5-13.2/1
Methanol	5/1
Nitromethane	1.7/1

*The listed air/fuel ratios are approximate. The stoichiometric for your engine may vary depending on the particular fuel blend and specific engine requirements.

Pound for pound, methanol and other alcohol chemicals aren't as energetic as gasoline, but they contain oxygen atoms. With a stoichiometric about half that of gasoline, you can burn almost twice as much liquid alcohol in the cylinders. This more than overcomes the lower energy content of alcohol and results in a net gain in power. It also aids greatly in cooling the cylinders and engine block.

It is estimated that a nitro-burning Top Fuel drag car engine develops a startling 6000+ horsepower. This is largely due to the very high energy content and low stoichiometric ratio of the nitromethane fuel. Nitromethane contains so much oxygen that, at certain temperatures and pressures, it requires no additional oxygen at all and is considered a *mono-propellant*. The fuel injection system on a Top Fuel dragster or funny car sprays well over five gallons of fuel into the engine in less than five seconds. By comparison, our 500 CID Pro Stock engines use only about a quart or so of racing gasoline throughout the burnout and run.

<u>Quench Areas</u> - Some of the gasoline that enters the cylinder fails to burn and enters the exhaust stream. Incomplete combustion can be caused by cylinder *quench areas*. A quench area is a region where the air/fuel mixture is very close to relatively cool metal surfaces. The cool surfaces draw heat away from the air/fuel mixture and prevent it from burning. One suspected quench region is the *squish/quench area* of the cylinder head. Another is the small space between the piston and cylinder wall above the top compression ring.

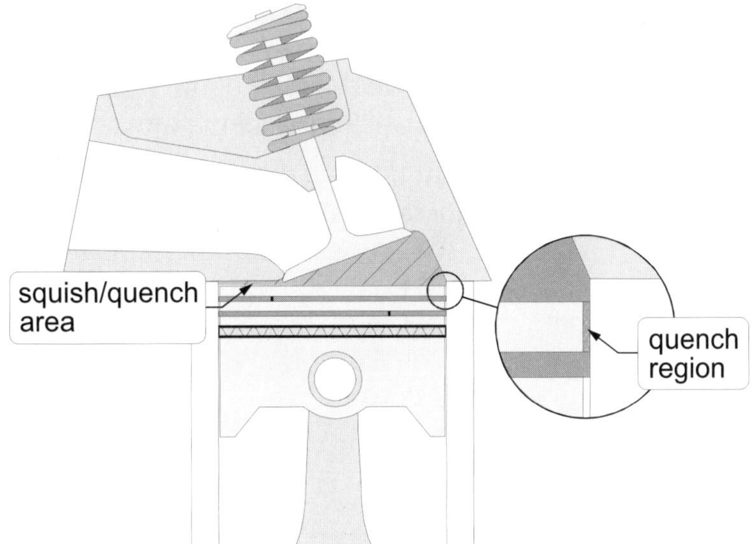

Cool metal surfaces can quench the combustion process between the cylinder head overhang (squish/quench area) and between the piston and cylinder wall above the top compression ring (crevice volume).

Spark Timing & Combustion Rates - Selecting the right fuel and maintaining the correct air/fuel mixture are important, but this is far from the end of the horsepower story. The precise moment when the charge ignites and the speed at which it burns is crucial to engine performance and longevity.

The combustion process cannot be a violent explosion (detonation), but rather must be a rapid, controlled burn. When the spark plug fires, a flame front travels through the combustion chamber at an average rate of about 50 meters per second. In about .0015 seconds, the flame travels across the combustion chamber and the combustion process is complete.

The burn must be started at the right time so that the greatest amount of pressure is on the piston when it is between 10° and 20° after top dead center (ATDC). This creates the most effective push on the crankshaft and keeps the engine rotating in a clockwise direction. The ideal spark timing depends on things like compression, spark plug location, fuel type, and combustion chamber/piston dome shape.

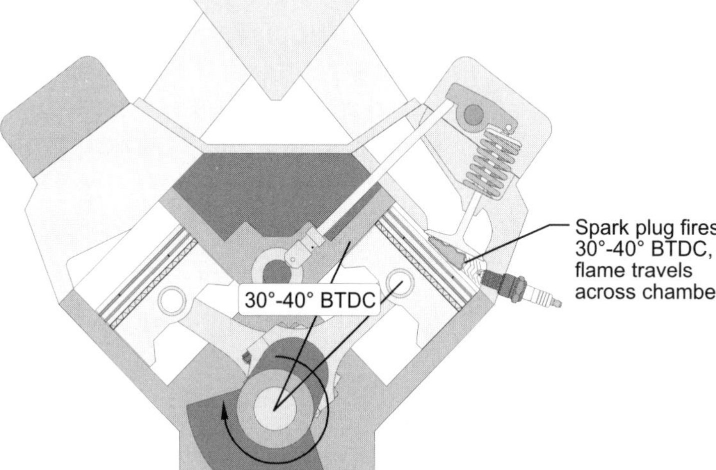

The spark plug in less efficient engines must fire 30° to 40° before the piston reaches the top (BTDC) in order to realize maximum cylinder pressure when the piston is 10°-20° ATDC.

If the flame front travels slowly, you have to fire the spark plug earlier (advance the spark timing) to achieve maximum pressure by 20° ATDC. However, advancing the timing means that the piston encounters more pressure on the way up to TDC. A truly efficient naturally aspirated gasoline racing engine will make its maximum power with only about 27°-30° of spark advance.

One good way to speed up the rate of burning is to increase the compression ratio. Higher compression helps in two ways. First, when the same amount of heat is released into a tighter space, there is more pressure to push on the piston. High compression also increases the rate of burning. A rapid burn means the spark plug can fire later and the piston will run into less pressure on the way up. There will be more heat energy and pressure left to push the piston down.

Detonation – Often, horsepower can be gained by running as much dynamic compression as possible without causing detonation. Detonation happens when the compression wave that is ahead of the flame front super-compresses the remaining air/fuel mixture pocket. This pocket explodes violently, rocking the piston, valves, spark plug, and combustion chamber.

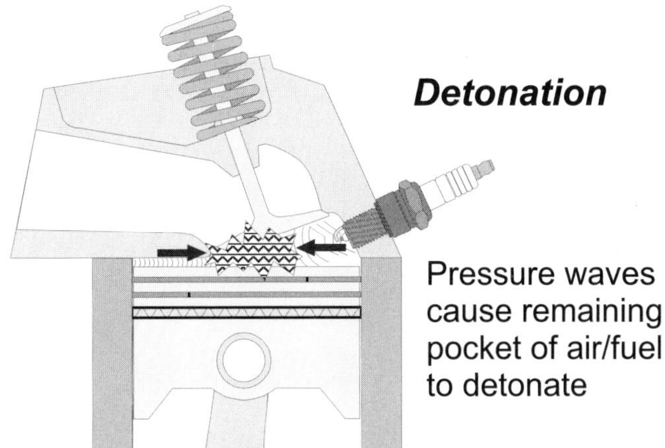

Too much engine compression results in detonation of pockets of air/fuel mixture.

Detonation is very destructive to a racing engine and can be heard as a knock or "ping" sound. If not corrected, detonation can crack pistons, cave in ring lands, shatter spark plugs, and hammer the engine bearings.

Pre-Ignition - As the name implies, pre-ignition means the igniting of the air/fuel mixture *before* the spark plug fires. Like detonation, pre-ignition can usually be heard as a knock or "ping" coming from the engine. The pistons run into combustion pressure before they get to the top the compression stroke. This robs power and, if it continues for long, can damage engine parts.

Pre-ignition is caused by something glowing red hot in the combustion chamber such as carbon deposits or metal burrs. Sharp edges and narrow ridges of metal should always be removed from pistons, head gaskets, and cylinder heads before they are installed in the engine to help prevent pre-ignition.

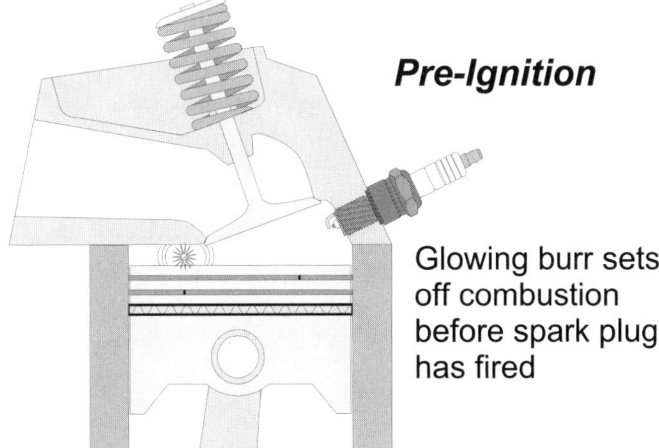

Burrs, sharp edges, and carbon deposits can cause pre-ignition.

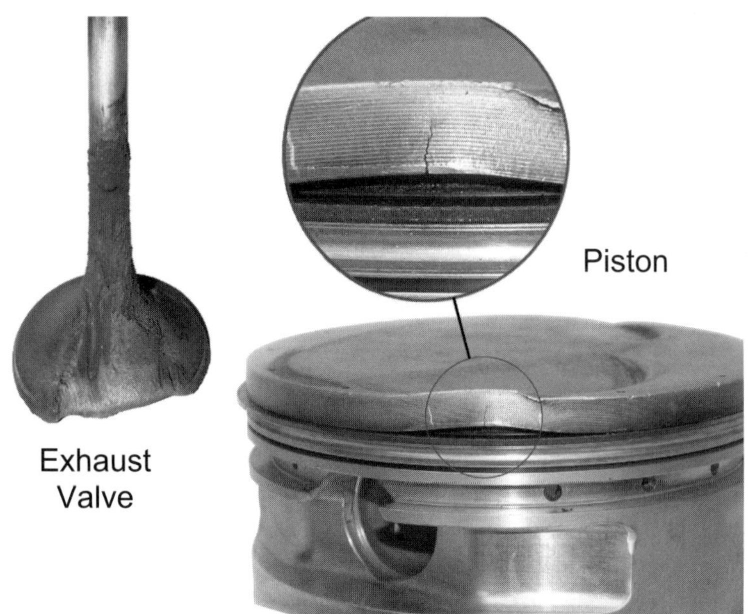

The damage to these parts was caused by severe detonation in a nitrous oxide equipped engine.

Fuel Octane Number Ratings - High *octane* racing gasoline resists detonation and allow the engine to run with much higher compression. Octane is actually a particular liquid hydrocarbon chemical that is used to rate the anti-knock properties of other fuels.

Common Misconception

Many people believe that high octane gasoline makes more power because it has more energy in it. Actually, most racing gasolines contain the same amount of heat energy - about 19,000 BTU's per pound. High octane gasolines resist detonation and allow a higher compression ratio. The tighter squeeze on the air/fuel mixture is what really makes the engine more powerful.

The octane number test was developed in the 1920's and is still used today. A particular fuel that is to be rated is run in a CFR (Cooperative Fuel Research) engine. This special one-cylinder engine, also called a *"knock engine"*, has an adjustable combustion chamber so that most any fuel can be squeezed until it detonates. Technicians start the engine and reduce the volume of the combustion chamber until the engine develops an audible knock. The combustion chamber volume setting is recorded, and then it is returned to the starting position.

Pure octane, or *ISO-octane* has been assigned an AKI (anti-knock index) of 100. Another liquid hydrocarbon chemical, *N-Heptane,* has been assigned an AKI of zero. Different percentage mixtures of ISO-octane and N-Heptane are run in the CFR knock engine until it knocks at the same combustion chamber volume as did the test fuel. The percentage of ISO-octane in the mixture is the assigned octane number rating for the test fuel. For example, if it takes a mixture of 95% ISO-octane and 5% N-Heptane to match the knock characteristic of a test fuel, that fuel will be labeled as 95 octane.

Octane Boosters - The octane requirement of a motor fuel depends on the dynamic compression of the engine and combustion temperatures. Recall that it is very difficult to measure dynamic compression. The table below lists the approximate octane requirements for fuels based on the static compression ratio of the engine.

Static Compression Ratio	****Approximate Octane Requirement***
8:1	87-92
9:1	92-98
10:1	100
11:1	104
12:1	108
13:1	110
14:1 & higher	112-117

* The listed octane ratings are intended for comparative purposes only. The actual requirement for your engine may vary.

Very few pure gasoline chemicals test higher than 100 octane. *Anti-knock additives* are blended with the fuel to boost the octane rating of racing gasoline. The most effective octane booster is TEL (tetra-ethyl lead). Tetra-ethyl lead releases atoms of lead metal during the combustion process. This has the effect of slowing the combustion rate and helps to prevent detonation.

NOTE: Federal law prohibits leaded fuels from being used in street-driven vehicles. Never run racing fuels containing lead in passenger cars.

There are limits to how much TEL can be added before it begins to reduce the power output. Rarely if ever does racing gasoline contain more than 6 grams TEL per gallon of fuel.

Gasoline tends to exhibit different anti-knock characteristics when run under load in the engine than they do at cruise. RON (Research Octane Number) is the result of a steady-state cruise test. Another octane rating, called MON (Motor Octane Number), is tested under high speed and high temperature conditions.

In the late 1960's, the US Congress standardized an octane number rating (ONR) system for passenger car motor fuels that is an *average* of the RON and MON. In racing, we are less concerned about the performance of the engine at cruise. For this reason, racing fuels are usually listed by their slightly lower MON rating.

These are some common types of racing gasoline with the MON ratings:

Fuel	***Recommended Uses***	***MON Rating***	***grams TEL (tetra-ethyl lead)***
VP-C11	Circle Track Racing, under 12:1 compression	104	4.23/gal.
VP-Red	Sportsman engines, under 12.5:1 compression	105	4.23/gal.
VP-C14+	High HP engines, above 14:1 compression	115	6.0/gal.
VP-C19	Drag racing engines, 16:1 compression or higher	117	6.0/gal.
VP-C25	Spec. fuel for NHRA Pro Stock drag racing engines, 16:1 compression or higher	113	6.0/gal.

Check your rulebook and read all of the warning labels before you pour an octane booster into your tank. Additives that contain alcohol may be prohibited by your race sanctioning organization. Some may damage rubber seals after prolonged use or in excessively high concentrations. Also, check with the manufacturer of your car for additive recommendations and related warranty information.

Gasoline additives that contain oxygen are called *oxygenates.* When an oxygenating compound is added to gasoline, more fuel can be burned. This can mean substantial increases in horsepower. However, some oxygenating chemicals are dangerous, and many are banned by race sanctioning organizations for most race car classes. For this reason, we will cover only racing engines that run on pure racing gasoline in this book.

<u>Other Fuel Characteristics</u> - Although high octane ratings are necessary to operate a high compression racing engine, a higher octane rating does not necessarily mean a better racing gasoline. These are some other important fuel characteristics:

- Energy Content
- Burning Rate
- Density
- Cooling Effect

The amount of heat in gasoline can be expressed by the BTU's per kg. (kilogram). A BTU (British Thermal Unit) is the amount of heat that is required to raise one pound of water 1° Fahrenheit. A gallon of racing gasoline contains about 19,000 BTU's per lb. weight. Those with less heat content may not produce as much horsepower in the engine.

Some types of racing gasoline have relatively fast burn rates while retaining superior anti-knock characteristics. These are desirable fuels because they require less spark timing advance.

The density of a fuel affects the adjustment of your fuel delivery system. Fuel density is a measurement of the weight of the gasoline per unit volume. It can be thought of as similar in effect to that of oil viscosity. High-density fuels flow at lower rates through carburetor jets (or injector nozzles) than do low density ones. Be sure to correct the jetting of your carburetor or fuel injection system if you change to a fuel with a different density. Generally, high-density fuels require larger jet sizes; low density fuels require smaller jet sizes.

When the fuel is mixed in the intake manifold, it is in the form of an *atomized* mist. Atomized means broken into tiny droplets. When these fuel droplets enter the hot combustion chamber, they turn into a *vapor* and absorb heat. Engineers call this effect *latent heat of vaporization*. It is an extremely important part of engine cooling.

A lean air/fuel mixture contains less liquid fuel than a rich mixture. This is why lean engines run so much hotter than those with the right air/fuel mixture. With less fuel entering the cylinders, less heat is absorbed and temperatures climb rapidly.

Cool, dense intake charges release more heat energy in the engine than do warm, expanded ones. For every 10°F that the intake charge is cooled, horsepower output will increase by about 1%.

A percent or two horsepower increase may not sound like much, but in some classes such as NHRA Pro Stock, there is probably less than a 2% horsepower difference between any two cars in the entire 16 car field!

It is possible to have too much cooling in the induction system. A great example of this can be seen on drag race cars that run pure methanol. The stoichiometric ratio for methanol (methyl alcohol) is less than half that of gasoline, so at least twice as much liquid fuel is required to avoid lean burning problems.

The large amount of incoming alcohol fuel draws off so much heat as it vaporizes that most alcohol dragsters and funny cars have no engine coolant or radiator at all. Alcohol racers typically have problems building enough engine heat prior to a run. It's not uncommon for frost to build up on the supercharger of an alcohol dragster or funny car during a run.

<u>Ethanol-Enhanced Gasoline</u> - In the last few years, ethanol (ethyl alcohol) has been added to pump gasoline in many US markets. Ethanol acts as an effective oxygenate to promote cleaner burning and also increases the fuel octane. It is part of efforts to reduce dependence on foreign oil. E-85 contains up to 85% ethanol and has a very high listed octane rating of 105 (R+M/2 method). For these reasons, E-85 is finding favor in some forms of racing. However, E-85 requires a much richer fuel mixture and may be incompatible with rubber and steel fuel system components.

Combustion Chamber Turbulence - A great way to improve combustion efficiency and create horsepower is to increase *turbulence* in the combustion chamber. The more the air/fuel charge mixes and swirls, the more rapid and complete the combustion process will be.

The squish/quench area of a wedge style cylinder head creates turbulence. As the piston approaches TDC, the air/fuel mixture is expelled from this region and swirls around the chamber. A wedge style cylinder head has a relatively large squish/quench region and tends to have superior combustion chamber turbulence and burning efficiency.

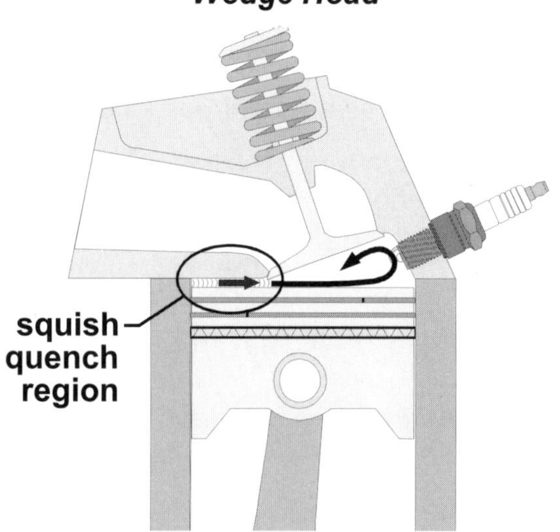

As the piston approaches TDC on the compression stroke, the air/fuel mixture in the squish/quench region is expelled, causing combustion chamber turbulence.

Nitrous Oxide - One way to increase the amount of oxygen available to the engine is by adding a *nitrous oxide* injection system. These systems are permitted by some race sanctioning organizations for specific classes. Nitrous oxide (N_2O) is like a molecule of air, but one that is oxygen rich (36.4% by weight compared to 21% for air).

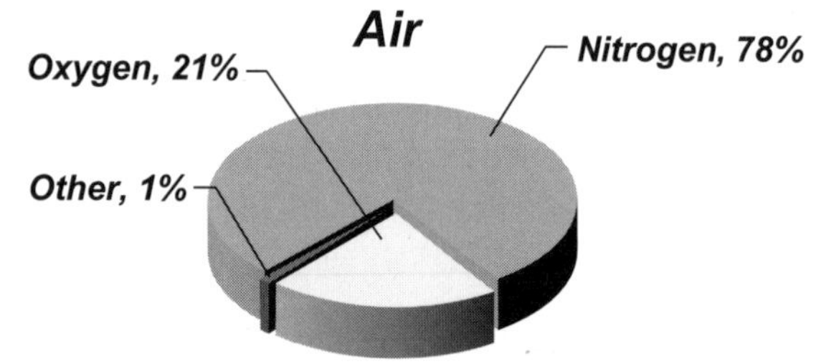

Air is mostly made up of nitrogen (N_2). Only 21% of air is oxygen (0_2) by weight.

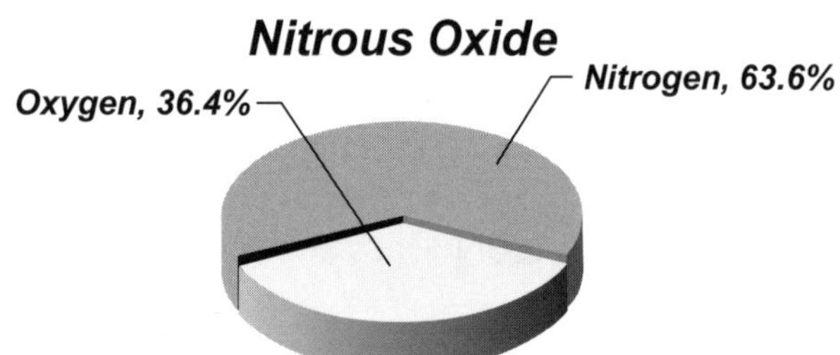

Nitrous oxide is oxygen-rich, 36.4% by weight.

Nitrous oxide (N_2O) creates additional cylinder pressure and horsepower in two ways. First, it provides more oxygen atoms for the combustion process. This means that additional fuel may be brought into the cylinder and burned.

Nitrous oxide also works by cooling the intake gases. Nitrous oxide is stored as a liquid under high pressure in a bottle. When it is released into the intake manifold, the liquid turns into a gas and absorbs a great deal of heat. The intake charge becomes much denser. More fuel and oxygen enter the cylinder and more heat and pressure are released during combustion.

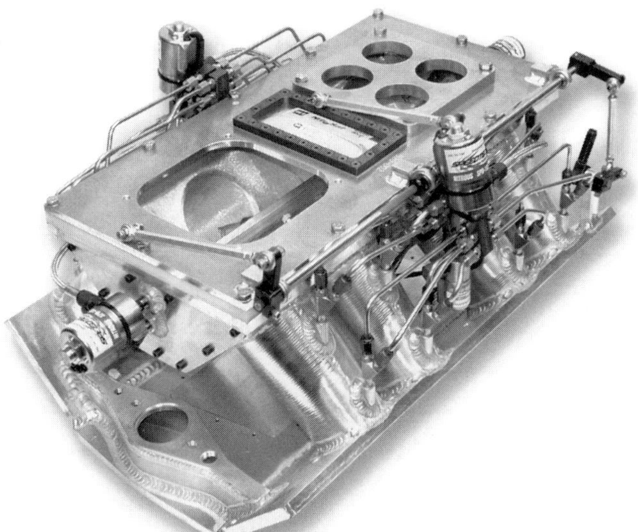

This multi-stage nitrous oxide system is a complex series of regulators, tubes, and nozzles that inject both nitrous oxide gas and fuel into the intake manifold. It can add several hundred horsepower to a big block racing engine.

Adding <u>only</u> nitrous oxide to an engine will make the air/fuel mixture lean and result in serious engine damage. A nitrous oxide system must inject both the gas (N_2O) and additional fuel in order to produce more power and avoid lean mixture problems.

Because it takes temperatures over 572° F to break nitrous oxide molecules apart, the gas remains relatively non-reactive and safe until it enters the combustion chamber. Nevertheless, flame-backs in the intake manifold and carburetors can and do occur in cars equipped with nitrous oxide injection systems. Be sure you have a fire extinguisher on board nitrous oxide equipped race cars in accordance with the rules of your race sanctioning organization.

WARNING: It is unlawful and dangerous to store nitrous oxide in non-approved containers. Violent explosions, injuries, and deaths have occurred when people have attempted to fill non-approved containers or used other oxygen bearing gases and fuels. Never experiment with other gases, fuels, or homemade delivery systems. Read all of the safety and installation information provided by the nitrous oxide system manufacturer. Handle and store nitrous oxide and gasoline in strict accordance with all rules and regulations. Only certified and experienced professionals should fill nitrous oxide bottles.

Improving Volumetric Efficiency:

Rules usually do a good job of creating a "level playing field" for competitors in terms of engine displacement, fuel type, and basic construction. If two engines are identical in these areas, the one with a higher *volumetric efficiency* will make more horsepower.

Volumetric vs. Thermal Efficiency - An engine can be thought of as a type of pump. It draws in air and fuel, and then pushes out exhaust. Volumetric efficiency is a means to express how effectively the engine acts as a pump for its size. It is calculated by this simple formula:

$$\textbf{Volumetric Efficiency (VE)} = \frac{\textbf{actual volume of air \& fuel drawn into the cylinders}}{\textbf{engine displacement}}$$

These are approximate volumetric efficiency values for different types of naturally aspirated engines:

Engine Type	*Volumetric Efficiency (VE)*
Stock	.85 - .95 (85% - 90%)
Modified	.91 - .95 (91% - 95%)
Competition Drag Race (Super Series)	1.01 to 1.14 (101% - 114%)
Pro Stock	1.15 - 1.26 (115% - 126%)

You may be surprised at how high the VE values are for full race engines—well over 100 percent volumetric efficiency. This may sound like a mechanical impossibility, but remember, we are adding a lot of energy into the system in the form of burning gasoline. The extra "kick" to the pistons makes the overlap portion of the 4-stroke cycle draw in additional air & fuel.

A supercharged engine can have even a much higher VE, at least two or three times greater than that of a naturally aspirated engine. But, this VE level comes at a significant cost—supercharged engines burn a lot of fuel. It can take over 500 horsepower to run the blower on a Top Fuel car, but so much fuel is burned that there is still plenty of power left over.

In terms of its *thermal efficiency*, an engine looks less impressive. Some of the heat released when fuel is burned in the cylinders pushes the pistons down, but a lot more of it is wasted as heat in the exhaust system, engine block, and radiator.

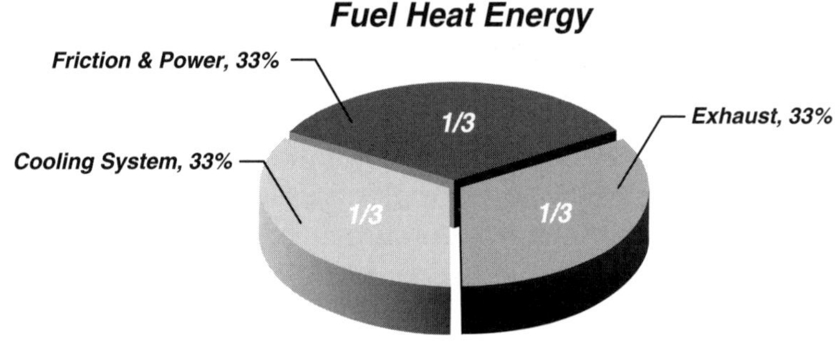

Only about a third of the heat released in the cylinder winds up pushing pistons down. The rest winds up in the cooling and exhaust systems. The high combustion efficiency of a racing engine can increase the thermal efficiency to about 38%.

The thermal efficiency of an engine depends largely on how it is operated. During extended part throttle operation, much more heat winds up in the cooling system than it does during brief intervals at wide open throttle.

In road racing or circle track racing, there is usually a significant amount of part throttle and off throttle operating time. These cars must have very efficient cooling systems with large radiators that dissipate a lot of heat.

Drag racing engines are a different matter. They run briefly at wide open throttle and extremely high rpm's. Air flows into and out of the cylinder heads at very high speeds and burn rates are very fast. In a matter of seconds, the engine is shut down, so there is little time for heat to build in the cooling system.

Look under the hood of a drag race car and you'll often see a radiator that was designed for a 4-cylinder passenger car. Drag race cars that run on alcohol or nitromethane usually do not require coolant passages or radiators at all.

Remember that every time you find a way to eke out another horsepower through improved volumetric and combustion efficiency, you add a little more heat to the cooling system. If the cooling system is unable to remove the extra heat fast enough, cylinder temperatures may rise to the point of detonation.

The tiny radiator in this Pro Stock car can remove enough heat for seven seconds at wide open throttle, but would be entirely inadequate for a road race or NASCAR stock car.

Due to rulebook and other practical limitations, improvements to the volumetric efficiency of the engine hold the most potential for creating more horsepower. Substantial improvements in power can be realized through modifications to:

- *Carburetion*
- *Intake Manifold*
- *Camshaft & Valve Train*
- *Cylinder Heads & Valves*
- *Exhaust Headers*

Reversion - *Reversion* is an unwanted reversal in the normal direction of gas flow through the engine. Reversion can happen on the intake or exhaust side and reduces the volumetric efficiency and power of the engine.

Intake reversion happens because of the late closing of the intake valve. With a racing camshaft, the piston can be as far as 2/3 of the way up on the compression stroke before it finally closes. This works great at high engine speeds because the momentum of high-velocity intake gases keeps them flowing in the right direction—into the cylinder.

But at lower engine speeds, there is insufficient velocity and the piston starts to turn the gases around and push them right back into the port. Intake reversion results in less air/fuel mixture being trapped in the cylinder. That's why racing engines idle roughly and don't have a lot of power until they are brought up into their operating rpm range. Intake reversion also kills manifold vacuum and upsets carburetor operation. Street vehicles with performance cams may not build sufficient manifold vacuum to operate power brakes and other vacuum-operated systems.

Valve operating instability is an issue related to this reversion problem. If you choose the wrong valve springs and valve hardware for an application, it's not uncommon to lose control of valve operation. New high speed camera technologies have allowed us to study the action of valves and valve train components in slow motion to better understand what is really happening. The result of this research has been rather startling.

Valve train dynamics in a poorly matched system are in a state of near chaos, with components flexing, turning, and bouncing at various rpm's throughout the engine operating range. Under these conditions, an intake valve can actually bounce off the valve seats five times at certain engine rpm's. When the intake valves bounce, they leak some of the intake gas pressure in the cylinder, reducing engine power.

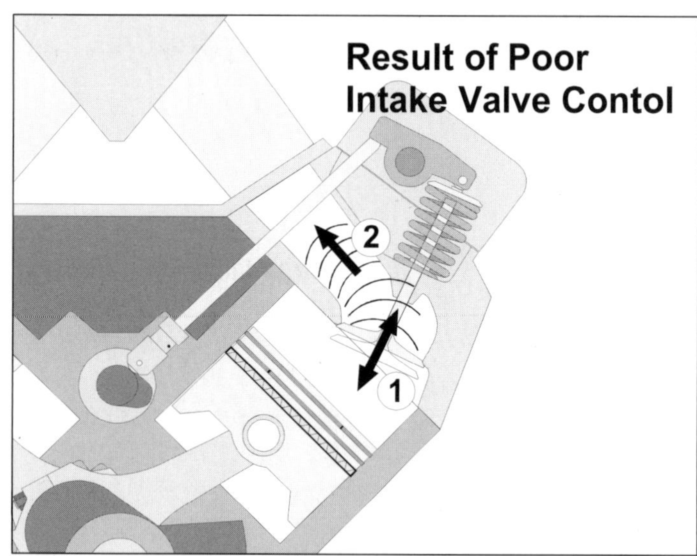

1. *In a valve train with poor dynamic control, the intake valve slams shut and bounces several times.*
2. *When this happens, cylinder pressure leaks from the cylinder, greatly reducing engine power.*

Exhaust reversion is the unwanted reversal of exhaust gas flow back into the cylinder during the exhaust stroke. Unlike intake reversion, the effects of which are often visible as a fuel cloud hanging over the carburetors, the effects of exhaust reversion happen inside the cylinders and are very difficult to study.

One theory is that exhaust reversion happens shortly after the valve opens on the exhaust stroke. The gases burst into the header pipe and create a region of very high pressure. Like a compressed spring, the gases uncoil in both directions. Some of the exhaust gases travel back through the port in into the cylinder.

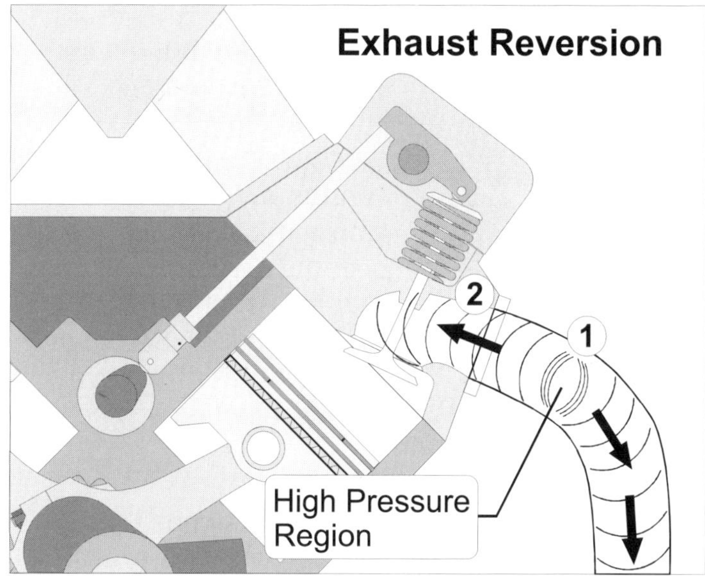

1. *An exhaust pulse in the header pipe creates a region of very high pressure.*
2. *The high pressure region expands in both directions. A reversion wave travels back through the exhaust port.*

Controlling Reversion - The most common cause of reversion is a mismatch of port size to engine displacement. Excessively large cylinder head ports do not maintain the high gas velocities and inertial forces needed to resist reversion. Reversion problems that are related to valve harmonics can best be controlled by selecting lightweight valves and good, high pressure racing valve springs that are appropriate for your application.

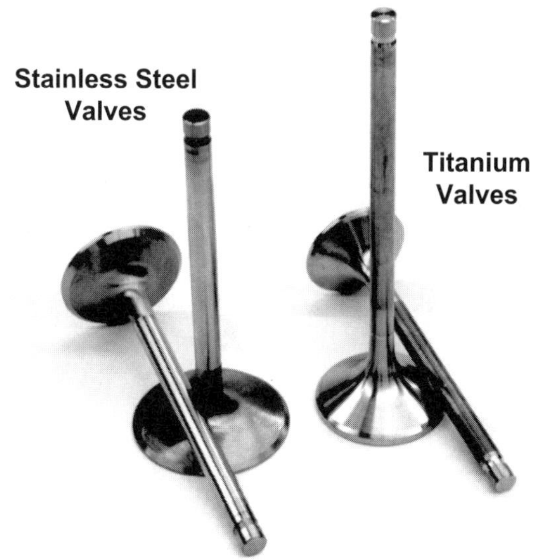

Low mass titanium valves can help eliminate intake reversion problems. We feel strongly that they are well worth the additional cost for many racing engine applications.

Valve spring selection is one area where you should rely on information from your engine builder and high performance parts manufacturers. Different types of valve springs can have very different harmonic characteristics in an engine.

A number of years ago, we had a race car that would nearly shut off from fuel standoff over the carburetors at a certain point in a run. A simple change of valve springs cured the intake reversion problems and transformed the engine into a winner.

Choosing the right valve springs is extremely important in a racing application. The correct springs will help prevent high rpm clash with pistons, dampen harmonics, and extend valve train life. See your engine builder for valve spring selection advice.

Buying really stiff valve springs is not necessarily the answer. The springs that transformed our engine into a winner actually had *less* seat pressure, *less* pressure rise at opening, and *less* pressure over the nose of the cam than the springs that caused us all the problems. This is why you must consult your engine builder or contact the camshaft manufacturer for valve spring recommendations.

The valve attaching hardware including the *retainers* and *keepers* must be strong enough to stay together, but as light as possible. It's hard to beat titanium retainers for most medium to high horsepower racing applications.

The lightweight titanium retainers on this RMRE Raptor BBC cylinder head help reduce valve harmonic and reversion problems.

Reversion Dams - To help reduce reversion, some racing engine builders like to create *reversion dams*. An intake reversion dam is an intentional mismatch between the port in the head and that in the manifold.

The intake reversion dam theory works like this—the air/fuel mixture can flow in the correct direction without obstruction. When reversion occurs, the gases are slowed due to turbulence created by the overhanging ledge.

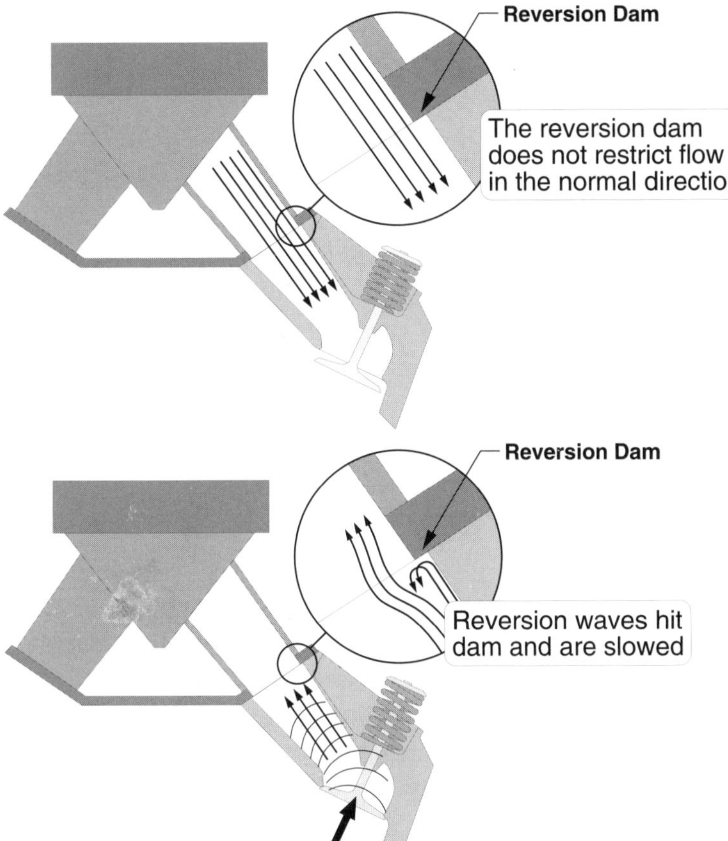

The theory of an intake reversion dam is that the gases can flow over the reversion dam ledge in the right direction with little or no effect.

When the intake gases try to flow the wrong way in reversion, the dam creates turbulence that restricts backflow.

All of this intake reversion dam theory looks good on paper, but we don't find it to be an effective way of controlling reversion problems. However, a reversion dam is effective on the exhaust side of the engine. The size and shape of the exhaust ports create a reversion dam with the round tube on the header.

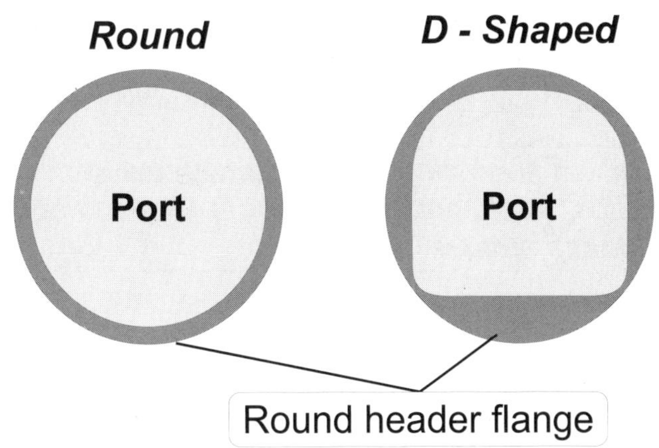

The exhaust port size or shape can create a reversion dam (shown as darkened areas).

One interesting attempt at creating an exhaust reversion dam is the use of *ditch-cut exhaust valves*. A ditch-cut is a trough milled into the back side of the valve head near the seat. Any exhaust gases that flow the wrong way (into the cylinder) will become turbulent as they follow the trough contour. The theory is that the resulting turbulence creates a partial barrier to exhaust back flow.

This ditch-cut exhaust valve is supposed to help control exhaust reversion.

Although some engine builders have reported measurable horsepower gains with ditch-cut exhaust valves, we have not found them to be an effective way to control exhaust reversion problems. The best approach for controlling both intake and exhaust reversion is to match port size with engine displacement to maintain high velocities, then gain control over valve harmonics by installing the right valve train components.

Sealing Cylinder Pressure:

Much of the effort and expense you put into an engine to increase cylinder pressures will be wasted if the engine does not seal the pressure effectively. If the engine block, piston rings, gaskets, cylinder heads, and valves have been properly inspected, machined, and installed, they will not leak cylinder pressure in any significant amount. The greatest concern and potential for cylinder leakage is in the area of ring seal.

> ***NOTE:*** For more information about piston ring function, selection, measurement, and installation, refer *Unit III - Short Block Component Selection & Preparation and Unit VI - Short Block Pre-Assembly Measurements.*

Reducing Parasitic Drag

Although you may have done an excellent job of maximizing engine thermal and volumetric efficiency, *parasitic drag* can rob the engine of precious horsepower. Parasitic drag draws off energy and slows the acceleration of the crankshaft. These are some common sources of parasitic drag in a racing engine:

- *Inertial Losses*
- *Windage Drag*
- *Sliding Friction & Viscous Drag*
- *Accessory Component Drag*

Inertial Losses:

Inertia is the force that causes an object to resist changes in motion. It takes energy to overcome inertia and accelerate the moving parts in the engine. It also takes energy to reverse the motion of reciprocating parts. These are some of the reciprocating engine parts that are subject to inertial losses:

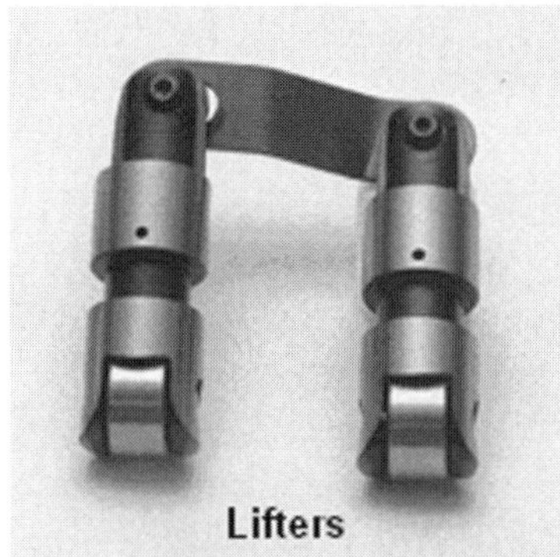

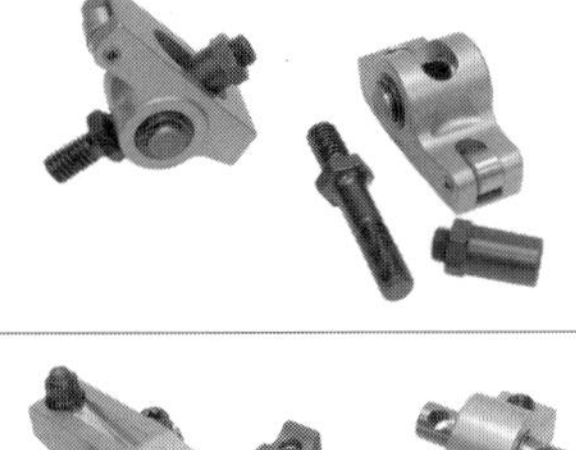

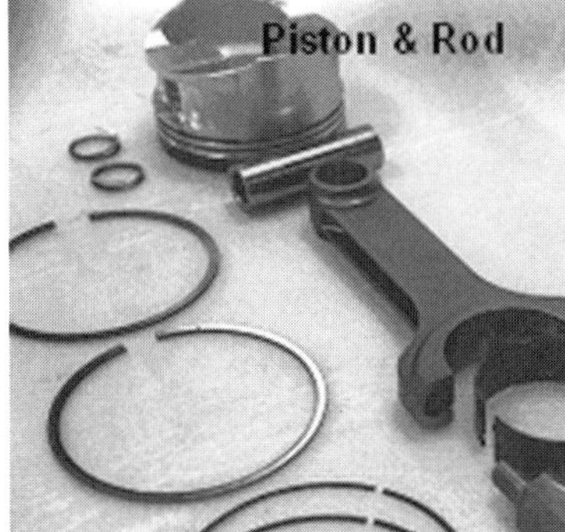

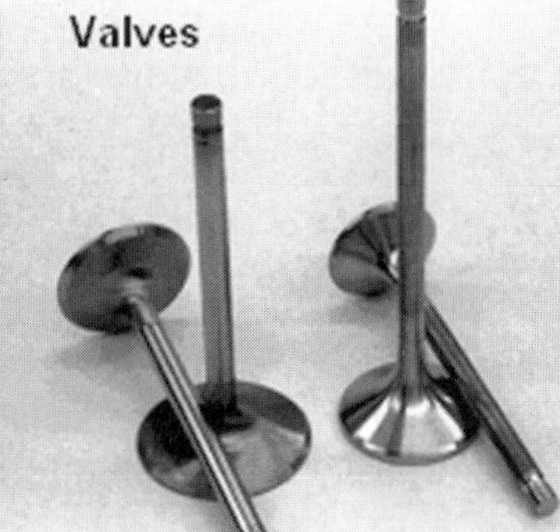

All of these engine parts reciprocate and create inertial energy losses in an engine.

Reciprocating parts have significant losses due to inertial forces. Pistons and rods work against normal crankshaft rotation each time they reverse direction. Inertia forces also increase the loadings on engine bearings and add to frictional losses.

The repeated stretching and compressing of reciprocating parts stresses and work-hardens them until they eventually fail. This is why we must replace our aluminum connecting rods after only 50-70 runs in a Pro Stock engine.

Heavy valve train parts are particularly bad in a high rpm racing engine because they necessitate very stiff valve springs in order to close the valves on time. The valve springs must also reverse the direction of other valve train parts including the retainers, rocker arms, pushrods, and lifters. The result is higher parasitic losses in the form of increased frictional drag on cam lobes, cam bearings, and the cam drive system. High pressure valve springs also get very hot from torsional flexing of the spring wire—yet another source of lost energy in the engine.

The problems of inertial losses get worse rapidly as engine rpm's rise. The inertial energy stored in a part is a function of the *square* of the velocity. This means that if you double the velocity of a part, the forces go up by a factor of four. At triple the velocity, the forces go up by a factor of nine!

There are only two ways to reduce inertial losses in a racing engine—lower the component velocities or reduce component mass. Reducing velocities is not often possible because the reciprocating parts must keep up with crankshaft rpm's. Your goal should be to select the lightest possible parts that are still strong and durable enough to survive in the engine. A good racing engine builder can help you select cost-effective parts that are lightweight, but with a proven track record of reliability.

Windage Drag:

Lower End Components and Modifications - The crankshaft and rods encounter significant resistance as they slice through crankcase windage. Windage can rob 40 or more horsepower from a racing engine. There are at least five good ways to reduce the parasitic drag caused by crankcase windage:

- *Install a crankcase evacuation system*
- *Install a quality racing oil pan and a windage tray (w/o dry sump system)*
- *Install a dry sump system*
- *Install a crankshaft with streamlined counterweights*
- *Smooth the sharp edges in the engine block*

The oil pan design can have a lot to do with the amount of drag from oil windage. A kicked-out pan provides the needed extra space for oil spray on the right side of the engine. A windage tray can also help reduce parasitic drag.

<u>Crankcase Evacuation</u> - Many years ago, it was discovered that if you create a vacuum in the crankcase of a racing engine, there is a substantial (2% to 5%) increase in horsepower. This is probably due to one or more of the following:

- *Reduced Crankcase Windage*
- *Improved Oil Control*
- *Improved Piston Ring Performance*

An effective crankcase evacuation system causes a substantial reduction in windage drag. With less air and other gases in the crankcase, the oil droplets have no medium in which to mix and tend to fall into the oil pan. The crankshaft throws and counterweights cut through air that is much thinner and contains far fewer oil droplets.

As the pistons reciprocate, they move a lot of air and gas back and forth in the crankcase. This pumping action draws off power and contributes to windage. By reducing the amount of gas in the crankcase, these effects are significantly reduced.

Another benefit is the improved oil control in the engine. Motor oil has very poor combustion characteristics. It reduces the octane rating of the fuel charge and can add soot to the combustion chambers. Vacuum in the crankcase helps keep the oil from getting past the compression rings. Racing engine builders call this “keeping the cylinders dry”.

We find that 18 to 20 inches of vacuum (in. hg.) is optimal for producing horsepower. There are three common ways that racing engine builders create crankcase vacuum:

- *Passive evacuation system (Vac-U-Pan)*
- *Dry sump oil pump adjustment*
- *External pump*

A passive exhaust scavenging system takes advantage of the Bernoulli effect in the exhaust headers. The Bernoulli effect principle states that high velocity air creates low pressure (vacuum). This can be easily demonstrated by this simple experiment:

Bernoulli Effect

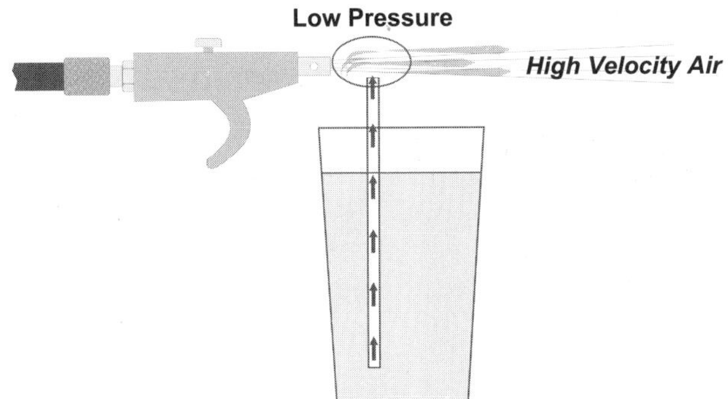

Insert a soda straw into a glass of water. Shoot a stream of air over the top of the straw with a blow gun. The water is drawn up the straw into the area of low pressure created by the high velocity air and sprays out with the air stream.

A passive crankcase evacuation system takes advantage of the Bernoulli effect created by the high velocity exhaust gases in the header collector pipes. A tube is welded into the exhaust header collector at an angle. The low pressure draws crankcase blow-by out of the engine and into the exhaust stream. A check valve ensures that an exhaust backfire cannot ignite fuel fumes in the crankcase. The passive crankcase evacuation system has been around for a couple of decades and is sometimes called a Vac-U-Pan system.

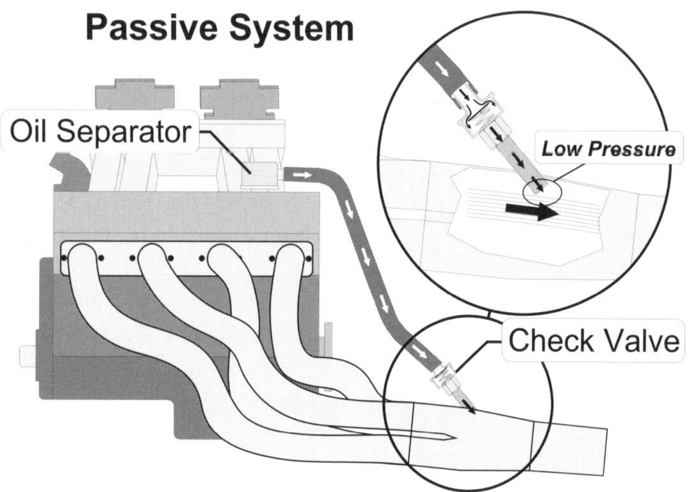

This passive crankcase evacuation system uses high velocity exhaust gases to pull a vacuum in the engine crankcase. An oil separator cap minimizes the amount of oil droplets that are pulled into the exhaust stream.

The amount of blow-by produced by an engine increases dramatically with engine speed. A passive evacuation system is better than nothing, but it cannot create the amount of vacuum (18-20 in. hg.) needed for substantial horsepower gains. With a dry sump oil system, you may be able to find a pump speed that pulls plenty of crankcase vacuum throughout the rpm range.

The pumping volume and crankcase vacuum are determined by the drive ratio of the crank and pump pulleys. You may have to try several combinations to achieve the desired (18-20 in. hg.) crankcase vacuum.

Even a dry sump system may not be enough to pull the kind of vacuum that provides maximum gains. We often add a belt-driven pump to our 500 cubic inch Pro Stock engines to ensure the pumping capacity required for the unusually high 24-26 in. hg. vacuum that works best on these engines.

The belt driven pump on this 500 cubic inch Pro Stock engine supplements the vacuum created by the dry sump system.

Although a vacuum pump may look like just another source of parasitic drag to the engine, there is something of a tradeoff. If you use the dry sump pump to pull all of the vacuum, it must be adjusted for a higher pumping rate. This increases the drag on the engine. If you add a vacuum pump, you can reduce the pumping rate and drag in the oil pump. This offsets most of the drag created by the vacuum pump.

Sliding Friction & Viscous Drag:

Sliding friction occurs between moving engine parts. It robs the engine of power and erodes the surfaces of the parts. All moving parts have some frictional losses. This not only drags power from the engine, but the wasted energy becomes additional heat that must be radiated away.

Viscous drag is the resistance to pumping fluids (oil & water) through the engine. These are factors that affect the amount of power lost in an engine because of sliding friction and viscous drag:

- *Oil Viscosity & Type*
- *Engine Component Fit & Finish*
- *Engine Rpm's*
- *Accessory Component Drag*

Oil Viscosity & Type - *Viscosity* means thickness. The viscosity rating for a motor oil is a standardized numerical system developed by the SAE (Society of Automotive Engineers). Thin oils are rated in "weight" numbers under SAE 20. Thick oils range from SAE 30 weight to SAE 50 weight.

Thin oils offer less viscous drag as they are pumped through the engine. Many *synthetic racing motor oils* have a very low viscosity—between 0 and 5 weight. Some are so thin that a different and more sensitive metric scale called *centistokes* is being used to rate their viscosity. One problem with using a thinner oil is that it sprays out of engine bearings more rapidly. If you decide to use a thin oil, be sure your oil pump has enough flow rate to maintain adequate pressure.

Oil flows through most racing engines at a rate of 8-12 gpm (gallons per minute). One way to reduce this flow rate is to install roller cam bearings. When you install roller cam bearings, the outer races cover the oil holes in the cam bores of the block. This saves about one gpm of oil flow through the engine. Oil spray off the crankshaft provides all the lubrication the rollers need.

Roller cam bearings can save a little power by reducing the oil volume requirements for the engine. They also do a little better job of controlling the cam than standard babbitted bearings.

Synthetic racing motor oils often have superior lubricating qualities that can reduce the sliding friction between engine parts. This helps keep the engine cooler, and the lower viscosity of synthetics helps reduce pumping losses. For these reasons, we think synthetic motor oils deserve serious consideration for use all racing engine applications.

IMPORTANT: Synthetic motor oils should not be used on new engine assemblies. They lubricate so well that the cylinder walls may never conform to the rings. We apply standard SAE 30 weight oil to the cylinder walls during engine assembly and fill the crankcase with the same non-synthetic oil. After the break-in period (usually a few dyno pulls), we drain the oil and replace it with a quality synthetic racing motor oil.

Engine Component Fit & Finish - Tight bearing and piston-to-wall clearances can greatly increase the frictional losses in a racing engine. A good rule of thumb when building a racing engine is that a little too loose is better than too tight. Some parts like the crankshaft journals have less friction with a smooth, consistent finish. This is why we polish crankshaft journals to a high luster with worn polishing cloth.

Polishing a crankshaft with the right materials and techniques is an important part of reducing frictional losses. We recommend that you stay very close to the lower engine clearance and finish specifications included in this book.

Engine Rpm's - Rpm's are of equal importance to torque in the horsepower equation, but there are limits as to how fast an engine can go. Parasitic losses due to inertia and friction take their toll on the engine as rpm's climb. Breathing (volumetric efficiency) also suffers as gases try to move in and out of the cylinders with ever-increasing velocities. Heat may build in the cylinders faster than it can be dissipated.

Horsepower reaches a peak when everything gained by high rpm operation is offset by these losses to crankshaft torque. As rpm's climb higher, horsepower begins to fall off rapidly.

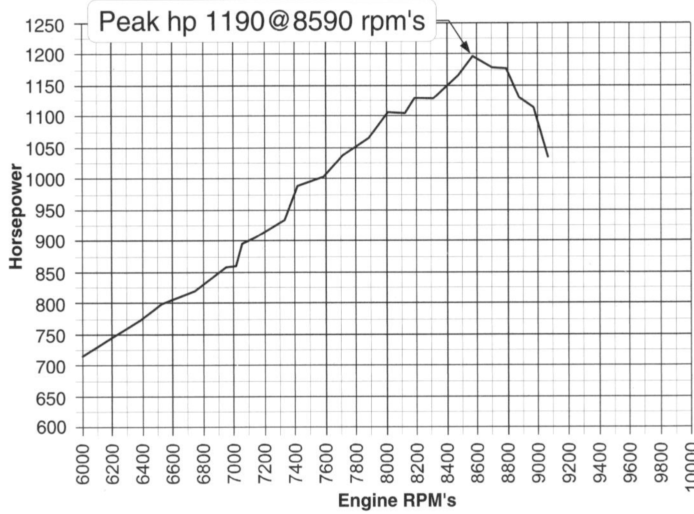

Parasitic losses and other operating inefficiencies rob torque from the engine at high rpm's. The power of this engine peaked at 8950 rpm's, and then fell off rapidly.

The rpm range in which a racing engine can operate depends largely on the breathing efficiency of the heads, the mass of the pistons, and the length of the stroke. Big bore, long stroke engines like the 800 cubic inch monsters run in IHRA Pro Stock cars run out of steam a couple of thousand rpm's lower than their 500 cubic inch NHRA counterparts. Dyno testing is the only way to really know where your engine will run its best.

Dyno testing will reveal the horsepower peak and help you determine the most effective operating rpm range for your engine.

Accessory Component Drag - All crank-driven accessories that you add to an engine consume horsepower. Most race cars do not need power steering or air conditioning, so these systems are not usually installed. Drag car batteries can be recharged between rounds, so you may also be able to eliminate the alternator. Before you remove the alternator, give some thought to the electrical system operating voltage.

Common Misconception

Many people think that a car has a 12 volt electrical system. When the engine is running, the charging system maintains about 14.5 volts. All car electrical devices, including the ignition system, are designed to operate at this higher voltage level. With no alternator, the output of a stock ignition system may be reduced by as much as 15%.

There are several factors that increase the demand on a racing ignition system. First, as engine rpm's increase, there is less and less time in which to charge and discharge the ignition coil. It takes significantly higher voltage to fire a spark plug in a high temperature/high pressure environment. Battery voltage may not be high enough to overcome these problems, and the engine may lose spark at high rpm's.

To maintain a strong spark without the voltage boost of an alternator, many drag racers prefer to use a special 16 volt racing battery. The higher voltage also provides more cranking power to help start a high compression racing engine.

These 16 volt racing batteries ensure a hot spark and reliable cranking in a drag car with no alternator.

Photo courtesy of New Castle Battery Mfg. Co.

NOTE: Be sure to read the voltage requirement information included with your ignition system and other accessory components. Always recharge the battery after every run.

A crank-driven water pump consumes about 1½ to 3 horsepower from the engine. An electric water pump can eliminate this small power loss, but it has far less pumping capacity than a crank-driven type. We don't recommend electric water pumps for high-heat endurance racing applications like stock car engines.

However, if rules permit, an electric water pump is a very attractive option for many drag race cars. It usually has enough capacity for these engines since they only run for a few seconds.

A small amount of power can be saved in drag race cars by using an electric water pump. The stock car engine on the right must have a crankshaft driven pump to stay cool throughout the race. Note the smaller pulley on the crankshaft to reduce the driven speed of the pump.

Endurance racing engines need a belt-driven fan, but some power can be saved in these applications by using a *flex fan.* The blades on a flex fan flatten at higher speeds and save some drag on the engine. When a typical stock car is running at high speeds, air pressure in front of the race car is usually enough to push plenty of air through the radiator without the full pitch of the fan blades.

An electric fan can often be used on a drag race car to eliminate the parasitic drag from the engine causes by a belt-driven fan. Most drag racers find that they only need to run the fan between rounds or while waiting to stage. They just click it off prior to the run to eliminate the drain on the battery and to reduce the electrical interference caused by running an electric motor.

This electric fan mounts on the radiator. It is usually adequate for a drag race car and eliminates the drag of a belt-driven fan.

A high performance electric fuel pump eliminates the drag of a mechanical fuel pump and delivers greater volume and pressure.

Powerful engines consume a lot of fuel. An electric fuel pump not only eliminates the parasitic losses of a mechanical pump, it provides the volume and pressure required for high-horsepower racing engines.

NOTE: The power to run electric motors isn't free—it must come from somewhere. If you have an alternator on your car, you'll only trade the drag eliminated by removing mechanically driven accessories for increased drag in the alternator.

Review Questions

1. What is horsepower? Do engine components make horsepower? What is the real source of engine power? What is the force component in the horsepower formula below? What is the distance component? What is the number 5252 for?

$$\textbf{Horsepower} = \frac{\textbf{Torque} \times \textbf{RPM's}}{\textbf{5252}}$$

2. What are three ways to increase engine torque?

3. What is engine displacement? Does increased displacement always mean increased torque? Why or why not?

4. Name four ways of increasing cylinder pressures.

5. What is "hydrocarbon" fuel? Describe the combustion process with a hydrocarbon fuel. What are the byproducts of the complete combustion of a hydrocarbon fuel?

6. What is a "rich" air/fuel mixture? What is a "lean" air/fuel mixture? What does the term "stoichiometric" mean? Why is the stoichiometric different for different fuels?

7. Explain what happens when a rich air/fuel mixture is burned. What are the byproducts of the incomplete combustion of a hydrocarbon fuel?

8. What is a "quench" area? Where can cylinder quench occur?

9. Why is it important to fire the spark plug at the right time? How does the combustion rate affect the spark timing in an engine? What is the advantage of using a fuel that burns quickly?

10. What is detonation? What causes detonation? What are some symptoms of detonation?

11. What is pre-ignition? What causes pre-ignition? What is a symptom of pre-ignition?

12. What is octane? How are fuels tested for octane ratings? What is the most effective and common octane-boosting gasoline additive? What is the difference between motor octane number (MON) and research octane number (RON)?

13. Name four important fuel characteristics other than octane rating. About how much energy is in a pound of gasoline? What effect does fuel density have on engine tuning? How does the fuel cool the combustion chamber? Why is this important?

14. Explain the importance of combustion chamber turbulence. What cylinder head design creates the most turbulence? How does it do this?

15. What is air made of? What is nitrous oxide? How does a nitrous oxide injection system increase engine horsepower? What are some safety considerations when using or handling compressed nitrous oxide?

16. How is engine volumetric efficiency different from thermal efficiency? What is the approximate volumetric efficiency of a racing engine? What is the thermal efficiency of a stock engine? What is the thermal efficiency of a racing engine?

17. What is reversion? What causes intake reversion? What causes exhaust reversion? What are some ways to control reversion?

18. Name three types of crankcase evacuation systems. Why does crankcase vacuum increase engine power output? What is the Bernoulli principle? Explain how a passive crankcase evacuation system works. How can a dry sump oil pump be adjusted to create crankcase vacuum? What is the purpose of a belt driven vacuum pump on a racing engine?

19. Why is it important to maintain a good cylinder seal?

20. What are parasitic losses in a racing engine? Why are heavy moving engine parts undesirable in a racing engine?

21. What are five possible sources of engine frictional losses?

22. What is oil viscosity? How does the viscosity of oil affect parasitic drag in the engine? What are some advantages of using a synthetic motor oil in a racing engine? Why should you not use synthetic motor oils for engine assembly and break-in?

23. Explain the importance of proper engine component fit and finish. What is a good rule to follow concerning engine clearances?

24. What is the relationship between engine rpm's and parasitic drag?

25. What is windage? How does crankcase oil windage reduce engine power? Name five ways to improve oil windage control in a racing engine.

26. Name some common sources of accessory component drag. How can some of these parasitic losses be eliminated in a racing engine? Why do some racing batteries have a higher 16V rating?

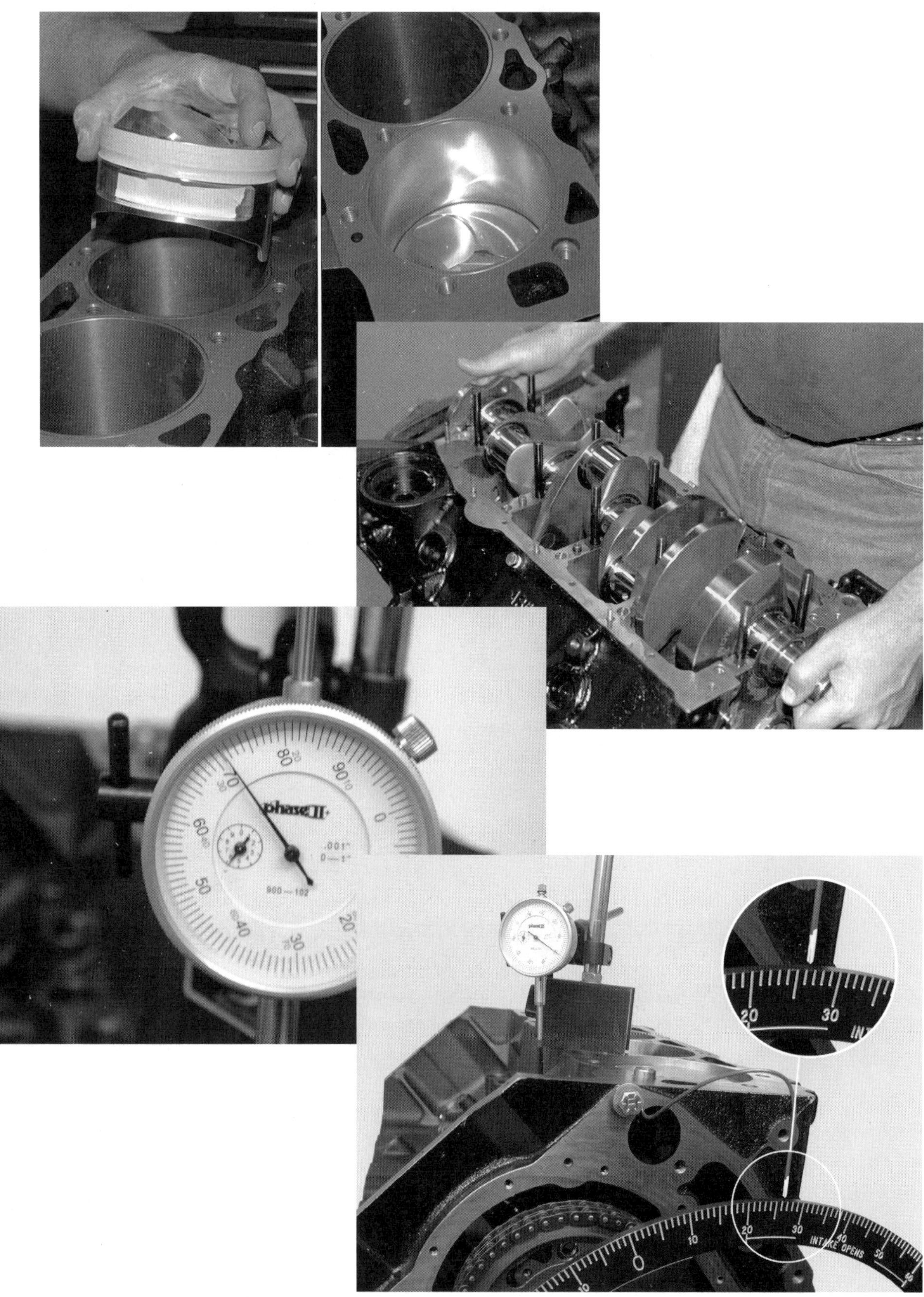
phaseII
.001"
0—1"
900—102
INTAKE OPENS

Championship Engine Assembly

Unit III - Short Block Component Selection & Preparation

The lower engine assembly is the very foundation on which horsepower and reliability are based. The crankshaft, connecting rods, and pistons must endure forces in the tens of thousands of pounds without breakage. Every part must be machined, balanced, and measured to very close tolerances. In this unit, you will learn how to select the right parts and prepare them for assembly.

Building reliable power begins in the short block assembly. This is not the time to get in a hurry. A number of pre-assembly checks, measurements, and parts modifications are required before you can bolt it all together.

Engine Block

The type and quality of engine block that you choose for a racing engine affect both the durability and power output potential. The base metal must be strong and hard in order to maintain shape under extreme loads and high temperatures. A racing block must be free from cracks or other non-repairable defects. It should have uniform wall thickness, especially around the cylinder bores to help the rings maintain a good seal.

Ferrous Blocks:

The vast majority of the racing engines we build have *ferrous* blocks. Ferrous metals contain iron and will attract a magnet. Although cast ferrous blocks are relatively heavy and difficult to weld or repair, they have other very desirable characteristics for building racing engines.

Unlike stock pieces, the special aftermarket racing ferrous blocks we use are extremely rigid and hard, making them an excellent base for building a racing engine. The cylinder walls are thick and strong, allowing them to be bored without losing their shape or durability.

This Dart Big M big block V8 ferrous casting is an excellent choice for a medium to high-horsepower racing engine because of the very high strength and hardness of the base material.

When machine work is performed on the engine block, it is not possible to duplicate the exact temperature variations and stresses that are present under racing conditions. Some distortion of machined surfaces can be expected when you run the engine, resulting in a partial loss of ring seal or increased frictional losses. Ferrous blocks are very rigid and have low rates of thermal expansion that help reduce these problems.

One drawback of ferrous materials (other than weight) is that many types of damage cannot be repaired—if there is just one small crack, it is often less expensive to scrap the entire piece. Despite this problem, we still recommend ferrous blocks for most racing applications.

Non-Ferrous Blocks:

Most non-ferrous engine blocks are cast from high-strength aluminum alloys. Aluminum blocks weigh about half of their iron counterparts and there is almost no degree of damage that cannot be successfully repaired by welding.

However, there are significant drawbacks to aluminum blocks that can compromise the power of the engine. It's not uncommon to lose 30-40 horsepower in a big block engine when you use an aluminum block.

Aluminum is very soft, so the cylinders must be sleeved with iron to withstand the wear from sliding pistons and rings. Because it has a higher rate of thermal expansion, the sleeves can move around in the block. Aluminum has a relatively high *modulus of elasticity*. All of this means that important machined tolerances change in operation and it becomes very difficult to maintain a good ring seal.

Aluminum blocks are also expensive—often several times the cost of a ferrous block. Unless weight is a critical issue, we recommend that you select a racing ferrous block as the foundation for your competition engine.

Block Availability:

GM Performance Parts, Dart, Brodix, and other companies offer great engine block choices that are desirable because of the thickness of the casting, hardness of the material, and high strength 4-bolt main bearings caps.

Dart makes a great new block that we use in our Super Series engines called the "Big M". It has an improved oiling system, splayed 4-bolt main caps, and other nice features for the racing engine builder.

All big blocks were originally cast for 4.840" bore centers and accept most available heads, crankshafts and camshafts. Today, however, new bare big blocks with bore centers of 4.900", 5.000" and even 5.200" are available. Most require custom machining operations and the use of many specialized components.

For some high-horsepower applications, we install steel billet main bearing caps. These cost more and the engine must be align honed to fit them, but they are the strongest caps available.

Due to the wide range of racing block options, such as the casting material (iron or aluminum), main bearing cap types (ductile or steel billet), deck heights, cam locations, bore center spacing, and bore diameters, it would not be practical to print a list here. Before you buy a block, we recommend that you obtain a catalog or call the manufacturer for additional information.

Seasoned vs. New Engine Blocks:

Ferrous materials are molded at very high temperatures. As the metal cools, areas contract at different rates and leave stresses in the block. As these stresses relax, critical engine clearances can change and cause the engine to lose power.

A *seasoned* block is one that has been in service for a number of months or years. Over time, the block stresses relax as the engine repeatedly heats and cools in service. This aging process also tends to harden the cast iron.

It would make sense to build a racing engine out of a seasoned engine block, but the problem is in finding one that will work. Nearly all of the blocks installed in passenger cars and trucks are too thin and weak to hold up in a racing engine. Many old blocks have cracks, stripped bolt holes, or other mechanical damage that makes them unsuitable for use. Even if you find a good seasoned racing engine block, it may already have been overbored, leaving very little material in the cylinder walls for engine maintenance.

NOTE: The amount of overbore that a block can tolerate varies by the particular part number. Check with your engine builder for maximum bore recommendations or refer to listings in the block manufacturer's catalog.

The real difference in power output between identical engines built with seasoned versus new racing blocks is negligible. You'll do far better if you put your time and money into places where the big gains are found, such as the cylinder heads and the upper engine assembly.

We have tested many block casting treatments including thermal & vibrational stress relieving processes and even cryo-freezing to harden the iron. Unless you are involved in a professional class such as Pro Stock where every horsepower counts, seasoned blocks and exotic treatments have little or no importance.

This RMRE Super Series big block V8 engine was built with all new parts and produces well over 900 horsepower.

Block Cleaning:

Before you inspect and measure a block, it first must be thoroughly cleaned. Cleaning makes cracks and other flaws visible and removes dirt or metallic particles that can affect the accuracy of measurements. Remove the oil gallery plugs with a hex key wrench and clean the passages thoroughly with long rifle barrel brushes.

Rifle barrel brushes can reach all the way through the oil galleries and remove the dirt, oil, and metal particles.

A high pressure blast of soapy water is best for removing oil and dirt deposits. Be sure to clean all internal water passages and block surfaces.

IMPORTANT! Spray a water blast through <u>all</u> oil passages to be sure that none were partially drilled at the time of manufacture.

Rinse the block with plenty of water to remove the soap residue, dry it with a blast of air, and then immediately apply oil to discourage rust formation.

Spend time cleaning your block. Spray water through all the oil passages to be sure that they are open. Apply oil immediately after drying the block.

If your engine block was a used piece, it is internally caked with dirt, rust, and scale. The best way to get it really clean is to take it to a machine shop that has a *hot tank*. The hot tank is filled with an aggressive chemical that digests organic materials, leaving only the ferrous metal. Remove the core plugs (freeze plugs) and camshaft bearings before you have this cleaning operation performed.

Remove the core plugs and cam bearings before hot tanking a seasoned block.

If you do not have the correct tools for cam bearing and core plug removal & replacement, your machine shop can perform these procedures for you. After cleaning, apply oil to the machined surfaces to prevent rust.

Block Inspection:

Cast ferrous blocks can have cracks or other damage that may make them unsuitable for use. Before investing in machine work, you should check the block for the following:

- Cracks and Thread Damage
- Cylinder Bore Damage
- Main Bore Damage
- Core Shift
- Deck Surface Damage
- Blocked Oil Passages

Cracks and Thread Damage - If you find any cracks in the casting, a ferrous block should be discarded. Also look for problems such as broken bolts and stripped threads. Broken bolts may take time to drill and remove. Stripped or damaged threads can be repaired by the installation of Heli-Coils or a similar thread repair system. A bright light will reveal large cracks, but fine cracks are much easier to find with a Magnaflux or Zyglo process.

For a ferrous block, the Magnaflux process is most often used. The machinist places a large magnet over the area that is being inspected. Iron particles applied to the area gather around any disruption in the magnetic field, clearly indicating the presence of a crack.

A magnet and special Magnaflux spray can be used to make fine cracks visible. Notice the crack in the lifter valley of this block. The coolant freezing in cold weather probably caused this. Do not use a cracked block when building a racing engine.

Cylinder Bore Damage - Look for cracks and gouges in the cylinder walls. If the engine suffered a serious problem such as a broken connecting rod or if a metal part entered the cylinder, the damage is often too severe to repair with overboring (see *Machining Operations*, *Cylinder Boring*).

Main Bore Damage - If the main bearings lose lubrication in operation, they grip the crankshaft and spin. This leaves deep scars in the precision-machined main bores. If you see any scars in the main bores, the block will require align honing or may be unsuitable for use in a racing engine.

Deck Surface Damage - Inspect the deck surfaces for cracks and discard the block if any are found. Blown head gaskets expose the deck surface to cylinder heat or water, leaving a blackened or rough appearance. This can burn a trench into the deck surface. If the trench is too deep to be repaired by milling, the block may have to be discarded.

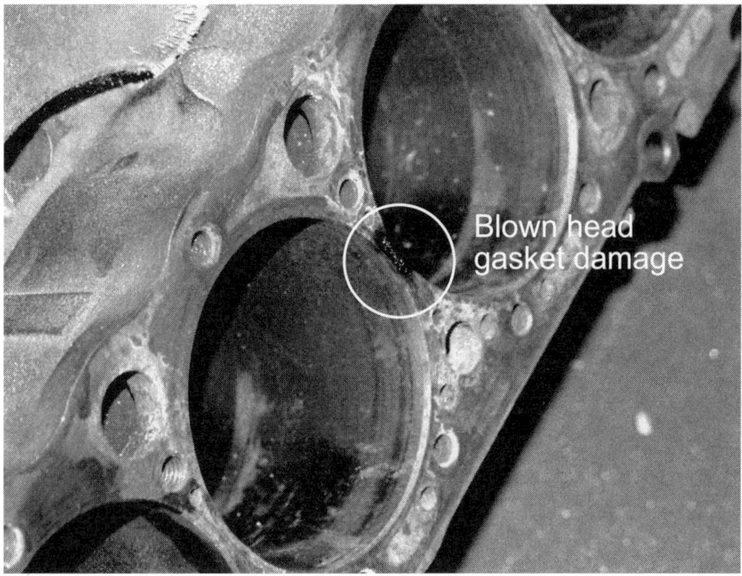

Inspect the surfaces closely. This damage was caused by a blown head gasket. If it is not too deep, surface milling may repair it. See your machinist for advice if you see this kind of damage on your block.

Core Shift - At the time that the casting molds are joined together or when the raw casting is mounted on a milling machine, some degree of misalignment is possible. This is called *core shift,* and the cylinders will have inconsistent wall thickness. As the engine block warms in operation, the cylinder walls distort. The result is lost piston ring seal and power.

The best way to determine if a block has consistent cylinder wall thickness is through *sonic testing*. This test utilizes sound waves to measure the thickness of the cylinder walls in a number of locations. There are companies that can provide this service for you, but the new GM racing blocks are shipped with the sonic test results.

If you are going to use an older block, there are telltale signs of core shift that you can easily spot. Look closely at the lifter bores. They should be centered in the bosses molded into the valley area of the block. If the holes all appear to be offset, the block probably has core shift.

These offset lifter bores are a telltale sign of significant core shift. It would be a good idea to find another block with less core shift for your racing engine.

Blocked Oil Passages - If you are using a seasoned block that ran with no difficulties, the oil passages are probably all there and may only need cleaning. However, new blocks may have oil passages that are either partially drilled or haven't been drilled at all. Always have an experienced engine builder inspect the oil passages before you build an engine with a new block.

Block Measurements:

After cleaning, a number of measurements should be performed to determine what machine work will be required including:

- Deck Height
- Cylinder Bore Diameter
- Cylinder Out-of-Round
- Cylinder Taper
- Main Bore Diameter & Alignment
- Cam Bore Diameter & Alignment

Deck Height - Deck height is the distance from the crankshaft centerline to the block deck surface.

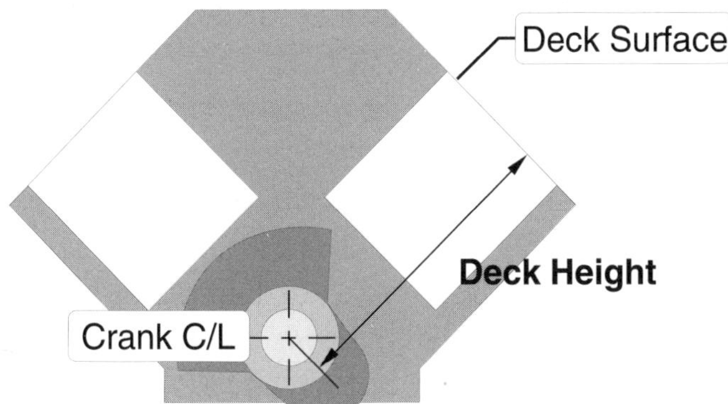

Have your machine shop measure the deck height of your block.

Most GM small blocks have an original deck height of 9.025". For GM big block engines, there are two common available block deck heights:

- Short Deck Big Block (9.800" deck height)
- Tall Deck Big Block (10.200" deck height)

GM Cast iron and aluminum performance blocks are now available from so many sources, (GM, Dart, Brodix, Donovan, etc.), and in so many configurations, that to attempt to list them here would not be practical. We suggest you obtain a catalog or contact the manufacturer to get the most updated information and availability for a block suited for your specific engine building project.

The short deck blocks (9.800") are good choices for most racing engines with strokes of 4.250" or less. The tall deck blocks (10.200") have deeper cylinders that can handle strokes from 4.250" to 4.750", but you will have to do some grinding along the pan rails to make clearance for the connecting rods (see the *Checking for Interference* section of this unit).

NOTE: Never assume that the deck height of your block matches the original specification, especially if the block is used. The deck surface may have been milled or it may not be parallel with the crank bores.

Special fixtures are required to measure the block deck height. Have a machine shop perform this measurement for you. This information is very important when choosing bore/stoke combinations, rod lengths, and piston compression height measurements (see the *Connecting Rods, Calculating Rod Length, Stackup* section of this unit).

Cylinder Bore Diameter - Use an *inside micrometer* or *bore gauge* to measure the bore at a location 1/2" below the deck surface. If the block is seasoned, this is where you can normally expect to find the greatest amount of wear from the piston rings. Also measure the diameter at points deeper in the cylinder.

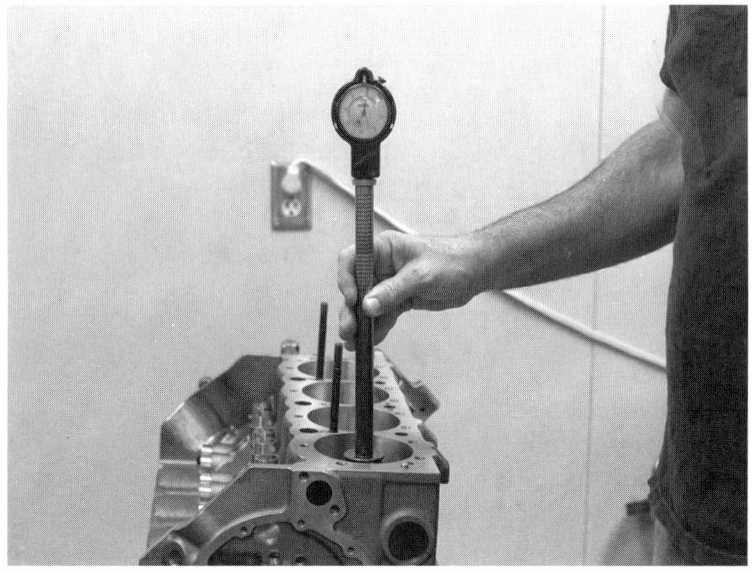

This machinist is using a bore gauge to measure cylinder diameter.

Cylinder Out-of-Round - The pistons lean hard on the *major thrust face* as they push on the connecting rods during power strokes. This tends to wear the cylinder into an "egg" shape.

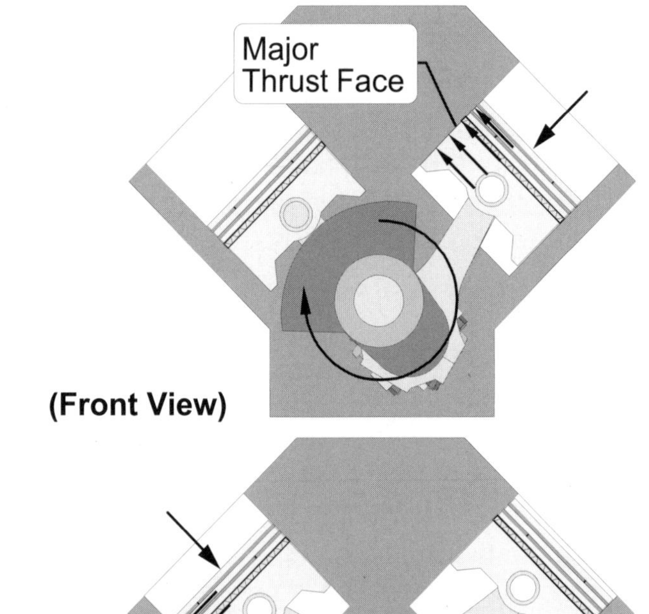

The pistons on the driver's side (left) cylinder bank wear against the inside cylinder walls.

The pistons on the passenger's side (right) cylinder bank wear against the outside cylinder walls.

Use a bore gauge to measure the diameter across the major & minor thrust faces at the midpoint of the cylinder. Then measure the diameter at 90° to the thrust faces. Subtract the two measurements to find the amount of cylinder out-of-round.

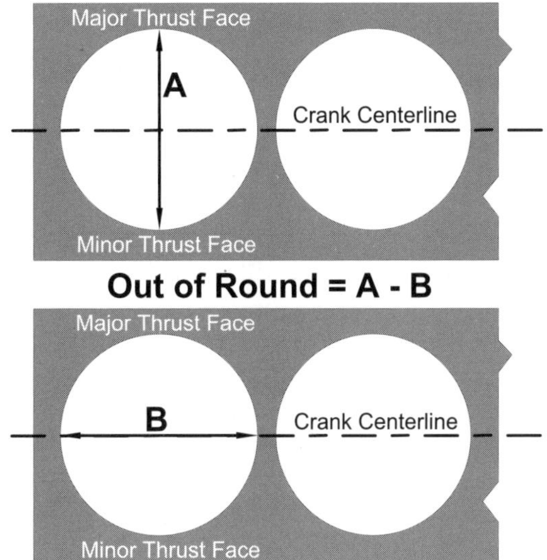

Subtract these bore measurements to determine cylinder out-of-round.

Cylinder Taper - Piston rings do not wear the cylinders walls evenly because the pressures that push them against the cylinder walls are much higher near TDC. An outward taper develops near the top, but does not extend all the way to the deck surface. This is because the top compression ring is below the top of the piston. In time, a noticeable overhanging ledge, or *ring ridge* is left at the top of each cylinder.

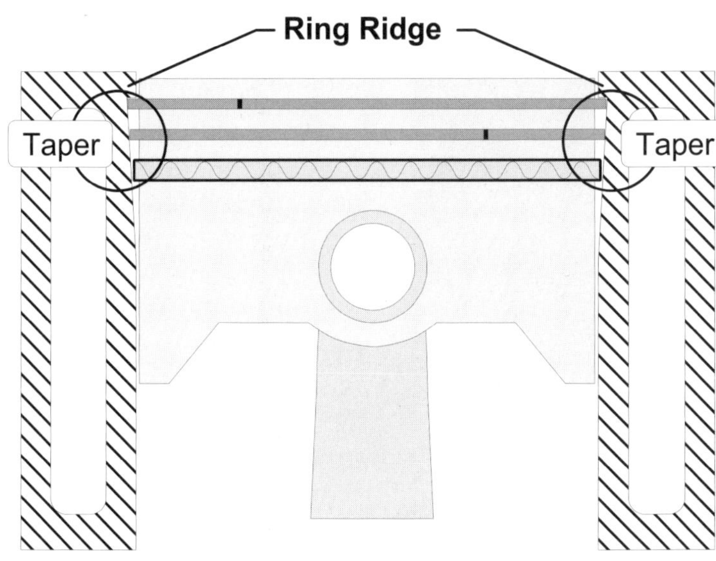

Heat & pressure on the piston rings wears a taper near the top of the cylinder. This causes a ring ridge to develop.

If the engine block has a visible ring ridge, you can be sure that it also has large amount of cylinder taper. You must still measure the amount of taper so that you know how much the cylinders will have to be bored to clean up the damage.

Check cylinder taper by measuring the diameter of the cylinder near the bottom, then again at a point near the top, but under any ring ridge. Taper is the difference between these two measurements.

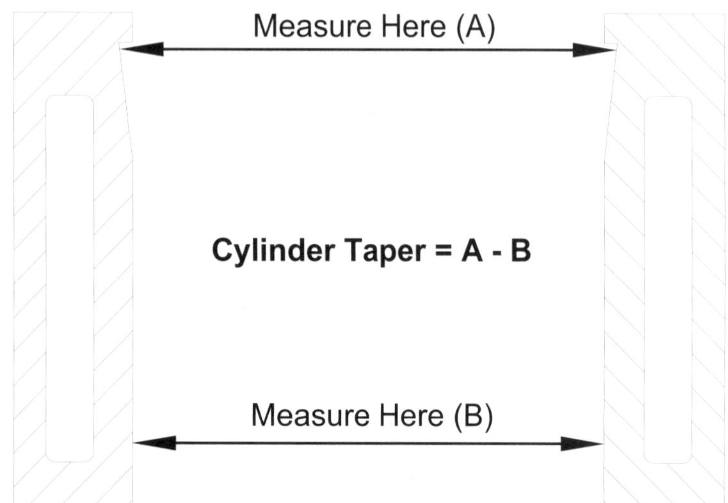

To find cylinder taper, subtract the diameter at the bottom of the cylinder (B) from the diameter at the top of the cylinder (A).

<u>Main Bore Diameter & Alignment</u> - The diameter and alignment of the block *main bore* is critical to avoid bearing failures. A bore gauge can be used to measure the diameter of each main bore. Bearing problems can result if the bore diameters reduce the vertical bearing clearance by more than .0005".

This technician is checking main bore diameters with a bore gauge. Have the block align honed if any the bore diameters are out of spec. It is especially important to be sure that they aren't tight vertically—this would reduce the critically important vertical bearing oil clearance.

Over time, individual main bores in a block can become misaligned. Excessive main bore misalignment adds undue pressure between the bearings and crankshaft. A machine shop can check the main bore alignment for you. If any main bore is out of alignment by more than .0015", you should have the block align honed.

If you don't have a main bore alignment measuring kit, you can perform a quick test to get some idea if the main bore alignment is in need of correction. The first thing you need is a straight crankshaft. Here's one way you can check crankshaft straightness without a special fixture.

Place one bearing insert at each end of the main bores. Lubricate the bearings and lay the crankshaft on the end bearings. Mount a dial indicator so that the plunger rests on the middle main journal. Slowly rotate the crankshaft and measure runout at the middle journal. A runout of .001" or less indicates that the crankshaft is straight enough for this test.

Lubricate and install the main bearings into the block and main caps. Install the crankshaft without a rear main seal. Torque the main caps to specs and rotate the crankshaft. It should turn freely by hand. If it is tight, loosen one main at a time until it turns freely. This indicates that the mains are misaligned and align-honing is required.

Our philosophy at Reher-Morrison is to align-hone every block. For the time it takes to check main alignment by any method, we can already have the block honed and ready with full confidence that there will be no problems related to main alignment.

<u>Cam Bore Diameter & Alignment</u> - As with the main bores, cam bearing bores can be the wrong bore size or misaligned. A bore gauge should be used to check the cam bore diameters. If any diameter is out of specification by more than ±.0005", cam bearing problems can result. A machine shop can check cam bore alignment for you. We do not like to assemble an engine with bore misalignment greater than ±.0015".

Have a good machine shop check the cam bores for diameter and alignment.

Machining Operations:

After you inspect and measure your block, it's time for a trip to the machine shop. Most problems that were found when making measurements can be corrected at this stage. Common racing engine block machining operations include:

- Main Align Honing
- Cam Align Honing and Bearing Installation
- Cylinder Boring
- Cylinder Honing
- Lifter Bore Honing
- Lifter Bore Sleeving
- Deck Milling
- O-Ringing the Block
- Deburring, Chamfering, & Thread Chasing

IMPORTANT! - The tolerances and consistency of machine work are extremely important to the power and reliability of a racing engine. If clearances are wrong or bores and deck surfaces are warped, a lot of power will be lost in the engine, or it may come apart in a catastrophic failure.

There is usually no visible difference between the best work performed by true professionals and that performed by less reputable shops that use improper techniques and poorly maintained machinery. You'll be ahead in money and performance if you deal with shops that have a proven record of producing championship-caliber racing engines.

Main Align Honing - All machine work starts with the main bores. The main bores must be as straight as possible, not only to prevent binding of the crankshaft, but also because the cylinders and deck surfaces are machined in relationship to the mains. We align-hone the mains of every block, new or used, to ensure that they are straight.

This special machine can accurately align hone racing engine blocks.

To align hone the mains, the machinist removes the main caps and mills a small amount of material off the base of the caps. When the caps are bolted back onto the block the holes are no longer round. A honing tool is run through the mains to restore the original size and create proper main alignment.

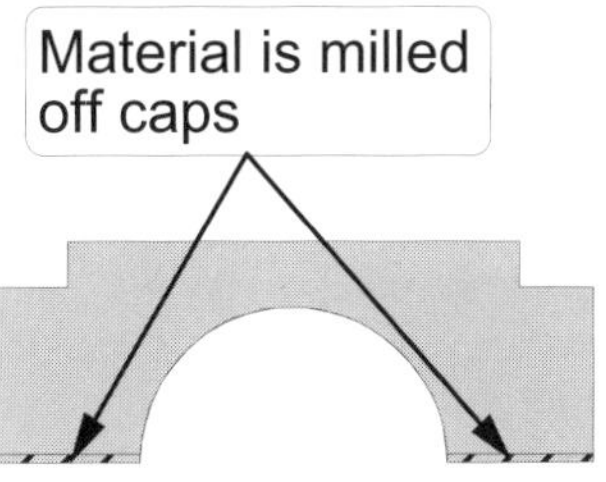

To align bore or hone a block, some material is first ground off the caps.

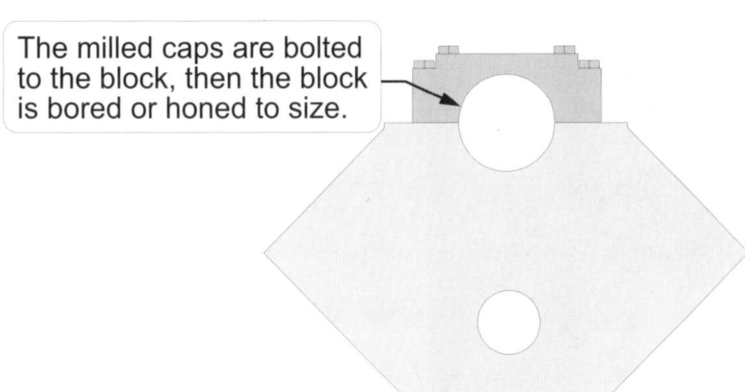

The caps are bolted onto the block and torqued to specifications. A special tool hones the oblong holes back to the original size. This corrects both main bore diameter and misalignment of the mains.

Cam Align Honing and Bearing Installation - Because the cam bores have no caps, the only way to correct cam bore alignment is to overbore the holes and install oversize cam bearings.

This machinist is removing the old cam bearings with a special tool in preparation for align honing the cam bores.

Babbitted cam bearing installation is particularly tricky because the bearings press-fit into the block and have oil holes that must be aligned. If a cam bearing oil hole is not properly aligned, the bearing will not have an adequate oil supply. This work should only be performed by trained professionals.

Cylinder Boring – You must correct any cylinder taper and out-of-round by having the block overbored and honed. All cylinders should be bored to the same size. The only way to be sure that the bores are perpendicular with the crank bores is with a machine like the one shown below.

The machinist carefully adjusts the cutting tool before boring the block. Be sure your machine shop has the right equipment for this job.

Pistons and rings can be purchased for almost any bore/stroke combination. Unless you are trying to increase the engine displacement, have the machine shop bore the block to the minimum size that cleans up the cylinders. This leaves the cylinder walls more rigid and allows you to re-bore the engine again to keep it fresh.

NOTE: Some builders install sleeves to repair severely damaged cylinders. To accommodate a sleeve, the cylinder must be bored to a very large size. This leaves the cylinder walls and deck thin, leading to cracks around the head bolt holes. If the boring tool cuts into the water jacket, the deck is no longer supported and the pressed-in sleeve will almost surely leak coolant in the crankcase.

For these reasons, we do not consider cylinder sleeving to be an acceptable repair procedure. Any block with cylinder wall damage that cannot be removed within the manufacturer's recommended maximum bore size should be discarded.

Overboring increases engine size and compression. If your class has restrictions on engine displacement or compression ratio, you must be careful not to exceed the maximum limits.

Cylinder Honing - The cylinder boring tool leaves the cylinder walls extremely rough with sharp, abrasive peaks that would cause wear to pistons. For this reason, the machinist always bores the block a few thousandths of an inch too small, then moves the block into a cylinder honing machine to bring the bores to the desired finish and bore size. The honing stones knock down the peaks into plateaus, while retaining valleys that hold oil for lubrication and to help seal the rings.

Cylinder honing is one of the more critical steps in block preparation. Piston rings seal best when the finish is right and the bores are straight and round. The cylinder honing machine applies pressure to rotating and reciprocating stones leaving a smooth, crosshatched pattern.

No block machining process is more important than cylinder honing. This expensive machine and an experienced operator are a must to create cylinder walls with the right finish and shape.

Cylinder head bolts or studs create wedging and pulling effects that distort the round shape of the cylinders and the block deck surfaces. For better ring seal, a *torque plate* must be installed to duplicate these stresses before honing the cylinders. We select a torque plate that is made of the same type of material as the heads and install it using the same type of gasket and fasteners.

A torque plate is a must to duplicate the cylinder wall distortion caused by head bolts or studs. This engine will have aluminum heads and studs, so an aluminum torque plate and the same type of studs and gasket are installed before honing the block.

Cylinder honing is a good example of where art and science come together. Abrasive stone pressures, rotation rpm's, and stroke rates must be closely monitored during the honing process. The machinist makes frequent measurements to ensure that the cylinder walls are round, straight, and the right size for the application. A continuous flow of honing oil removes metal particles and prevents the stones from clogging.

Cylinder honing requires expensive equipment, continuous monitoring, and careful measurements by an experienced machinist.

The resulting crosshatch pattern can be seen in the close-up of a finished cylinder wall shown below. Depending on the type of pistons and the ring package, we use stones between #280 and #400 grit to obtain the correct crosshatch finish. This pattern and texture will ensure rapid ring seating with plasma/moly piston rings.

This crosshatch pattern was created with #400 grit honing stones. It is the right finish to form an exceptional seal with plasma/moly racing rings.

Inexperienced operators or shops with manually operated honing equipment can do a lot of damage to your block, leaving you with inconsistent bore diameters or tapered and out-of-round cylinders. The result will be poor ring seal and lost performance. Be sure to take your block to a qualified and experienced racing engine builder.

Lifter Bore Honing - The lifters bores must be properly located and must allow the lifters to glide smoothly without sticking or galling. The size of the bore is also important because oil pressure is supplied to the lifter through holes that connect to the lifter oil galleries. If clearances are too tight, the lifters may bind. If clearances are too loose, too much oil will bleed around the lifters and reduce the engine oil pressure.

If the lifter bores were located and machined properly at the time of manufacture, most blocks require only a quick touch with a lifter honing tool. This tool can be operated in a hand-held electric drill if you have some experience. Be sure to control drill rpm's and adjust your stroke speed to create a smooth, crosshatched finish. Use a liberal application of honing oil and remove as little material as possible to clean up the bores.

The lifters must fit without binding or looseness in the lifter bores. This machinist is using a dial indicator to measure the diameter of the lifter bores.

Lifter Bore Sleeving - The extreme valve spring pressure on modern racing engines puts a lot of angular pressure on the lifters. Bronze lifter sleeves can be installed to correct the angle and operation of the lifters or to repair worn and damaged bores. To install lifter sleeves, the machinist mounts the block in the boring machine and sets the angle of the reaming tool. After the bores have been opened, bronze sleeves are press-fit into place. The sleeves are then reamed and honed to the finished size.

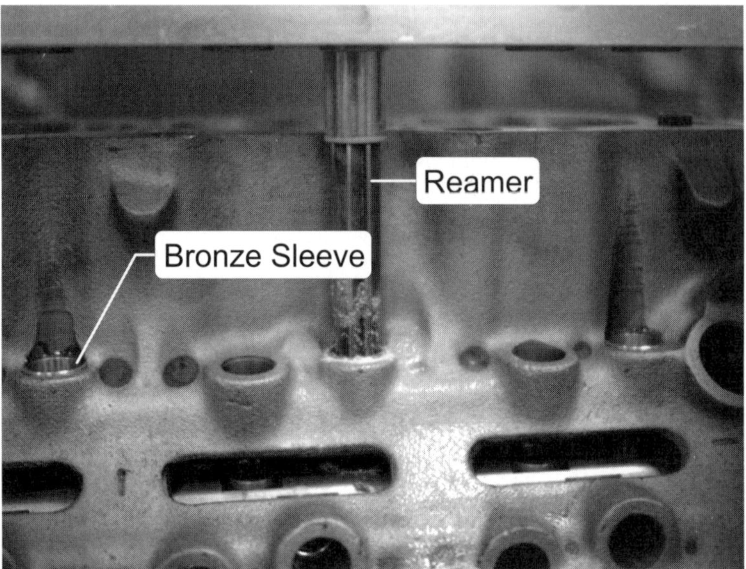

This lifter bore is being reamed for the insertion of a bronze sleeve. The sleeve is pressed into the bore, then trimmed, beveled, and honed to size.

Deck Milling - The deck surfaces should be milled just enough to make both sides of the block straight and equal in height. The block is located by the mains to ensure parallelism with the deck surface.

The machinist mills the engine block to correct deck straightness and parallelism, or to reduce the deck height. Oil should be applied after this procedure to discourage the formation of rust.

NOTE: The block should be milled to a pre-determined height so that your combination of crank, rods, and pistons provides the required total deck clearance. For more information, see *Connecting Rods, Calculating Rod Length* in this unit.

O-Ringing the Head/Block - Racing engines often have problems maintaining the integrity of the head gasket seal. High cylinder pressures tend to lift the heads off the block. Differences in rates of thermal expansion between aluminum heads and ferrous blocks cause a sliding action against the head gaskets.

In high-horsepower/extreme cylinder pressure applications, we sometimes add steel O-rings to the head around each cylinder. The O-rings compress the copper head gasket into a receiver groove in the block to create a very effective barrier to gas pressure losses. This procedure effectively eliminates head gasket sealing problems in these engines.

This head has been O-ringed to help maintain a good head gasket seal.

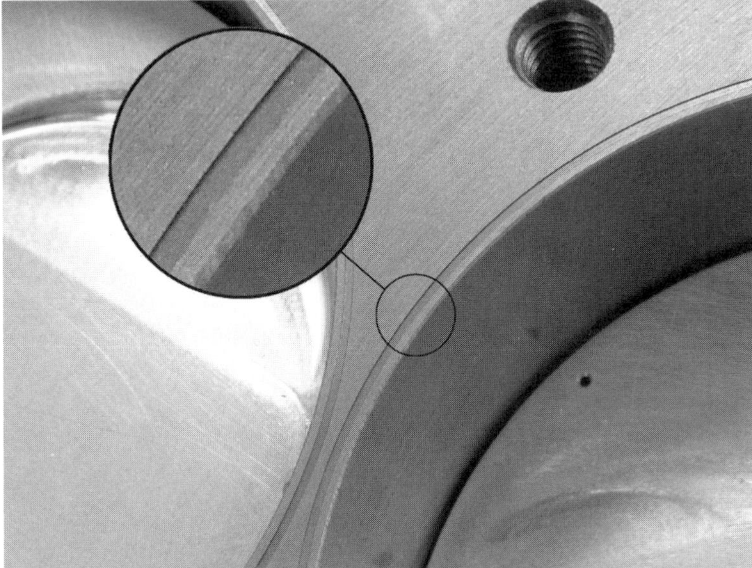

The copper gasket is compressed into receiver grooves that are cut around each cylinder.

Sometimes, the engine builder doesn't cut a receiver groove. In that case, the steel O-rings are installed into grooves around the cylinders.

Deburring, Chamfering, & Thread Chasing - Metal burrs on newly machined edges may scratch moving parts or may break loose and become imbedded in engine bearings. When you get your block back from the machine shop, deburr all sharp edges with a pneumatic or electric grinder.

Smooth the sharp edges with a high speed grinder after the machine work has been completed.

Crankcase windage is a mixture of oil droplets and gases that slow the spinning crankshaft (see the *Crankshaft, Crankshaft Features* section of this unit). Smoothing the sharp edges in the crankcase can reduce horsepower losses by minimizing oil windage.

Threaded holes in the engine block may also have burrs or dents. Chase all the threads with a thread chaser and thread cutting oil. This is an important procedure that helps ensure proper bolt torque during engine assembly. The top of every hole must also be chamfered to allow some room for surface distortion when tightening the bolts.

Chase the threads of all holes to ensure proper assembly torque. Carefully chamfer the top of each hole with a 45° countersink bit in an electric drill.

Bearings

Engine bearings are used for the camshaft, crankshaft main journals, and crankshaft rod journals. There are two types used in racing engines—babbitted inserts and roller bearings. All crankshaft main and rod bearing are babbitted inserts that are split into two halves. Cam bearings are complete rings that are pressed into the block.

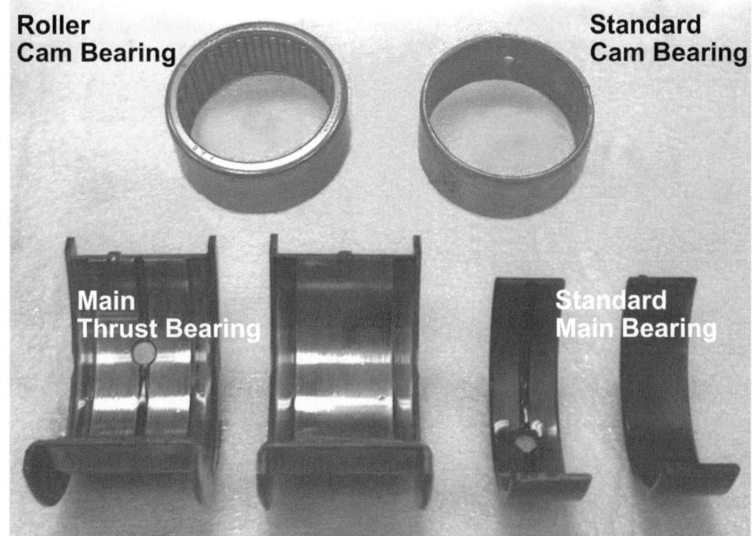

These are types of engine bearing inserts. Note the flanges on the sides of the main thrust bearing.

Bearing Insert Construction:

Bearing inserts have a smooth, flat surface into which oil is pumped to reduce friction against spinning journal. They have a stiff metal backing made of aluminum or steel to maintain the shape of the insert. A layer of heat-conductive copper is plated onto the metal backing. A layer of soft *babbitt* metal is applied to the copper.

Babbitt is a mixture of soft metals including tin, copper, and antimony. This material reduces wear on crankshaft journals and has a property called *imbedability*. Imbedability means that small particles of dirt or metal can become imbedded into the surface of the babbitt layer so they don't run around and scratch the journals. The top surface of a racing engine bearing is often coated with lead-iridium or Teflon® to reduce friction.

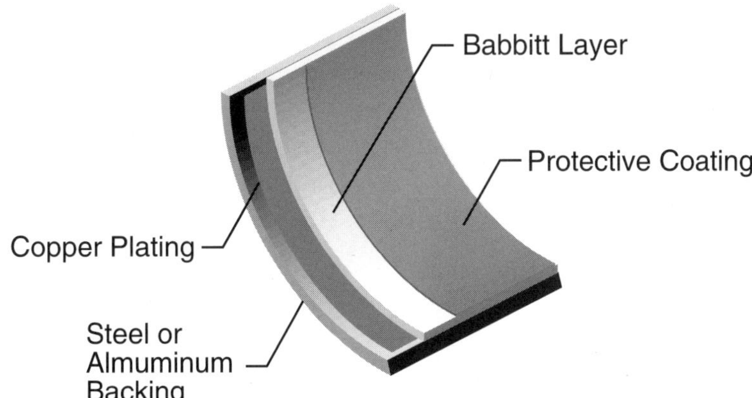

Race bearing inserts have a stiff backing, with layers of copper, babbitt, and a protective coating.

Bearing Insert Features:

To keep them from spinning, the bearing inserts extend beyond the parting line of the bores. This characteristic is called *bearing crush*. When the caps are tightened, bearing crush provides a high degree of friction between the backs of the bearings and the bores.

To make engine assembly easier, bearing inserts also have *spread*. The bearings are spread wider than the bore at the time of manufacture. When you press the inserts into place with your thumb, the tension created by the spread will keep them in place as you complete the engine assembly.

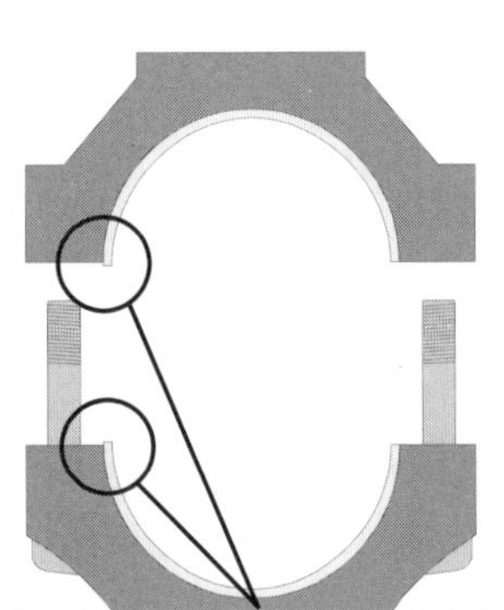

Bearing Crush - The insert extends beyond the parting line.

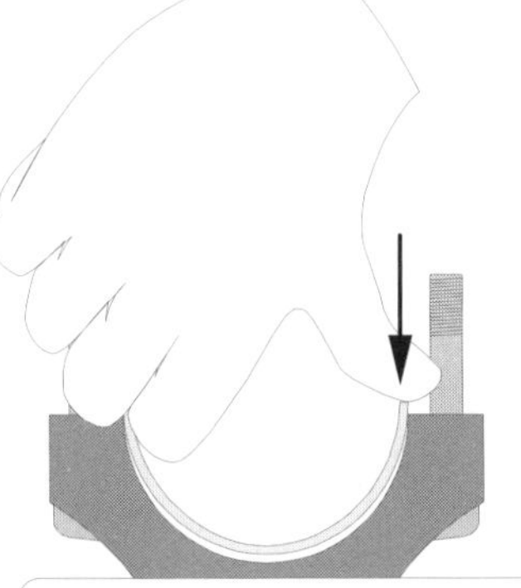

Bearing Spread - The insert is slightly wider than the bore.

Bearing crush and spread are two extremely important characteristics of engine bearing inserts.

Main bearings usually have an oil hole only in one bearing half. When you install bearing inserts, always place the main bearing insert half with the oil hole into the block, or you will cut off the oil supply to the bearing.

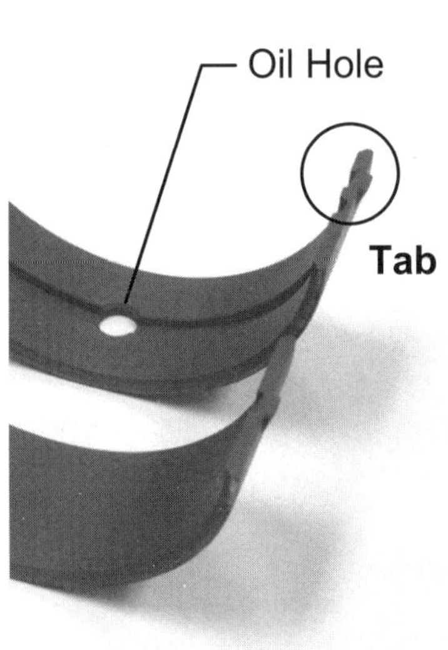

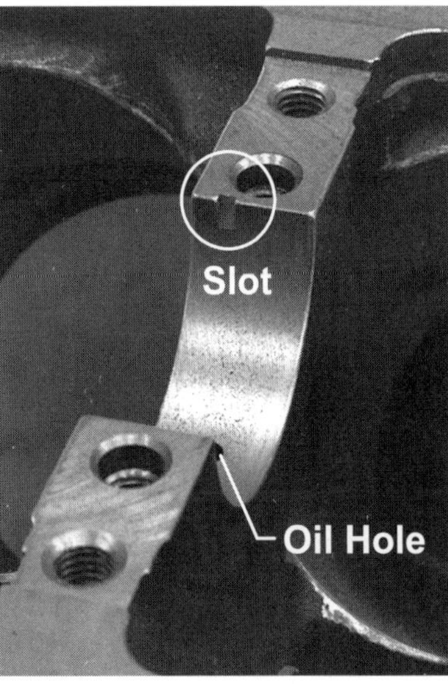

Always put the main bearing insert with the oil hole into the block, not the cap. The bearing tab must engage the slot in the bore.

Selecting Bearings:

Engine Bearing Inserts - We have used babbitted racing engine bearings from a number of suppliers without problems. You should talk to an engine builder or representative of a race bearing manufacturer for their recommendations.

Cam Bearings - In the past, cam bearings usually had a single hole. Today, most babbitted cam bearings have three oil holes and a groove that provides full flow all the way around the bearing. Oil holes must be carefully aligned when the bearings are pressed into the block. This procedure requires a special tool and is best left to an experienced machinist.

Roller cam bearings are expensive and require the use of a block that has been designed and machined for their use. However, roller cam bearings have important advantages if you are building a high-horsepower racing engine.

This high-horsepower GM small block racing engine is being assembled with roller cam bearings.

The rollers are in continuous contact with the cam journals, so they maintain better vertical cam positioning at all times. They can handle high loads and are a must when valve spring pressures of 1000 lb. or higher are used. Roller cam bearings also offer important advantages for the engine oiling system.

Oil flows through most racing engines at a rate of 8-12 gpm (gallons per minute). Anything you can do that reduces the amount of oil that must be pumped through an engine means less drag and more power. Although roller cam bearings may actually increase frictional drag as the rollers spin against the cam journals, the loss is more than offset by savings in oil flow demands.

Roller cam bearings get plenty of cooling and lubrication from oil splash off the crankshaft. When you press them into the block, the outer bearing races cover up the oil holes in the cam bores. This saves about one gpm of oil flow in the engine and results in a small net gain in horsepower due to reduced oil pump drag.

NOTE: Special modifications are often needed when using a belt-drive camshaft drive system with roller cam bearings. We have found that you if you try to run cam thrust washers alone with roller cam bearings, the block side of the thrust washer often wears excessively. For additional information about using roller camshaft bearings in belt drive applications, see *Unit IV - Upper End Component Selection, Camshaft Drive Assemblies, Belt Drives.*

Bearing Sizes:

Bearings are available in standard undersizes to fit reground crankshafts. The bearing undersize is stamped on the back of the bearing insert.

Undersize Markings

This bearing is .010" undersize.

Bearing Oil Clearances:

Bearing oil clearance is the difference between the inside diameter (ID) of the bearing and the outside diameter (OD) of the journal.

Bearing Oil Clearance = Bearing ID - Journal OD

The easiest way to measure bearing oil clearance is to adjust an outside micrometer to the crank journal and set the lock. Install the bearings and torque the caps to specifications. Adjust a good dial bore gauge to the outside micrometer so that it reads "0". The bore gauge will now read bearing oil clearance directly when it is placed into the bearing that corresponds to the measured crank journal. *Always make this measurement at 90° to the cap parting line.* These are the main and rod bearing oil clearances we use on our Super Series engines:

- *Main Bearing Oil Clearance - .003" - .004"*
- *Rod Bearing Oil Clearance - .003" - .004"*

Remember our rule about engine clearance—a little loose is better than too tight. If the bearing oil clearances are too tight, engine damage will result.

High rpm engine operation causes a bearing distortion problem that used to cause a lot of bearing failures. When the piston reverses at TDC, it places enormous stretching forces on the rod, pulling it into an oval shape. This pinches the bearing against the rod journal at the sides.

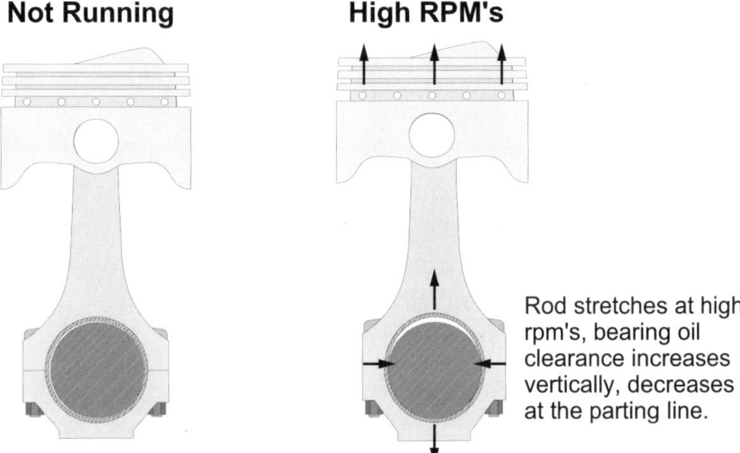

High rpm's distorts the shape of the rod, pulling the rod together at the parting line and pinching the bearing at the sides.

Racing engine bearings are now made thinner near the parting line to provide additional clearance at the sides. For this reason, bearing oil clearances must be measured vertically, at 90° to the parting line. If you measure horizontally from parting line to parting line, you'll find that the clearance is several thousandths of an inch greater.

Pinned Bearings:

If oil clearances are correct and the lubrication system functions properly, bearing crush should be enough to keep the bearings from spinning in a steel rod. With a high thermal expansion rate, aluminum rods tend to relax their grip on the bearing inserts. To help keep the bearing from turning in an aluminum rod, they must be pinned. Matching dowelled bearings are available from most manufacturers.

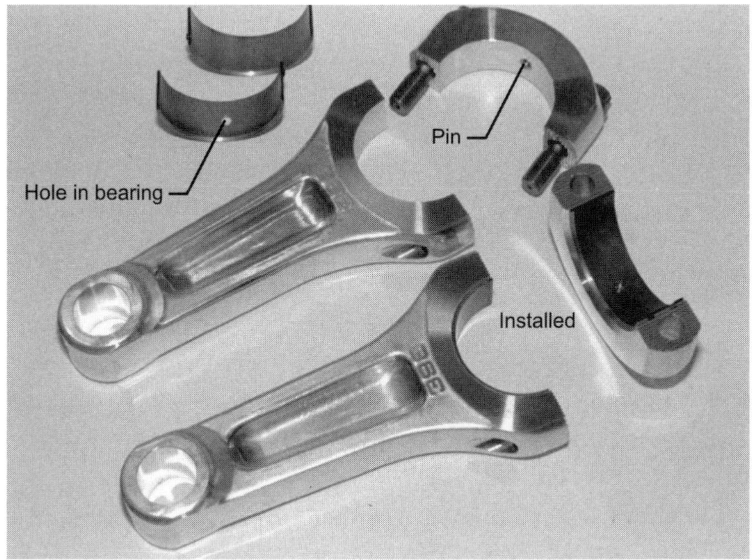

Pinning the rod bearings offers protection against spun bearings in aluminum connecting rods. This procedure requires a special drilling fixture.

Crankshaft

The type and quality of crankshaft that you choose for a racing engine affect both the durability and power output potential. There are three basic types of crankshafts; cast, forged, and billet steel.

Crankshaft Types:

Cast Nodular Steel - Cast nodular steel crankshafts usually have a grainy surface with a casting *flash line* where the molds were joined. If you tap lightly on a counterweight, you'll hear a dead "clunk" sound. This ability of a cast nodular crankshaft to *dampen* (deaden) harmonic vibrations makes them desirable for use in stock truck and a few extreme endurance racing applications. Although cast nodular steel is a premium ferrous casting material, the ultimate strength of these crankshafts is somewhat limited. For this reason, we do not recommend cast nodular steel crankshafts in most racing applications.

Forged Steel - Forged steel crankshafts are a little more expensive than cast steel crankshafts, but have superior internal metallic structure and are the strongest you can buy. A forged steel crankshaft has a smoother appearance on the un-machined surfaces than one that is cast. A forged steel crank has a distinctive "ring" when you tap on a counterweight. Forged steel crankshafts are available from the OEM (Original Equipment Manufacturer) or from several aftermarket manufacturers. They are a good choice for many short term racing applications and are available in several stroke lengths.

This forged steel crankshaft will endure the stresses in an 800+ hp. racing engine.

Billet Steel - These crankshafts are machined from a large blank (billet) of very high strength steel alloy. This allows the engine builder to obtain a custom piece with almost any journal size and layout without sacrificing too much strength. This makes a billet crankshaft a common choice for Pro Stock racing engines and other exotic, high-end applications. One big disadvantage of a billet steel crank is its price—a quality custom piece can cost several thousand dollars.

Crankshaft Features:

Counterweights - The weight of the offset rod journals, connecting rods, and pistons must be counterbalanced or the assembly would shake violently in operation. The crankshaft of a GM V8 engine usually has six counterweights.

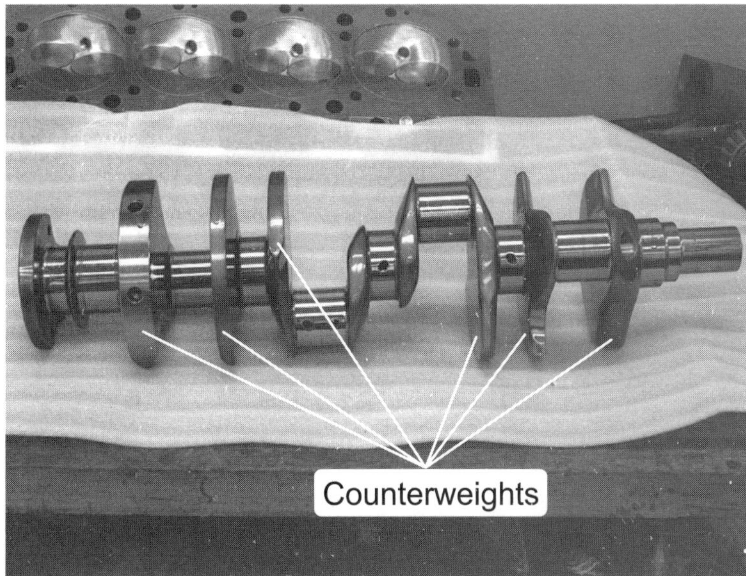

These six counterweights must be the right weight and in the correct position for proper engine balance.

The crankshaft acts like the blades of a blender, whipping oil droplets and crankcase gases into a circulating mist called *windage*. Windage slows the crankshaft and robs a lot of horsepower from the engine—up to 80 hp or even more!

To cut through the windage better, some racing crankshaft manufacturers "knife edge" the leading edges of the counterweights. However, sharp angles tend to deflect oil, rather than allow it to flow around the counterweight. We prefer a more aerodynamic teardrop shape, with a rounded leading edge and a sharper tailing edge to minimize turbulence and windage losses.

The leading edge of this counterweight is rounded to reduce the frictional losses from contact with oil windage.

Journals - Engine size is determined by the bore diameter, stroke length, and number of cylinders in the engine. The stroke is the distance from *Top Dead Center* (*TDC*) to *Bottom Dead Center* (*BDC*).

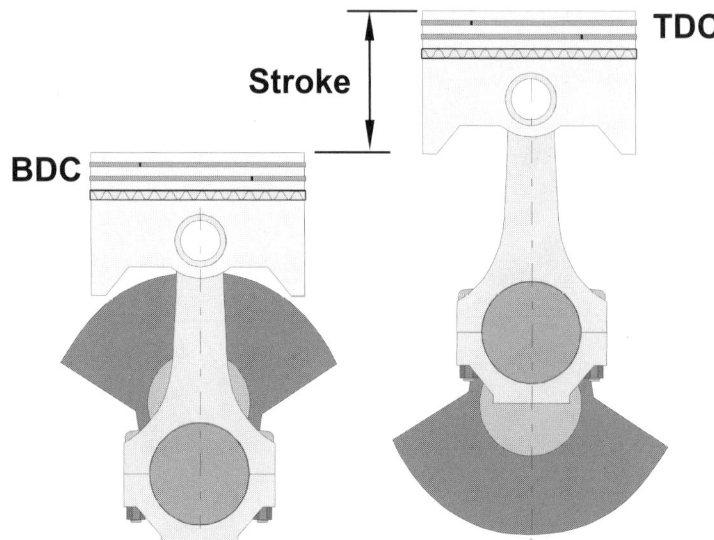

The position of the rod journals determines the stroke. "Dead Center" refers to alignment of the wrist pin, rod journal, and main journal.

Be sure that the crankshaft that you buy has the desired stroke for the engine displacement that you wish to build.

Main and rod journals must have a very precise diameter to provide the correct clearance with the bearing inserts. The journals must have a smooth, polished finish to reduce frictional losses. The sides of each journal must have a smooth radius to avoid sharp corners called *stress risers* that encourage the formation of cracks.

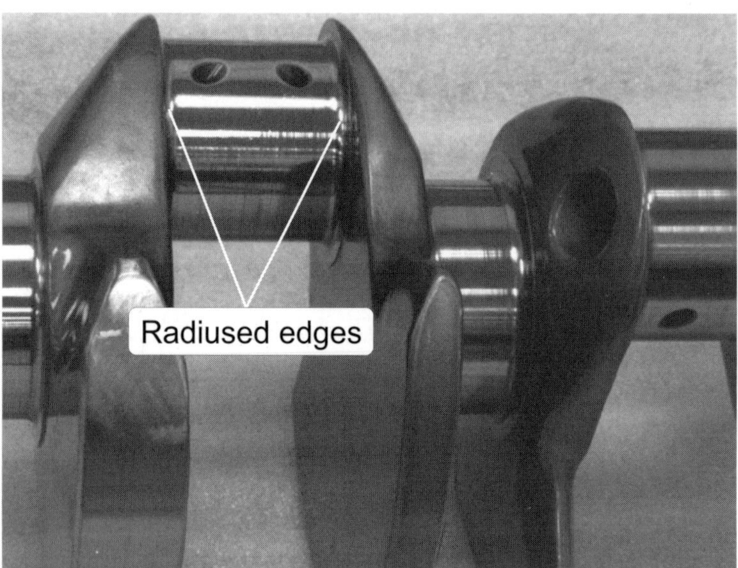

All journals must have a smooth radius at the edges to eliminate stress risers.

Also, note the sharper trailing edge on the counterweights that work with the rounded leading edge to create an aerodynamic teardrop shape.

Oil Passages - Oil is delivered under pressure to the main bearings in the block. The oil then travels through drilled passages in the crankshaft to lubricate the rod journals. At one time, it was believed that adding additional holes straight through the mains would help equalize oil flow to the bearings. This is called *cross-drilling* the crankshaft.

A cross-drilled crank may work in an engine that runs at relatively low rpm's, but experience proves that it has the opposite effect at very high engine speeds. Above 8000 rpm's, cross-drilled crankshafts starve the rod bearings and cause bearing failures. We believe this is a result of a "pin-wheeling" effect:

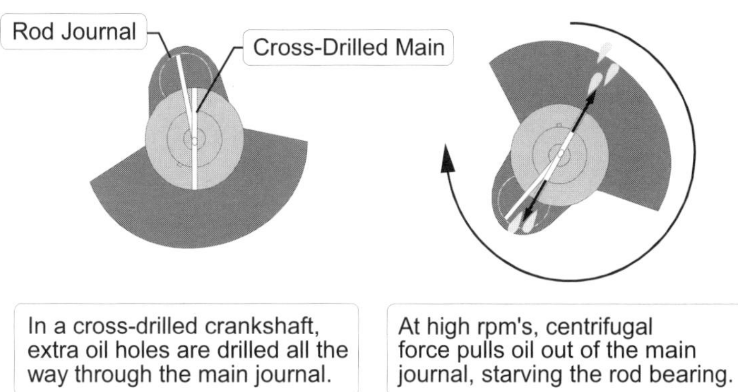

At high rpm's, cross-drilling allows centrifugal force to draw oil out of the rod journal oil holes. We call this a "pin-wheeling" effect.

You can check to see if your crankshaft is cross-drilled by inserting a piece of welding rod into the main oil holes as shown below. If the rod goes all the way through, the crank is cross-drilled and should not be used for high-rpm racing engines.

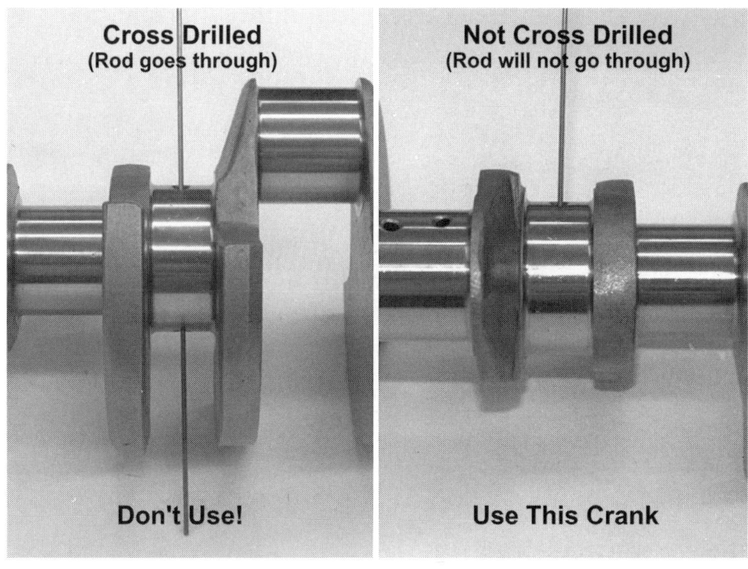

Before you use an old high performance crank, perform this simple test. Insert a welding rod as shown. If it goes all the way through (left photo), the crank is cross-drilled and should not be used if you plan to twist your engine above 8000 rpm's.

Crankshaft Inspection:

Clean the crankshaft in a parts washer, then check it for cracks and journal damage. A "tap ring" test may indicate an internal flaw if the shaft has a dead sound. A machine shop can Magnaflux your crank to reveal smaller cracks. Superficial scratches on journals may be polished away, but deep scratches require re-grinding.

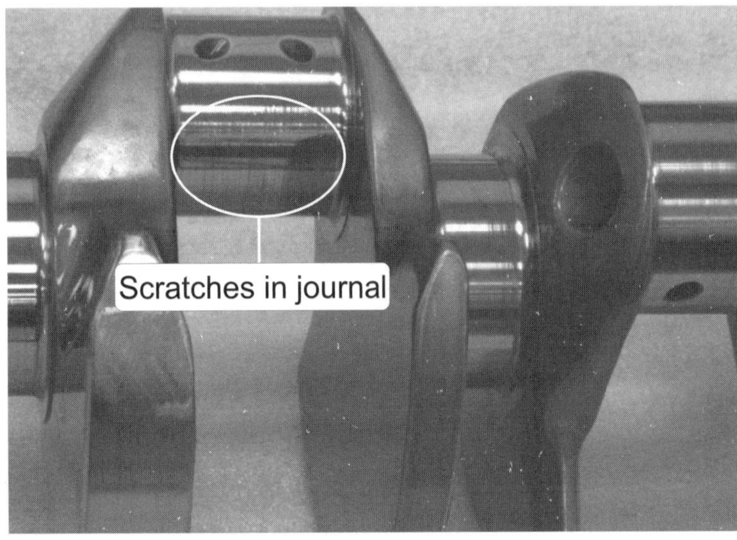

This crankshaft shows some light scratches that can probably be polished away by a machine shop.

Crankshaft Measurements:

After the initial cleaning and inspection, measure the crankshaft for the following:

- Straightness
- Journal Wear

Straightness - A racing engine builder can check and, in many cases, correct crankshaft straightness. The machinist chucks the crank into a special crank alignment fixture and measures runout at the center (#3) main journal.

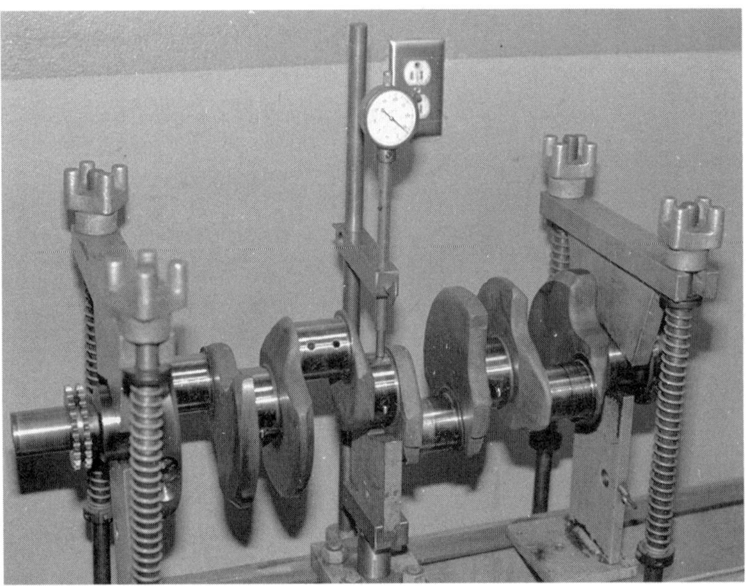

We measure and correct crankshaft straightness with this special fixture. If the crank is bent, the machinist applies pressure to the low point with a hydraulic jack located at the base of the machine.

Journal Wear - Ideally, bearings and crank journals should always have a layer of oil between them so that they never touch. However, during engine start up or conditions of extreme load or low oil pressure, bearing-to-journal contact can occur. Over time, the journals can be worn out of round. Measure the main and rod journals diameters and check for an out-of-round condition as shown below.

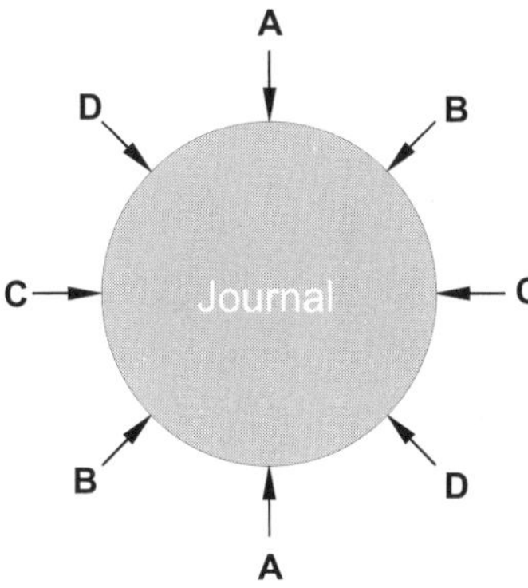

Measure the crank journal diameters at these points. Any differences in the dimensions indicate an out-of-round condition.

Use an outside micrometer with a minimum accuracy of ±.0001" for your crankshaft journal diameter measurements. A lot of time and practice are required to develop a "feel" for micrometer adjustments. Tighten the thimble until there is very light drag across the surface. We prefer to assemble engines with crank journal diameters within ±.0002" of the specified size for ease of obtaining correct bearing oil clearances.

Be sure to check the journals for taper. To do this, make several measurements at different points across the journals. Any differences in your measurements indicates crank journal taper. Repeat the measurement several times to be sure you have obtained an accurate reading.

Check the journals for taper. Slowly tighten the micrometer thimble until there is very slight drag when you pull it away.

Note that this engine assembler is holding the micrometer with a rag. This keeps body heat from expanding the frame and affecting the accuracy of the readings.

Crankshaft Machining Operations:

Regrinding - If the crankshaft has any measurable out-of-round or taper, it must be reground by a machine shop to one of several standard undersizes. The machinist mounts the crankshaft in a special grinding machine that is something like a lathe with a large, spinning stone wheel.

This large crankshaft grinding machine is used to restore the smooth round shape of the main and rod journals.

The machinist mounts the crankshaft and grinds the main journals, then offsets the chucks to grind the rod journals.

Crankshaft grinding is a very tricky machining operation that requires expensive equipment and a very skilled operator. The stone must be "dressed" often to keep it straight and many measurements and adjustments must be performed so that the desired journal size and stroke length are achieved. A sharp edge at the ends of a crank journal or a poorly contoured fillet radius often leads to crankshaft breakage. It is extremely important that your machinist creates the correct type of fillet radius on each journal.

Crankshafts are reground to standard sizes so that you can purchase companion bearing inserts to maintain proper oil clearances. These are some common main and rod journal regrind undersizes:

Common Crank Journal Regrind Sizes

±. 001" Undersize/Oversize	.030" Undersize
.010" Undersize	.040" Undersize
.020" Undersize	

Chamfering - Regrinding the crankshaft leaves sharp edges and burrs on the oil holes that can gouge the bearing surfaces. The machinist carefully *chamfers* each oil hole with a high speed grinder to remove these burrs and also to promote better oil flow.

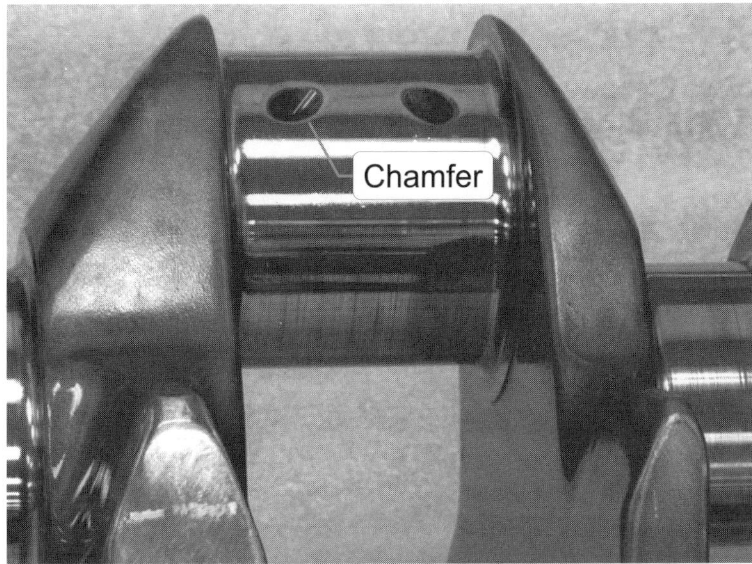

Oil holes must be carefully chamfered with a high-speed grinder to remove burrs and promote oil flow.

Crankshaft Polishing - Grinding stones leave a slightly rough finish on the journals. For this reason, the machinist must polish the crank journals. This process must be done with care to avoid making the oil chamfers too large or to add unwanted taper.

This crankshaft polishing machine rotates the crankshaft as an abrasive polishing cloth is run over the journal. We prefer to use a worn #600 grit polishing cloth to create a high gloss finish.

Polishing Technique - An inexperienced or careless operator can do a lot of harm to a crankshaft on the polishing machine. Polishing leaves a "nap" of microscopic metal structures that overlay in the direction that the polishing cloth runs across the journal surface. The operator must pay attention to the direction that the crankshaft spins against the polishing cloth or the nap will point the wrong way and wear into the bearings.

Another very important technique when polishing a crankshaft is to work only in one direction across the journals. If you work back and forth, the extra time that the cloth spends on the middle of the journal wears it into a taper.

Correct

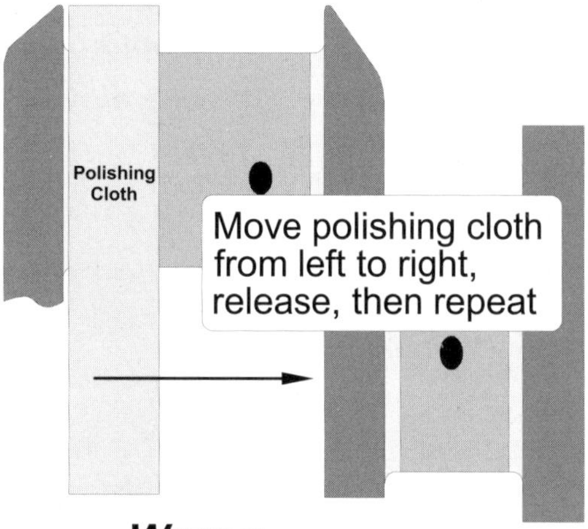

Polishing Cloth

Move polishing cloth from left to right, release, then repeat

An experienced operator moves the polishing cloth only in one direction across the journal. This helps prevent the tapering of the journal.

Wrong

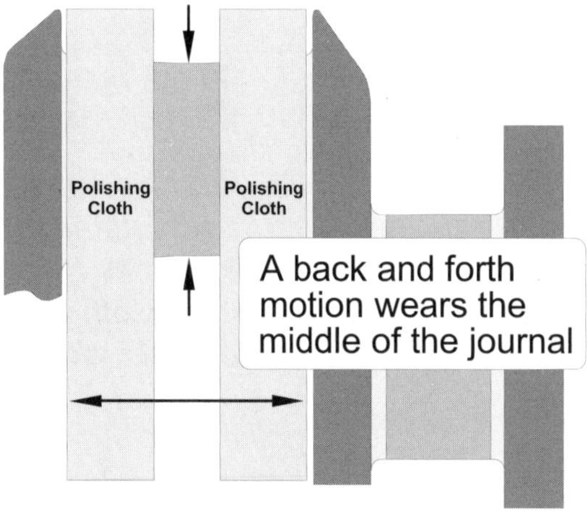

Polishing Cloth

Polishing Cloth

A back and forth motion wears the middle of the journal

Never run the polishing cloth back and forth across the journal. This causes greater wear in the middle.

The operator should make frequent micrometer measurements across the journal to be sure that the desired finished size has been achieved. After polishing, the crankshaft must be thoroughly cleaned, then oiled to protect it from the formation of rust.

Crankshaft Balancing:

A racing crankshaft must be balanced to the weight of the pistons and connecting rods. This is very important because an imbalanced engine will vibrate and fatigue the crankshaft until it breaks. Only an experienced machinist should perform crankshaft balancing.

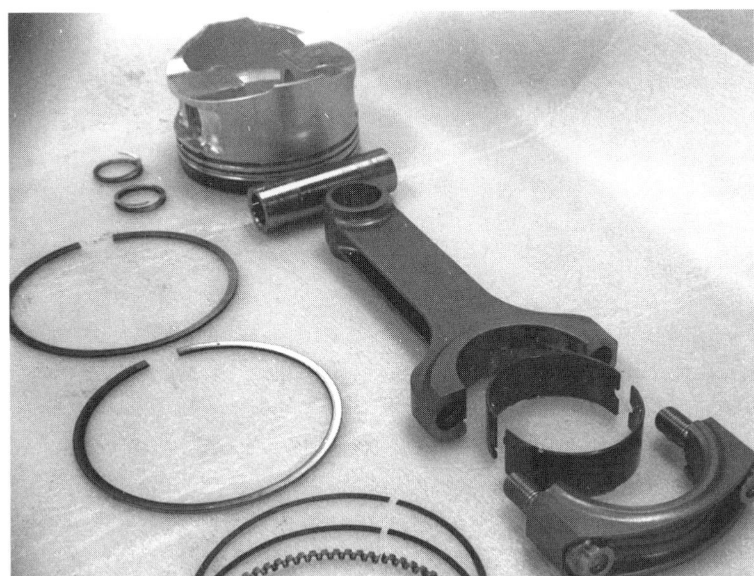

The mass of all these components must be counterbalanced for smooth engine operation.

> ***NOTE:*** Certain machining operations such as fly-cutting piston valve reliefs, shortening wrist pins, and clearancing pistons and connecting rods leave them lighter. Before you have the crankshaft balanced, you must know the final weight of each reciprocating and rotating component. For the most accurate results, have all operations performed to the components before you send them to the machine shop for balancing. Refer to *Unit VI – Short Block Pre-Assembly Measurements* for additional information about these procedures.

For each rod journal, the machinist prepares clamp-on "bob" weights that represent half of the reciprocating component weight (pistons, rings, pins & locks, and the small end of the connecting rods), and all of the rotating weight (big end of the rods, rod bolts, and bearings).

Once the bob weights are securely attached, the assembly is spun on the balancing machine.

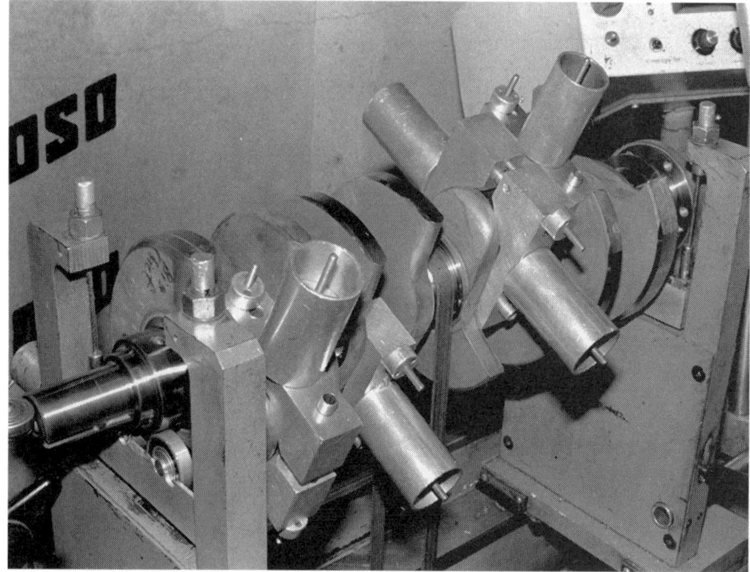

These clamp-on "bob weights" simulate the rotating and reciprocating mass of the rods, pistons, and rings.

The crankshaft balancing machine works something like a dynamic tire balancer. The weighted crankshaft is placed on precision bearings and then spun at high speed by an electric motor.

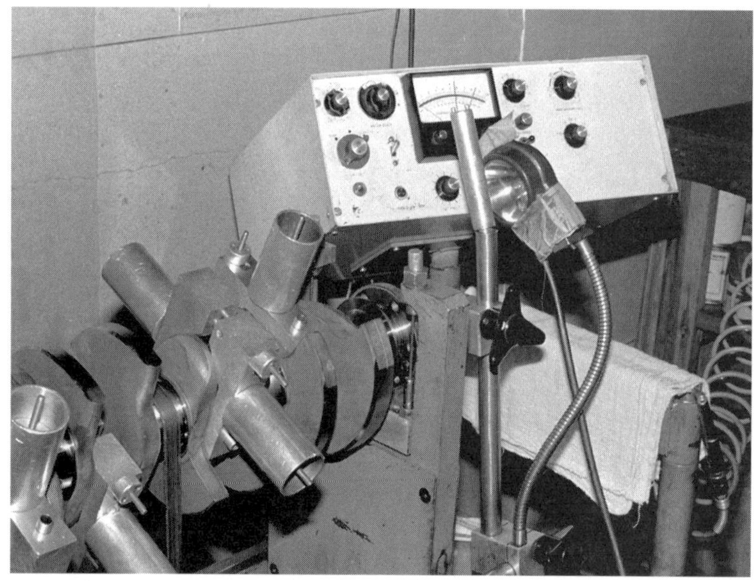

This crankshaft balancer uses a strobe light to freeze the motion of the spinning crankshaft to identify the correct amount and location for counterweights.

Vibration sensors send information to the electronics that determine the amount and location of weight needed to correct the imbalance. If the counterweights are too light, heavy slugs of tungsten metal are added to increase the mass. If the crankshaft counterweights are too heavy, the machinist mounts it in a lathe and cuts down the counterweights. A drill is then used to remove small amounts of material to "fine tune" the balancing job.

The crankshaft should be drilled in the side, not the end, of the counterweights for the heavy metal slugs. This ensures that the weight will not be expelled by centrifugal force when the engine is running. The photo sequence below shows how the heavy metal slugs are machined and installed.

After referring to a chart for the correct slug diameter and length, the machinist bores and reams the correct size hole into the side of the counterweight.

A heavy metal slug is machined to a diameter that is slightly larger than the hole and cut to length on a metal lathe.

The metal slug is pressed into the hole and ground smooth. With the counterweight now heavier, the machinist can drill away excess material until the correct counterweight mass has been achieved.

As with all types of dynamic balancing, crankshaft balancing involves a certain degree of error. Go easy when you remove weight from the crank counterweights. It's a lot easier to go back and drill more material than it is to add more weight.

Engine stroke length has a lot to do with the amount of mass required on the crankshaft counterweights. Long-stroke crankshafts usually require a lot of additional counterbalancing weight. This affects how the correct balance can be achieved within the space limitations of the block.

Internal Balancing - An *internally balanced* engine has all of the necessary balancing counterweight on the crankshaft. The flywheels and harmonic balancers on these engines do not have additional counterweights on them.

External Balancing - An *externally balanced* engine only has part of the necessary balancing counter weight on the crankshaft. The remainder of the counterweight is built into the flywheel and harmonic balancer.

The counterweight on the harmonic balancer on the right provides external balancing for a GM 502 cubic inch V8 racing engine.

Small displacement GM V8 engines (under 454 CID for big blocks, under 400 CID for small blocks) have relatively short strokes. The crank counterweights are usually large enough for internal balancing.

Larger displacement stock engines (454 CID big block and 400 CID small block engines) are shipped with external balancing by the factory. You must install the right counterweighted flywheels and harmonic balancers to avoid engine imbalance. However, many racing engine builders prefer to eliminate the counterweighted external parts by installing heavy metal slugs in the crankshaft.

Even components that are supposed to be balanced by the manufacturer may have some degree of imbalance. The best way to ensure correct engine balancing and long crankshaft life is to provide everything to the machine shop that reciprocates and spins in the engine, including the flywheel and harmonic balancer.

Pistons & Rings

Piston Types:

Pistons in racing engines must be very strong, but as light as possible. Stock cast aluminum pistons will not hold up under the stresses of racing. *Hypereutectic pistons* are better than cast types and work well in many street/strip or low-demand racing engines. However, quality forged aluminum alloy pistons have the highest strength-to-weight ratio and should be used in all serious high-rpm racing engines.

Piston Features:

These are some of the important features of a racing piston:

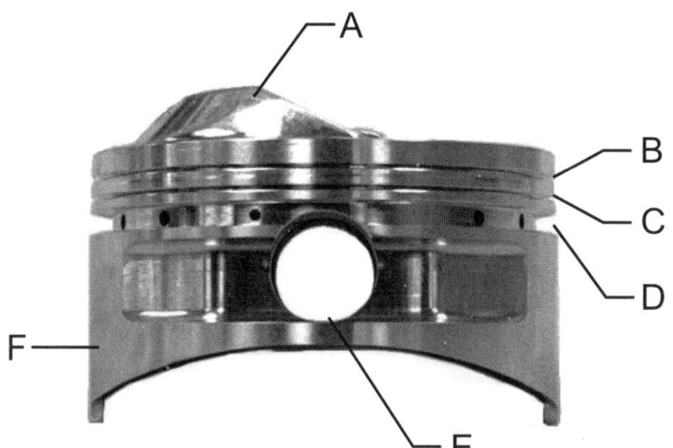

A. Compression Dome
B. Top ring groove
C. 2nd ring groove
D. Oil ring groove
E. Pin bore
F. Skirt

The goal of every piston manufacturer is to create a strong, lightweight piston that is as close as possible to a perfect cylindrical shape in operation. However, the uneven heat distribution in pistons and skirt loadings make this very difficult to achieve.

Piston skirts are subjected to forces under load that tend to flatten them. The tops of the pistons expand significantly as they are exposed to combustion temperatures that may exceed 1500° F. These factors distort the shape of the pistons when the engine is running.

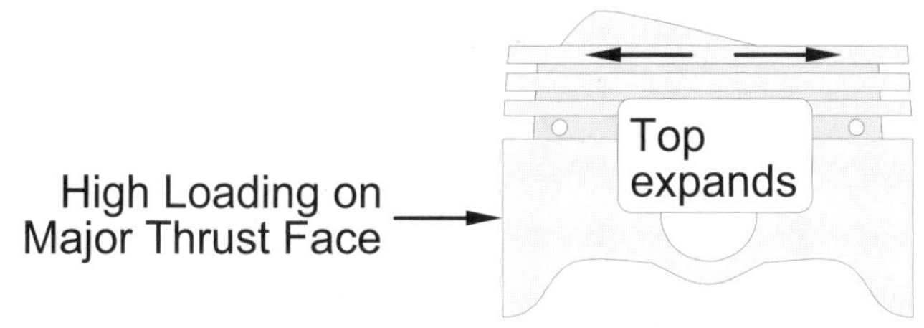

Heat and side loads tend to distort the shape of pistons when the engine is running.

Cam Grinding - To help allow for load distortion of the skirts, pistons are *cam ground.* This means that the measurement across the middle of the skirt is slightly greater than it is at the sides. Under high load, the skirt flattens into a nearly cylindrical shape.

Cam Ground Piston

(bottom view)

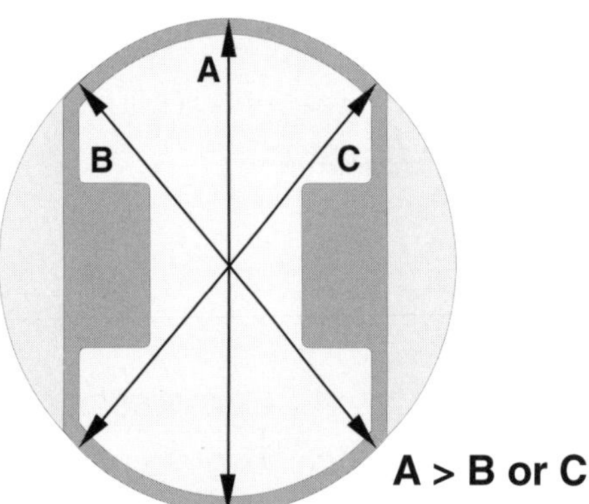

Racing piston skirts are cam ground. Measurement A (straight across the center of the skirts) is greater than dimensions B or C.

Racing pistons may be cam ground with a low-cam or high-cam skirt shape. The high-cam shape has a greater difference between the "A" and "B/C" dimensions. Both styles regain their round shape under heat and tend to run with the same frictional losses. The high-cam style allows a tighter cold piston-to-wall clearance (.006"-.007" for high-cam skirts as opposed to .010"-.011" for low-cam skirts).

Taper - The sides of pistons are tapered above the oil ring groove to allow for thermal expansion across the top surface. When cold, a piston measures significantly less (about -.040") across the top than it does below the oil ring groove. When racing, the top of the piston heats and expands. This makes the shape of the piston much more cylindrical.

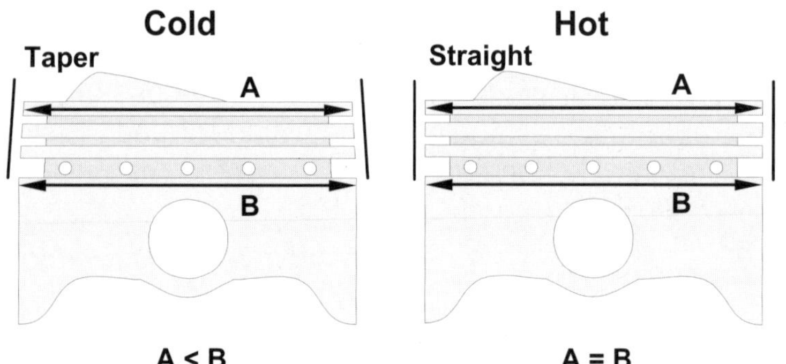

The top of the piston measures less than near or below the oil ring. This taper is necessary to allow for heat expansion.

Depending on the particular racing piston design, the skirt below the oil ring groove may also have some degree of taper to compensate for thrust loadings.

Compression Height - The piston *compression height* (or CH) is a measurement from the wrist pin centerline to the deck surface of the piston. This dimension is very important when selecting connecting rod length (see the *Connecting Rods, Calculating Rod Length* section of this unit).

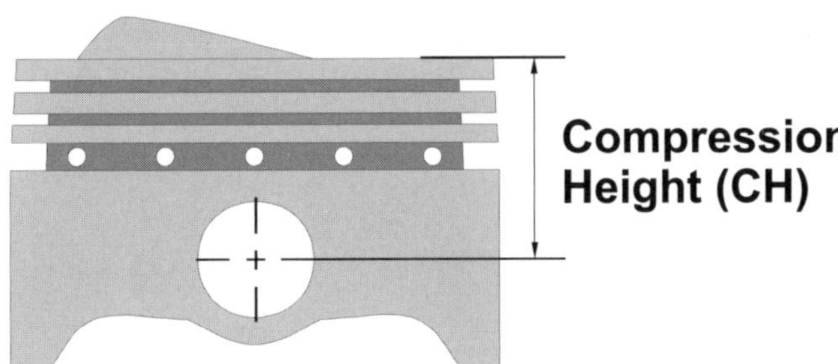

Compression height (CH) is the distance from the wrist pin centerline to the piston deck surface.

Valve Reliefs - If the valves hit the pistons in operation, catastrophic engine damage can result. This is most likely to happen to an intake valve when the piston is at 10° ATDC or to an exhaust valve when the piston is at 10° BTDC. *Valve reliefs* are cut into the piston dome to ensure adequate clearance between the piston and valves.

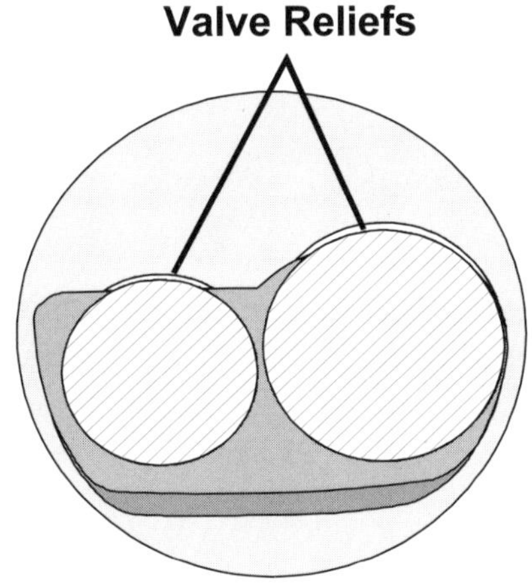

The valve reliefs must be deep enough to avoid interference with the intake and exhaust valves in operation.

Off-the-shelf pistons may have many compromises so that "one size fits all". We often find that these pistons have valve reliefs that are too shallow, unnecessarily deep, or cut at angles that don't match the valves angles in the cylinder head. Piston dome shape may also conflict with the combustion chambers. For these reasons, we prefer to do some of the final machining processes ourselves.

Retaining Wrist Pins:

Reliable wrist pin retention is a very important aspect of piston design. If the pin is allowed to move out of position, it will scrape and destroy the cylinder wall. There are three ways to retain the wrist (piston) pins:

- Press Fit in Rod
- Full-Floating w/Lock Rings
- Buttons

Press Fit in Rod - The wrist pins in passenger car engines are usually retained by a press fit into the small end of the connecting rod. With this arrangement, all sliding friction occurs between the pin bore and wrist pin. Press fit in rod pin retention is not recommended for racing engines.

Full-Floating w/Lock Rings – Full-floating wrist pins reduce friction because the pin is free to turn freely in both the rod pin bore and the piston pin bore. For this reason, the vast majority of racing engines are built with *full-floating* wrist pins. Lock rings retain the pin in the piston.

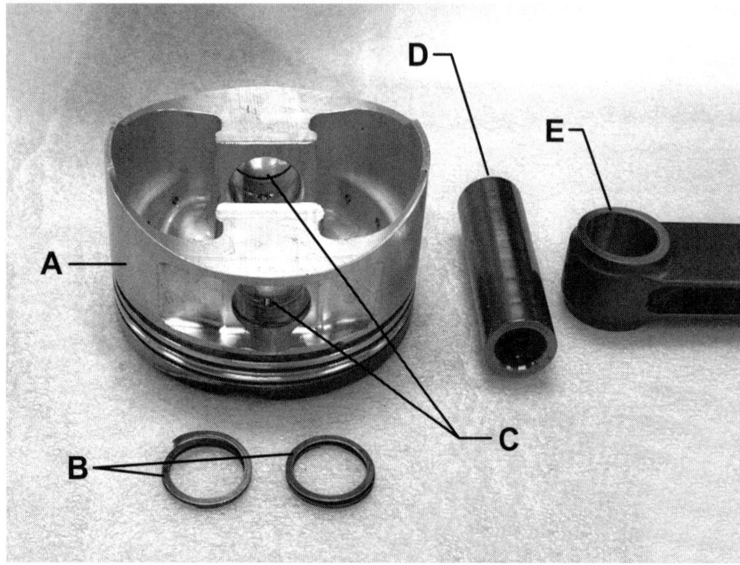

A. Full-Floating Piston
B. Lock Rings
C. Lock Ring Groove
D. Wrist Pin
E. Rod Pin Bore

There are several types of lock rings that are used to retain full floating wrist pins, including Spiro-Lox, round wire locks, and snap rings.

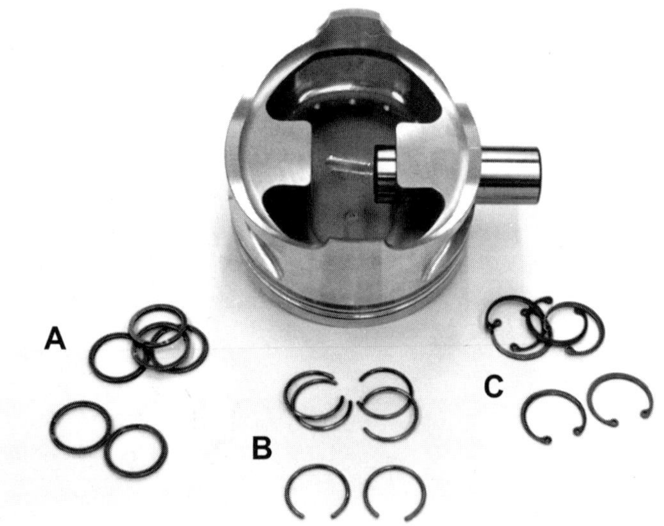

A. Spiro-Lox
B. Round Wire Locks
C. Snap Ring

Standard snap rings have two holes that can be gripped by special snap ring pliers. Spiro-Lox are a coil of flat, hardened steel. Round wire locks are another variety of snap ring that are used on some pistons. . If you are assembling a used set of pistons, be sure to discard the old lock rings and replace them with new ones

Buttons – *Buttons* are wrist pin inserts with smooth, rounded ends that ride against the cylinder walls. This positively controls lateral pin movement, but there are drawbacks to the use of buttons.

Buttons increase the mass of the piston & rod assembly and add more stress to connecting rods and crankshaft. They are often used in nitrous oxide and top fuel engines where rapid piston replacement is of utmost importance.

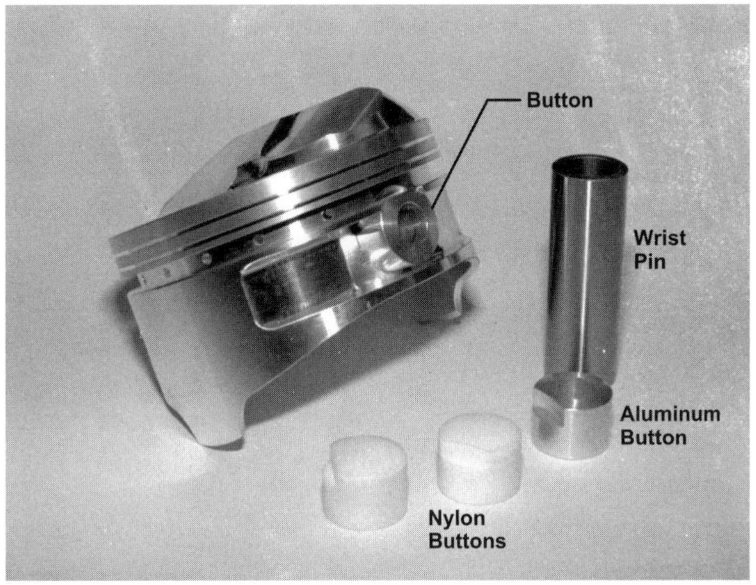

Buttons are another means of retaining wrist pins. Both aluminum and nylon button types are shown here.

Piston Ring Types:

Nearly all racing engines use a standard ring package that consists of two top rings and a three-piece oil ring.

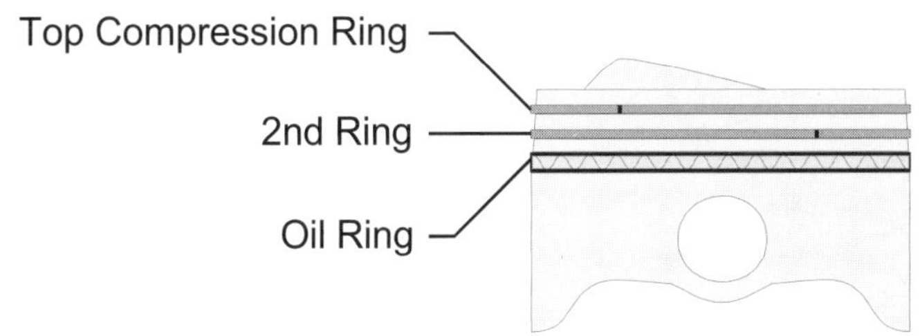

We build most of our racing engines with .043" thick top rings and a 3/16" thick oil ring.

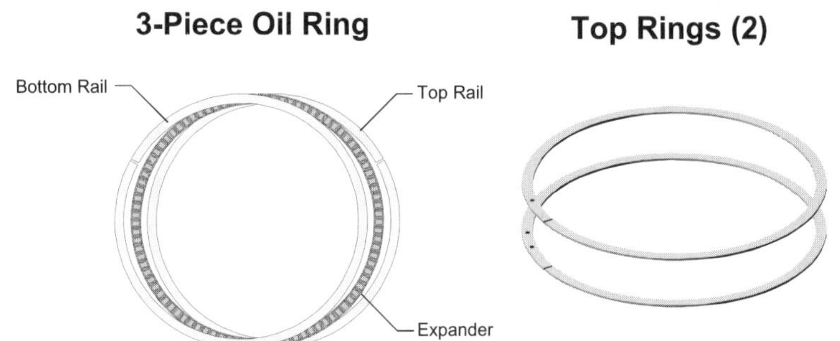

The oil ring (left) is made up of three pieces; two rails and an expander. There are two top rings (right).

Piston Ring Performance:

Poor compression ring seal causes a loss of engine power for several reasons. First, cylinder pressure is lost on compression and power strokes. Leaky rings are less effective at sealing vacuum, so less air and fuel is drawn into the cylinders on intake strokes.

Blow-By - Gases that leak past the rings are called *blow-by.* Blow-by contains unburned and partially burned fuel. It contaminates the motor oil and adds pressure to the crankcase. Crankcase pressure robs horsepower from the engine because it increases windage drag and reduces cylinder vacuum on intake strokes.

Ring seal is affected by:

- Top Ring Design
- Ring Tension
- Cylinder Wall Conformity
- Ring End Gap
- Ring Flutter
- Cylinder Hone Finish

Ring Design - A common misconception is that the top two rings serve the same function of sealing the piston to the cylinder wall. Actually, the top compression ring seals the piston to the cylinder while the 2nd ring primarily helps control cylinder wall lubrication.

It is particularly important to choose the right ring package for a racing engine. Stock rings that work perfectly well in a passenger car may perform poorly under the extreme speeds, pressures, and temperatures in a racing engine.

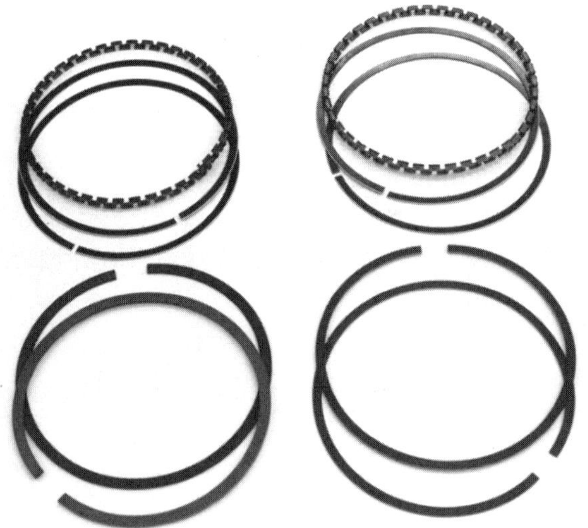

The ring package you choose affects both compression and oil control.

The better high performance top rings are made from steel blanks that are faced or filled with a very hard and wear-resistant plasma/moly material. The top compression ring primarily seals pressure. We prefer to use thin .043" top rings with a barrel face. The 2nd ring is also .043", but the face of the ring is slanted to scrape oil. Both rings have a chamfer on the inside diameter. The chamfer faces up on the top ring and down on the 2nd ring.

Ring Cross Sections

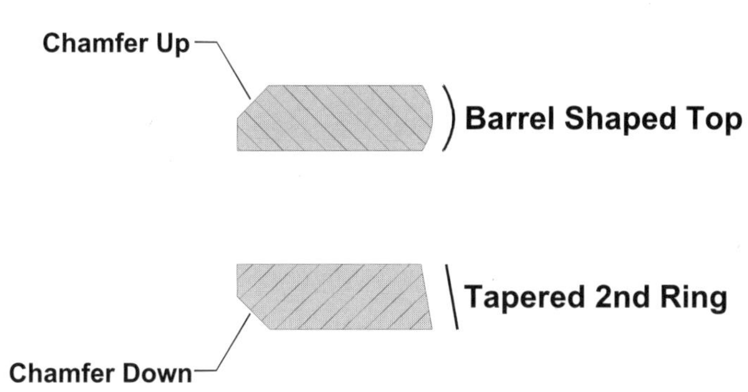

This diagram shows an exaggerated view of the top and 2nd ring cross sections. A hard plasma/moly coating is applied to the barrel face of the top ring. It is extremely important that the chamfers are orientated in the engine as shown.

The chamfer on the top inside corner of the ring makes it cone upward when it is compressed and installed in the cylinder. The 2nd ring has the chamfer on the bottom inside corner to make it cone downward.

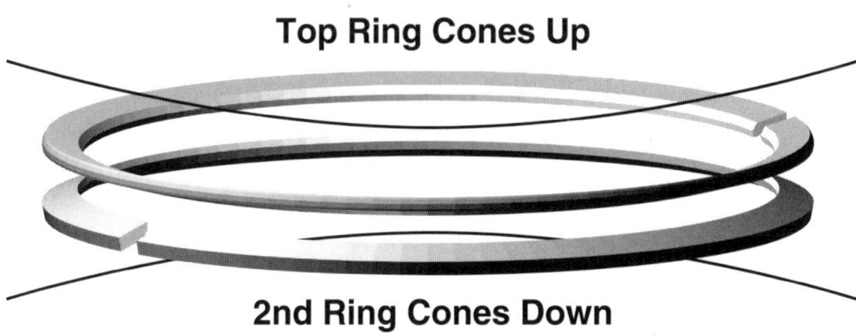

The top rings cone in opposite directions when compressed.

Coning stabilizes the rings by keeping them in constant contact with the ring grooves (lands).

This exaggerated view of the top rings shows how the "coning" keeps the rings in constant contact with the ring grooves. This improves ring performance.

Ring Tension - All piston rings must have some static tension against the cylinder walls to create an effective seal. However, the way rings seal on the compression and power strokes is often misunderstood.

Many racers think that ring seal is created soley by the static tension on the piston rings. In fact, it is cylinder pressure that largely seals the rings on compression and power strokes. Only on intake strokes is static tension the main force that seals the rings.

Let's take a look at how cylinder pressure increases the tension on the rings to create a good seal.

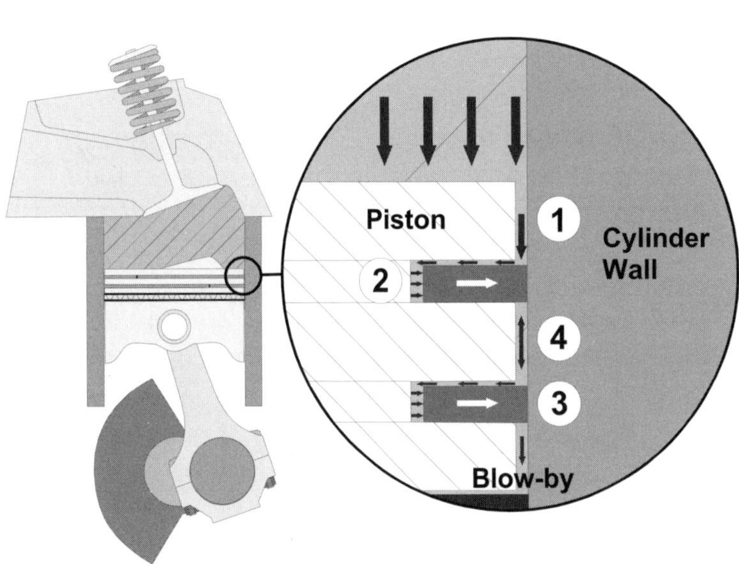

1. *Combustion pressure pushes on the top ring, seating on the ring land.*
2. *Pressure gets behind the ring, pushing it against the cylinder wall.*
3. *The pressure that escapes past the top ring pushes on the 2nd ring, seating it and pushing it against the cylinder wall.*
4. *Pressure builds between the rings, easing the pressure on the top ring land. Blow-by gases are those that get past the 2nd ring.*

The top compression ring handles most of the sealing chores when there is pressure in the cylinder. One common mistake by engine builders is to use a 2nd ring that seals *too well*. A small amount of ring leakage on the 2nd ring actually improves the overall ring seal.

Take another look at the previous diagram. If the 2nd ring seals too well, high pressure builds between the rings (location #4). This pressure tends to lift the top ring off the land and reduces the ability of the top ring to seal pressure.

There is some evidence that some 2nd ring compression leakage also helps to keep oil in the crankcase of the engine. This is very important because oil has poor anti-knock characteristics and can foul the spark plugs. Even small amounts of oil in the combustion chambers cause large power losses. Some leakage past the second ring helps push oil back down the cylinder and keeps the air/fuel mixture cleaner.

On unlimited engines like those built for Pro Stock, some builders cut a small amount of material off the piston between the top rings. This is called an *accumulator groove*. The theory is that the increase in volume slows the buildup of pressure between the rings that may unseat the top ring.

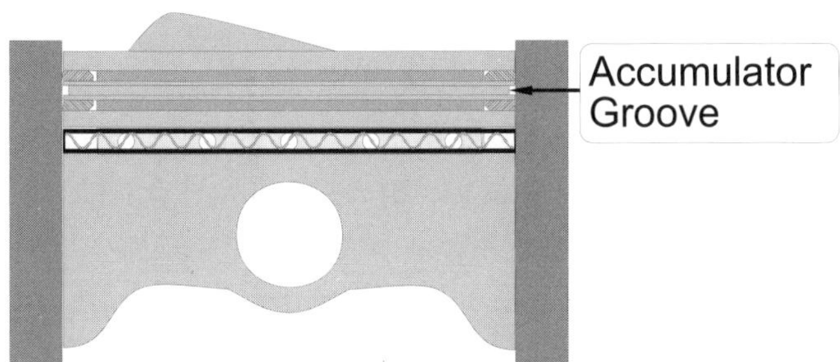

An accumulator groove increases the volume between the two top rings. This slows the rate of pressure buildup that can unseat the top ring.

Another high-end modification that receives a lot of attention is the use of *gas ports* in the pistons. Gas ports are holes drilled into the piston tops (or into the top ring lands from the side) to promote a rapid exchange of cylinder pressure behind the top compression ring.

When ring grooves are cut with very tight (.002" or less) vertical clearances, a problem is created in getting cylinder pressure into and out of the area behind the ring. This delays the proper sealing of the ring on compression and power strokes and creates extra drag on exhaust strokes because of the entrapped pressure. Gas ports solve this problem by creating a direct path for the exchange of cylinder pressure with the area behind the piston rings.

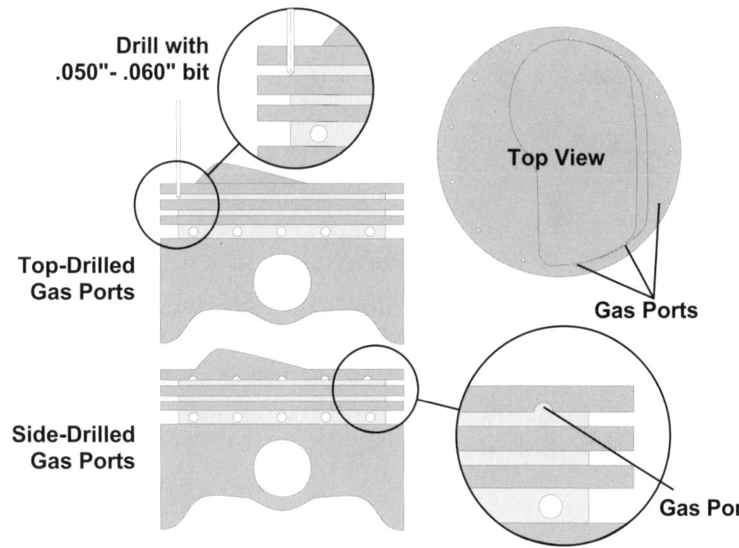

Gas ports are often used on high-end racing pistons along with custom-cut ring grooves. Some builders side-drill the ports to avoid carbon clogging or to meet rulebook requirements.

Ring groove depth should be no more than .005" deeper than the ring to keep the fill volume behind the ring as small as possible. This ensures quick fill/bleed times for rapid ring response. If you are using factory machined pistons and stock rings, there is usually adequate ring vertical clearance (.004"+) to allow the exchange of cylinder pressure with the area behind the rings.

All this sounds great, but drilling gas ports and machining pistons for the tightest possible ring clearances are expensive ways to gain power. If you are running in a sportsman class, we recommend that you don't become too wrapped up in exotic piston modifications and save these tricky procedures for applications where every horsepower counts.

Oil Rings - The two main concerns with oil ring performance are the amount of drag they add to the engine and the effectiveness with which they scrape excess oil from the cylinder walls. The expander puts pressure on the scraper rails. The rails remove much of the unwanted oil from the cylinder walls.

For an oil ring to be 100% effective at scraping oil, it would need to be under very high tension. Not only would this create additional drag, but the top rings also need some lubrication to seal and perform well. Oil rings are designed with only enough tension to remove part of the excess oil. As previously described, the 2nd ring provides the additional oil control that is required for the entire ring package.

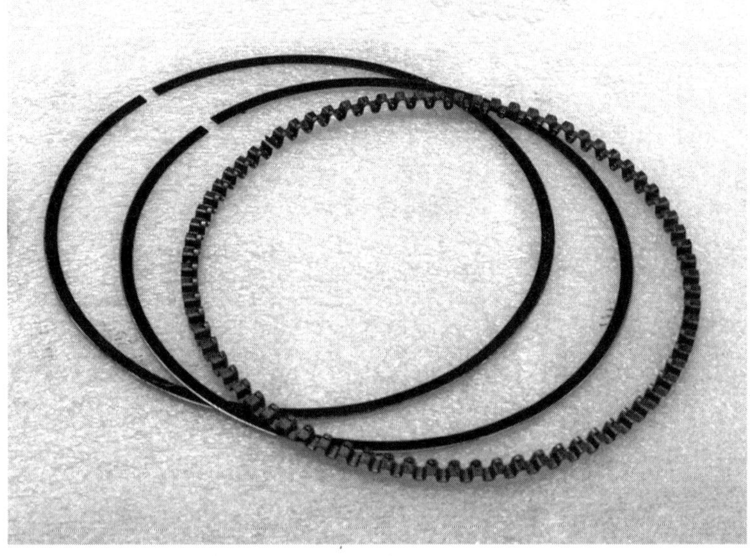

This three-piece oil ring provides adequate oil control when used with the rest of the racing ring package.

Racing piston ring manufacturers have built and tested many different ring types, configurations, and levels of tension. We recommend that you take advantage of the time and money they have invested in this research and development. See your racing engine builder or contact a reputable racing piston ring manufacturer for a ring package that meets the needs of your particular application.

Cylinder Wall Conformity - Rings require some running time to "break in" before the engine can display its true performance potential. Actually, the top compression ring surfaces are extremely hard and wear very little—it is the cylinder walls that must conform to the rings.

During the break-in period, high-spots and other small imperfections on the cylinder walls wear away and the surfaces work-harden to create the best seal and resistance to wear. The ring packages we use now seal extremely well with a very fine finish hone and usually make the best power in just a few pulls on the dyno.

Don't overlook the importance of cylinder wall finish and the value of using a good block that was designed for racing applications. Modern rings are very hard and only seal well against straight cylinder walls with the right finish and hardness.

NOTE: See the *Engine Block, Cylinder Honing* section of this unit for more information about cylinder wall finish.

Ring End Gap - A piston ring must have an end gap for several reasons. First, the gap allows you to stretch the ring and install it into the ring groove. Compressing the rings during installation provides the necessary static tension for compression and oil rings. The gap also provides a very important allowance for heat expansion. The ring end gaps close as the rings heat up in operation.

It is extremely important that compression rings have enough cold end gap so that the ends will not butt when the engine is running. If the ends do butt, the outside diameter of the ring will expand. This forces the ring into the cylinder walls, causing severe engine damage (see the upcoming section - *Checking for Interference, Measuring Ring End Gap).*

One interesting innovation is the "zero end gap" ring. The idea is to eliminate pressure losses that could occur through a ring end gap.

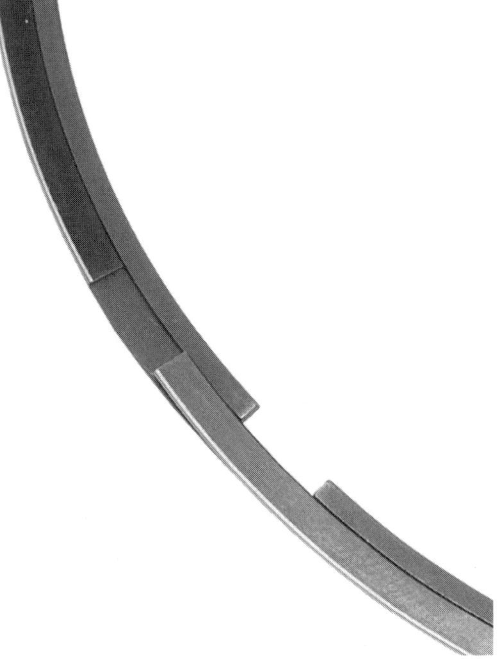

This Total Seal® gapless ring eliminates the end gap by making the ring in individual pieces.

NOTE: *The rings are shown upside down, with the end gaps positioned near each other for illustration purposes only. Install the rings with the top side facing up and 180° apart when assembling the engine.*

The theory of reducing compression losses by eliminating the end gap seems great, but remember that the gap largely closes in a standard racing ring when the engine is running. Also, piston-to-wall clearance is very tight (.006" - .012") so the portion of exposed gap is very small. The overall sealing advantages of a thin, barrel-shaped ring with a plasma/moly facing seems to outweigh any losses through end gap leakage.

The most common use for zero end gap rings is in alcohol engines. Alcohol is not compatible with racing motor oil. A zero end gap ring in the 2nd ring groove can help prevent motor oil contamination.

Ring Flutter - Compression ring flutter is a condition in which the rings release from the ring lands near top dead center as the piston reverses direction. Ring flutter can happen at mid to high engine rpm's and greatly reduces the ability of the rings to seal pressure.

Possible causes of ring flutter are loose ring grooves (excessive vertical clearance), high ring mass, excessive piston speed, and pressure buildup between the rings. The tighter the ring grooves can be with the sides of the compression rings without binding, the better they can control ring movement and flutter. For most racing engines with no gas ports, we maintain a vertical ring clearance between .001"-.0025". See the upcoming section - *Measuring Ring Vertical Clearance* for more information about ring clearances.

Thin, light rings tend to perform better because they have less inertial mass and can reverse direction in the cylinder more easily. This is why we use very thin (.043") compression rings and cut our own ring grooves in high-end racing engines. The slight amount of leakage that is allowed by the 2nd ring also helps relieve excessive pressure buildup between the rings to keep the top ring seated.

Cylinder Hone Finish - The cylinder wall finish and shape have as much to do with the quality of ring seal as the rings themselves.

Piston and Ring Measurements:

These are some critical piston and ring measurements:

- Weight (Mass)
- Dome Volume
- Piston-to-Wall Clearance
- Ring Groove Depth
- Ring Vertical Clearance
- Ring End Gap
- Piston-to-Valve Clearance
- Wrist Pin to Pin Bore Clearance

Weight - Racing pistons should have the lowest mass possible without sacrificing strength. This is important to reduce inertial forces that stretch rods and resist crankshaft acceleration.

For these reasons, racing pistons are made from lightweight high-strength aluminum alloy forgings. The overall weight of a piston depends mostly on the diameter, compression height, and dome configuration. They should not vary in weight from one another by more than 1-5 grams, depending on the application.

When looking for ways to reduce piston mass, there are few options. Nothing can be done to reduce the piston diameter because it must fit closely with the bore of the engine. The piston dome shape is determined by the contours of the combustion chamber and the amount of compression that you need for your application.

One piston dimension that you have some control over is *compression height* (CH). Compression height is the distance from the wrist pin centerline to the piston deck surface. Normally, the shorter the piston CH, the lighter it is. Reducing piston mass is a good idea, but there are practical limits as to how short the CH can be without compromising piston strength or ring performance.

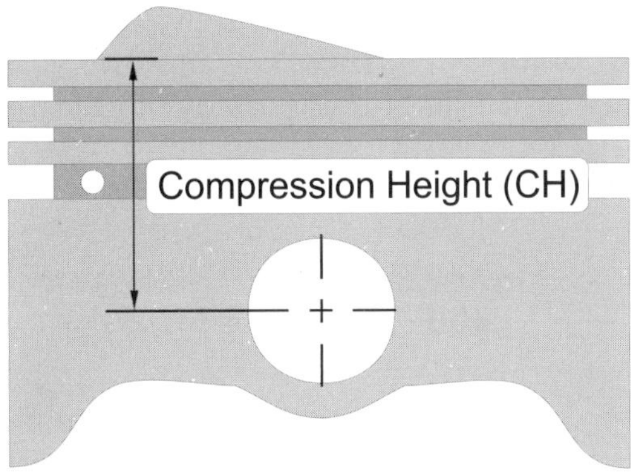

This important piston dimension is called the Compression Height or CH.

Sometimes the pistons must be made very short to solve internal engine clearance problems. This is often the case on long stroke engines where the pistons go deeply into the bores. Pistons with a standard configuration and CH height would run into the crankshaft counterweights.

The most cost-effective way of dealing with this problem is to cut the pin hole higher into the oil ring groove so that the piston can be made short enough to clear the crankshaft. When this is done, a support rail must be installed in the oil ring groove to restore support to the oil ring. This support rail adds some mass and may compromise oil ring performance to some degree, however it is usually the best way to solve long stroke engine clearance problems. The figure below shows the dimensions that make up piston compression height (CH) for different piston styles.

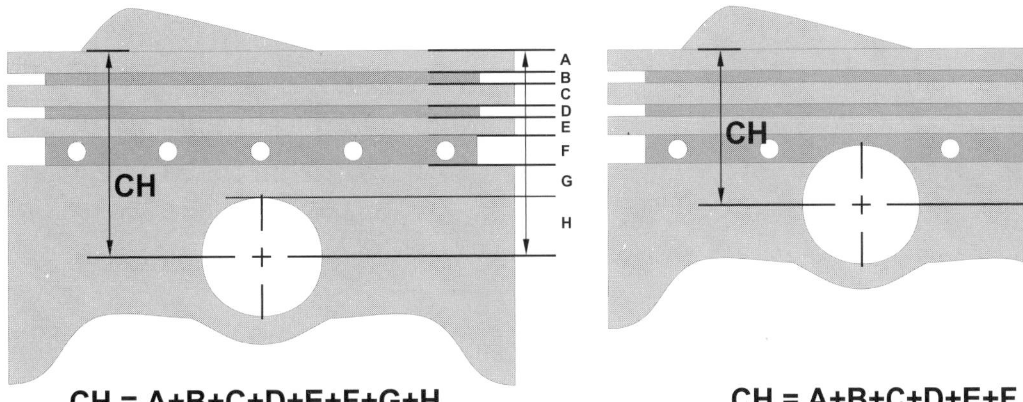

CH = A+B+C+D+E+F+G+H

This is a standard piston design with the pin bore below the oil ring groove.

CH = A+B+C+D+E+F

This piston is designed for a long stroke engine with the pin bore intersecting the oil ring groove.

The first dimension (A, Distance from the piston deck to the top ring groove) is limited by two factors:

- *The top ring cannot be less than .100" from the piston deck*
- *The top ring groove cannot cut into the valve reliefs*

If you move the top ring on a racing engine any closer than .100" from the piston deck, the aluminum will be too thin and weak. It will give way in operation, resulting in a total loss of ring control.

Often, the height of the top ring is not limited by the minimum thickness above the top groove, but by the location and depth of the valve reliefs. With many big block pistons, you will cut through to the intake valve reliefs if you locate the top grooves much higher than .240" from the piston deck.

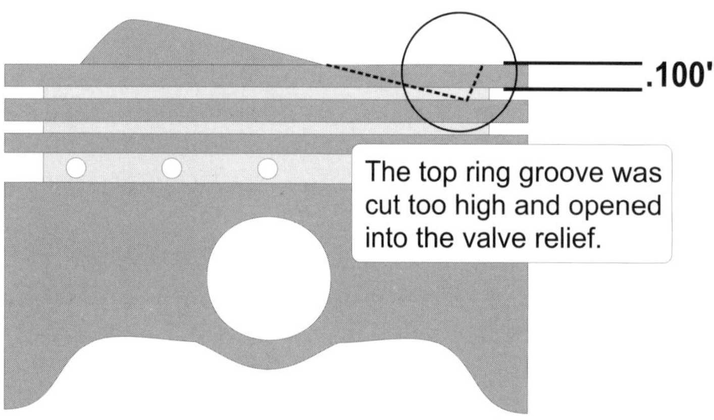

If you locate the top ring groove too high, it may cut into the valve relief.

These are some other minimum dimensions that are required for racing pistons.

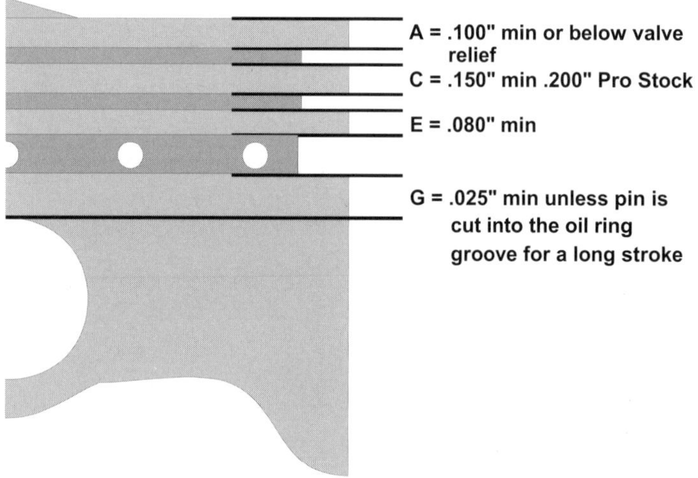

These minimum dimensions ensure that the ring lands will not collapse in operation. In most racing engines, the depth of the intake valve relief makes it impossible to locate the top ring at .100" from the piston deck.

Example:

You are building a 467 cubic inch GM big block engine. Find the minimum piston compression height for this engine. Refer to the previous figures for minimum piston dimensions and the information below to make your calculation.

- *Highest possible top compression ring location = .240”*
- *Compression ring thickness = .043”*
- *Oil ring thickness = .188” (3/16”, rounded to nearest thousandth)*
- *Wrist pin diameter = .990”*

This piston requires a very deep intake valve relief that limits the minimum distance from the piston deck to the top ring groove to .240” (dimension A). The top rings measure .043” thick, but there must be at least .001”-.003” vertical clearance with the ring groove. The same is true of the oil ring. For this example, we will add a vertical clearance of .001” to the ring thicknesses (.043” & .188”) to find the required oil ring groove width.

- *Top ring groove width = .044” (B & D)*
- *Oil ring groove width = .189” (F)*

Divide the wrist pin diameter (.990”) in half to find dimension H. Half of .990” is .495”. You now have all the necessary information to find the minimum compression height (CH).

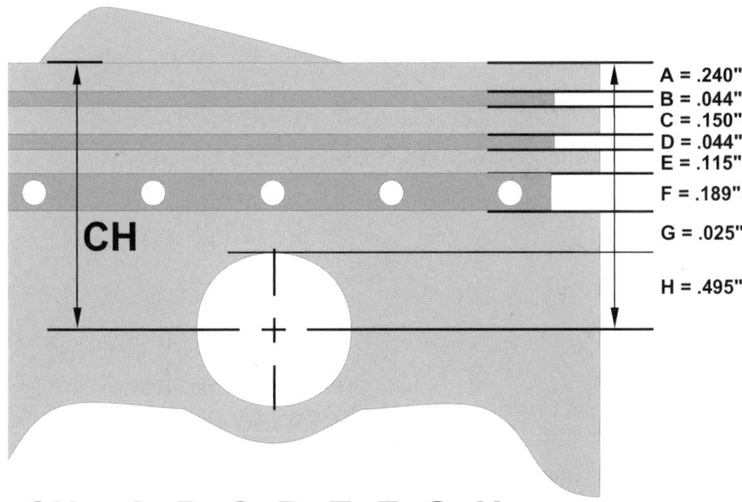

Dimensions A, C, E, & G are fixed minimums for this non-Pro Stock engine. Dimensions B, D, and F were found by adding .001” to the ring thickness. Dimension H is one half the wrist pin diameter. Add these dimensions together to find the minimum compression height (CH) for this engine.

CH = A+B+C+D+E+F+G+H

Add the numbers together to find the answer:

CH = .240"+.044"+.150"+.044"+.115"+.189"+.025"+.495"

CH = 1.302" (answer)

The minimum compression height for this example engine is 1.302”.

If you can't afford custom pistons, check with several manufacturers or engine builders to see if they have an available set of pistons that are close to the minimum compression height dimension. This will keep piston mass low and improve engine performance and longevity.

Often, we cannot find off-the-shelf pistons with all the right dimensions for our racing engines. We order semi-finished pistons by compression height (CH) and diameter, then cut our own ring grooves and reshape the domes as needed for each application. On some high-end racing engines, we perform special lightening procedures and add features like gas ports and additional oil holes.

A machinist is removing some unnecessary bulk from the pin bosses, skirts, and dome with this vertical mill. Such extreme piston lightening measures are only worth the time and money if you are building an engine for an unlimited professional application like Pro Stock.

The wrist pins and lock rings (or buttons) add additional mass to the reciprocating assembly. However, there is little that can be done to lighten a well manufactured racing wrist pin without seriously compromising its strength.

Purchase your pistons, wrist pins, and lock rings as a set from a reputable manufacturer. Always use new lock rings every time you reassemble the pistons.

Dome Volume - The dome volume is actually a net volume—it includes all of the material that is above the piston deck less what is lost by the valve reliefs in the piston deck. You must make an accurate measurement of net piston dome volume because it directly affects the static compression ratio of the engine.

Piston manufacturers list the dome volumes and approximate static compression ratios for their finished pistons, but use this information only for comparative purposes when selecting pistons. Modifications like re-contouring the domes for head clearance and cutting valve reliefs change the final net dome volume. Perform a net dome volume measurement after you have checked to be sure the domes fit the combustion chambers and have measured piston-to-valve clearances.

Piston-to-Wall Clearance - The difference between piston diameter and cylinder diameter is called *piston-to-wall clearance*. The required clearance varies widely by the type of pistons, so always refer to the manufacturer's recommendations. These are the piston-to-wall clearances we use for the majority of racing engines that we build with forged aluminum pistons:

- *.006" - .010" (most racing applications)*

Measure the piston diameter with an outside micrometer that is accurate to a ten-thousandth of an inch. Recall that pistons are cam ground and tapered. It is extremely important that you measure the piston exactly as indicated by the manufacturer. Usually, this is across the center of the skirts at a point in line with the center of the wrist pin as shown below.

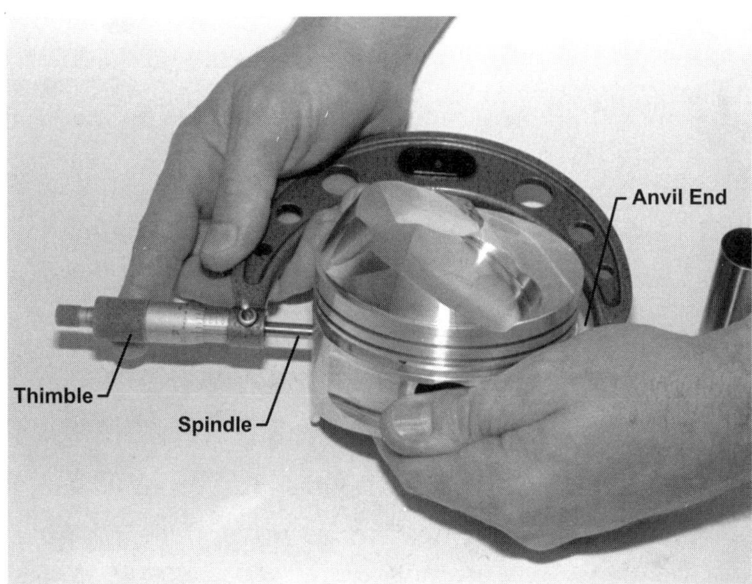

The designated place to measure this piston is in the middle of the skirts at 90° to the pin bore centerline. Once you've made the adjustment, set the lock.

Measuring piston diameter is very tricky because of the irregular shape and softness of the aluminum. If you are in doubt, see an experienced machinist for help.

Adjust a good dial bore gauge to the locked outside micrometer so that it reads "0". It will now read the piston-to-wall clearance directly when placed in the cylinder bore. Measure the bore in several places to be sure that the cylinder isn't tapered our out-of-round. Repeat this measurement for all eight pistons and bores. Match the larger pistons to the larger bores for consistent piston-to-wall clearance.

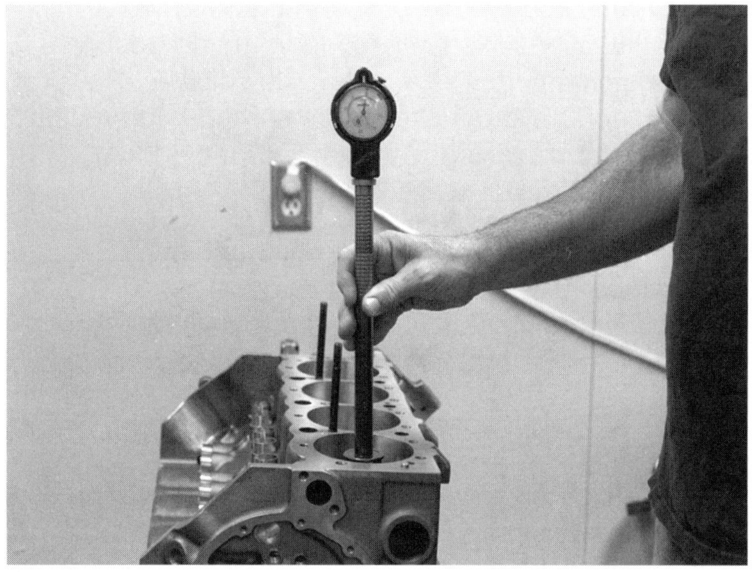

Measure and record the piston-to-wall clearance at a number of locations in the bore.

Remember that clearances that are too tight usually lead to engine damage. If the piston-to-wall clearance is below specifications, additional honing of the cylinder walls is required.

<u>Measuring Ring Groove Depth</u> - Recall that the tops of the pistons expand significantly when the engine is running. The ring grooves must be at least as deep as the rings to prevent them from jamming against the cylinder walls.

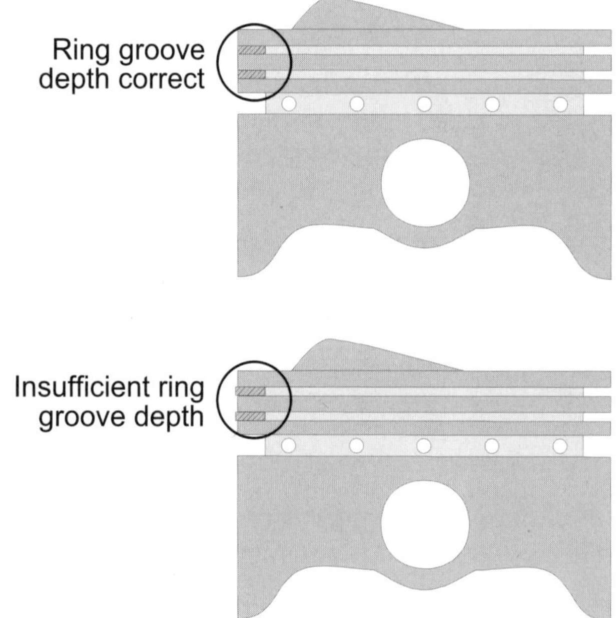

These ring grooves are deep enough so that the ring will not be forced into the cylinder walls when the piston expands.

These ring grooves are too shallow. The rings will be forced into the cylinder walls, causing a lot of damage.

An easy way to check for adequate ring groove depth is to place the ring in the groove as shown below. The ring should fit completely into the groove.

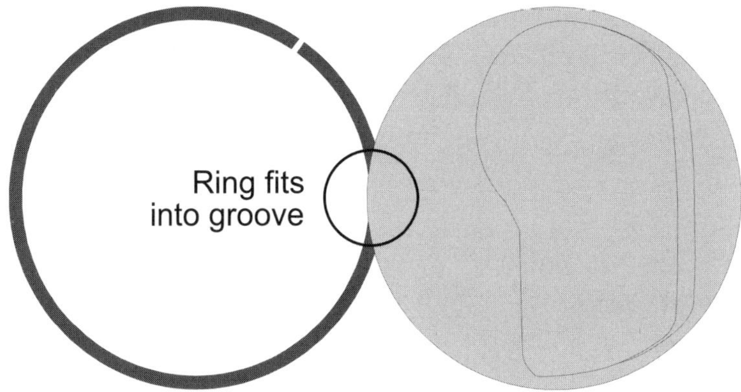

Check for adequate ring groove depth like this.

If the ring does not fit all the way into the groove, you will need to use different rings or have the ID's (inside diameters) of the rings cut by a machine shop. If you are building a high-end racing engine with gas ports, the ring groove depth should be no more than .003" greater than the rings to minimize ring response time.

<u>Measuring Ring Groove Vertical Clearance</u> – Often, the vertical ring clearance on off-the-shelf pistons is significantly more than we prefer. On pistons with custom-cut ring grooves and gas ports, the vertical clearance can be much tighter, .0005"-.0015". Place the ring into a clean ring groove in the piston and use a feeler gauge to measure ring vertical clearance.

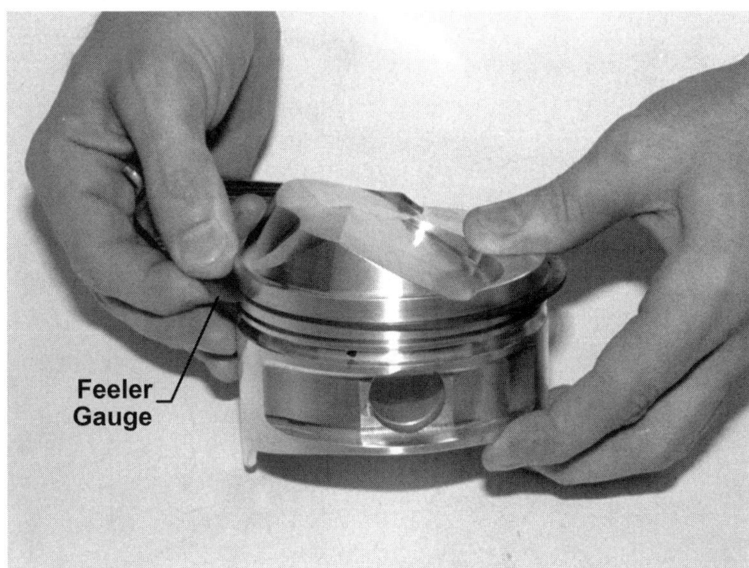

Use a feeler gauge to measure the ring vertical clearance as shown here.

Measuring Wrist Pin to Pin Bore Clearance - To avoid pin galling, it is important to have the correct oil clearance between the wrist pins and pin bores in the pistons. Check this clearance by measuring the piston pin bore ID with a good dial-type bore gauge. Then, measure the OD of the wrist pin with an outside micrometer. The difference between these measurements is the oil clearance. We will typically set wrist pin to piston pin bore clearance at .0015" on low-rpm (under 7800) and low HP (under 900) applications.

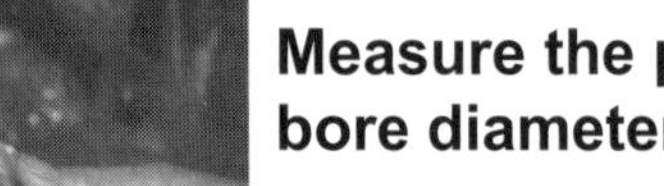

Measure the pin bore diameter

The wrist pin to pin bore clearance is the difference between these two measurements.

Measure the wrist pin diameter

If the wrist pin to pin bore clearance is already too great, oversize wrist pins are available in +.001, +.002, and +.003" for most applications. An experienced machinist slides the piston back and forth over the spinning pin bore hone. This is done manually for just a few strokes at a time. A constant stream of honing oil keeps the particles washed away. The result is a smooth, round hole with a crosshatch pattern. Then they slip the wrist pin into the bore for a quick check.

This special honing equipment is used for adjusting the pin to pin bore oil clearance as well as reconditioning connecting rods.

NOTE: If you are building a very high-end racing engine that will operate at extreme rpm's and under high-horsepower loads, it may be necessary to add a little additional wrist pin to pin bore clearance to prevent galling. Crankcase evacuation systems and dry-sump oil systems that create high levels of oil pan vacuum also tend to keep the pins "dry" and may require different clearances. It's best to check with your engine builder for wrist pin to pin bore clearance recommendations that are best for your application.

Measuring Wrist Pin to Lock Clearance - This is the side clearance between the ends of the wrist pin and the retaining lock. We have found that .005" clearance is adequate for most low rpm (below 7800 rpm) lower HP (900 Hp) non-vacuum equipped engines. With the installation of a vacuum pump or on dry sump applications we add additional wrist pin to lock and wrist pin to piston pin housing clearance to minimize galling of the wrist pins. The cutaway piston below helps demonstrate how we check the wrist pin to lock clearance with the depth measuring bar on an electronic digital caliper.

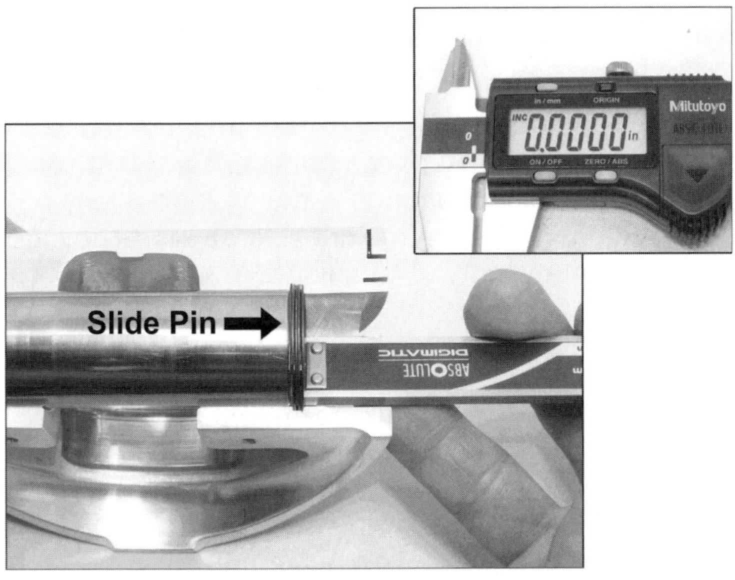

Slide the wrist pin to the right against the lock. Hold the body of the caliper against the lock and adjust the depth bar until it contacts the wrist pin. Zero the indicator.

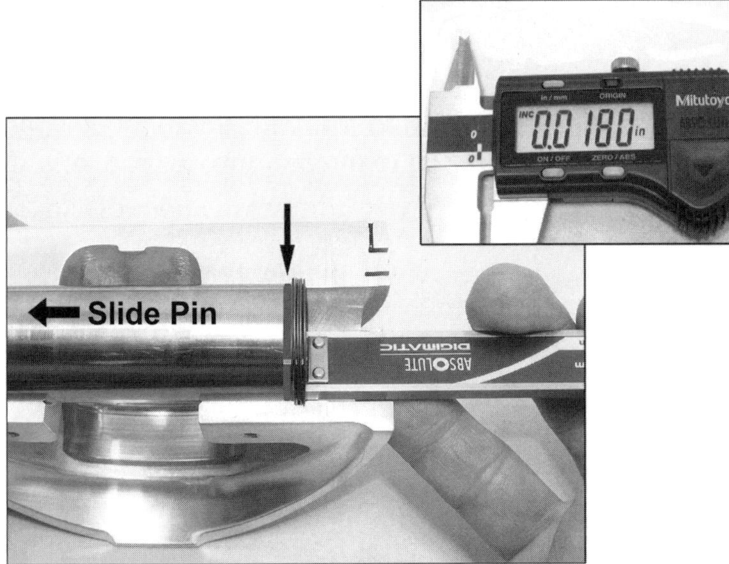

Now, slide the wrist pin to the left against the opposite lock. Adjust the depth bar until it contacts the wrist pin. It will indicate the clearance—in this case .018".

Connecting Rods

The connecting rods undergo enormous stresses in a racing engine. The stretching force when a rod reverses the piston direction at top dead center can exceed 12,000 pounds in a 500 cubic inch Pro Stock engine at 9000 rpm's.

Connecting Rod Types:

Stock Forged Steel - High performance forged steel rods are available from the manufacturer and some aftermarket suppliers. They can withstand higher stresses than standard passenger car connecting rods, but are not durable enough for high-rpm racing engines. Also, length choices in these rods are very limited.

Stock-type forged steel rods can be used in some low to medium performance applications.

Machined Forgings - These rods begin life as rough forgings, then undergo many machining operations. This leaves very few rough surfaces (*stress risers*) that can lead to the formation of cracks. We use machined forgings in many applications where strength, durability, and low maintenance are prime considerations. They are very reasonably priced and are available in a variety of lengths.

This H-beam machined rod forging is a good choice for many endurance or low maintenance racing applications.

Aluminum - For many high-horsepower/high-rpm drag racing applications, aluminum rods are the way to go. They have a very high strength to weight ratio and excellent dampening characteristics. They can be custom bored to almost any desired length.

Aluminum connecting rods have a very high strength to weight ratio and are available in almost any length.

The main drawback of aluminum rods is their very short life span. With every rotation of the crankshaft, connecting rods are stretched and compressed. Aluminum work hardens and fails more quickly than steel. This makes aluminum rods unsuitable for use in most endurance racing applications.

To avoid the risk of a catastrophic engine failure due to rod breakage, we replace the aluminum rods in our Pro Stock engines after only 50 to 70 runs, including dyno pulls. This adds to the time required to maintain these engines and really runs up the cost of racing, but it's valuable insurance against breakage.

Titanium - Recent advances in titanium rod technology have caused us to re-evaluate these exotic rods for use in our Pro Stock engines. They have the highest strength-to-weight ratio of any rod and appear to have a very long life cycle. However, titanium galls in contact with moving steel parts. Rod manufacturers have recently developed new coatings to help address this persistent problem.

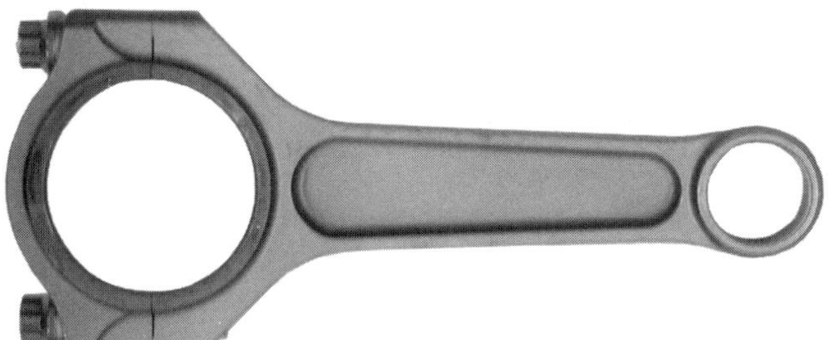

Exotic titanium rods like this may only be a practical choice in unlimited racing engines like those we develop for Pro Stock.

Titanium rods have other drawbacks. The initial cost is extremely high and the rod bolts gall after every torquing. This means that you must purchase new rod bolts each time you reinstall a titanium rod.

Connecting Rod Features:

The figure below shows some important features of a connecting rod:

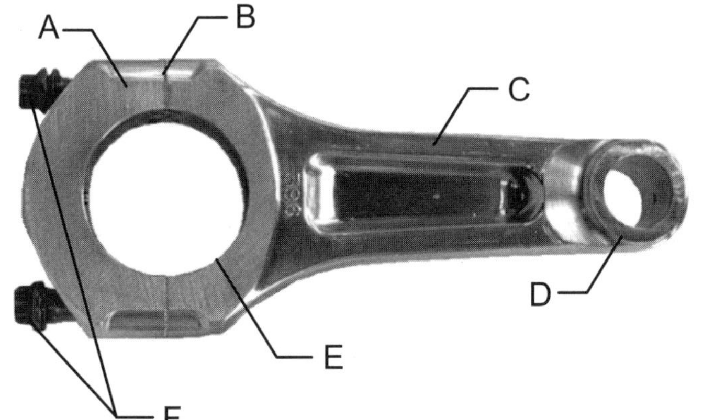

A. Rod Cap
B. Parting Line
C. Beam
D. Pin Bore
E. Crank Bore Chamfer
F. Bolts

NOTE: The crank bore is chamfered more on one side to clear the fillet radius at the side of the crankshaft journal.

Rod Length:

Connecting rod length is the distance from the center of the pin bore to the center of the rod bore.

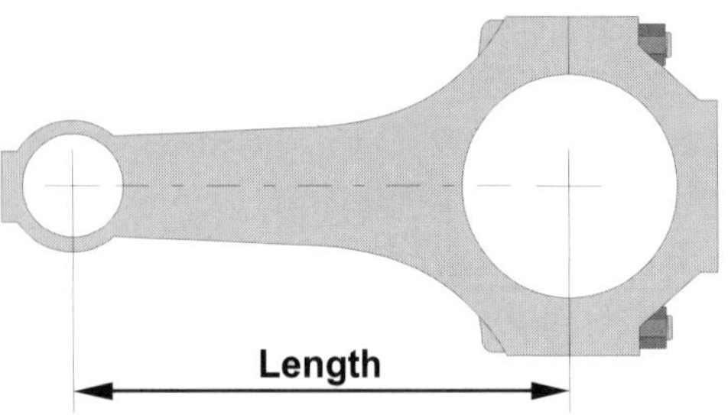

Rod length is a centerline measurement from the wrist pin bore to the crankshaft bore.

Connecting rod length affects engine *deck clearance* and *rod angularity*. Deck clearance is the distance from the top of the piston at TDC (top dead center) to the block deck surface.

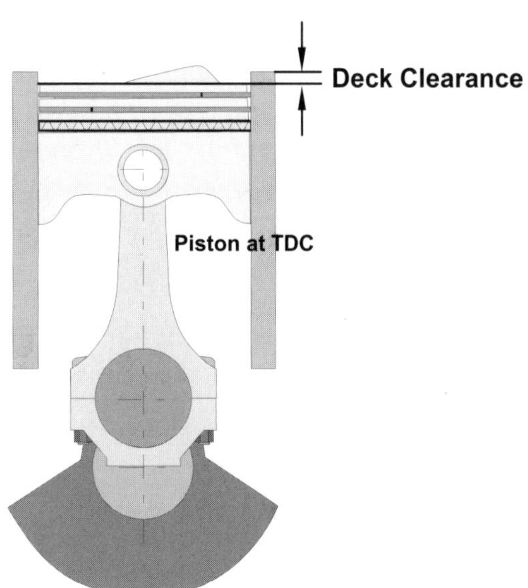

Deck clearance is an important short block measurement. You must select a rod length that provides the correct deck clearance measurement.

Rod angularity is the change in angle of the connecting rod as the piston moves up and down in the bore. Connecting rod angle is greatest when the crankshaft is at 90°. A short rod engine has higher rod angularity than a long rod engine. This increases piston skirt loading and can lead to failure.

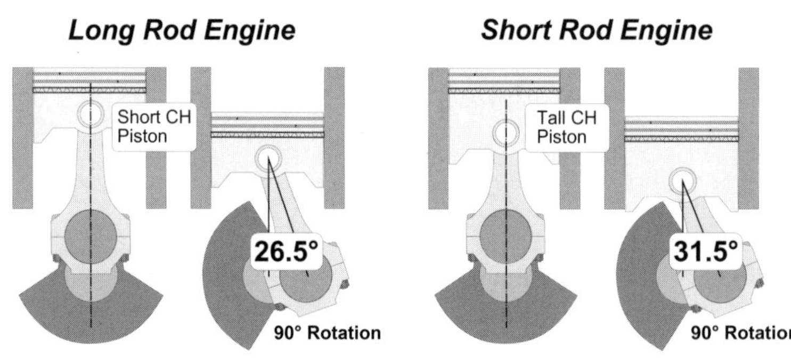

At 90° of crankshaft rotation, a short-rod engine has greater rod angularity than does a long-rod engine of the same displacement. This makes the piston taller and heavier. It also increases skirt loading.

Common Misconception

Many books and technical articles have been written concerning the supposed importance of connecting rod length to racing engine performance. Rod length actually has very little impact on power output. Choose your crankshaft and pistons first - they will dictate the rod length you need.

Conventional racing engine theory states that long rod engines have significantly different torque and horsepower profiles than do short rod engines. The theory is that the rod length affects the position and speed of the piston. Statements are often made that the piston lingers (dwells) near TDC on a long rod engine and that this affects breathing. This turns out to be largely untrue.

Does the piston really dwell near TDC long enough on a long rod engine to make a difference? Take a look at the computer-generated graph below. It shows a comparison of piston location by crankshaft degrees for three common rod lengths that are used in GM big block V8 racing engines.

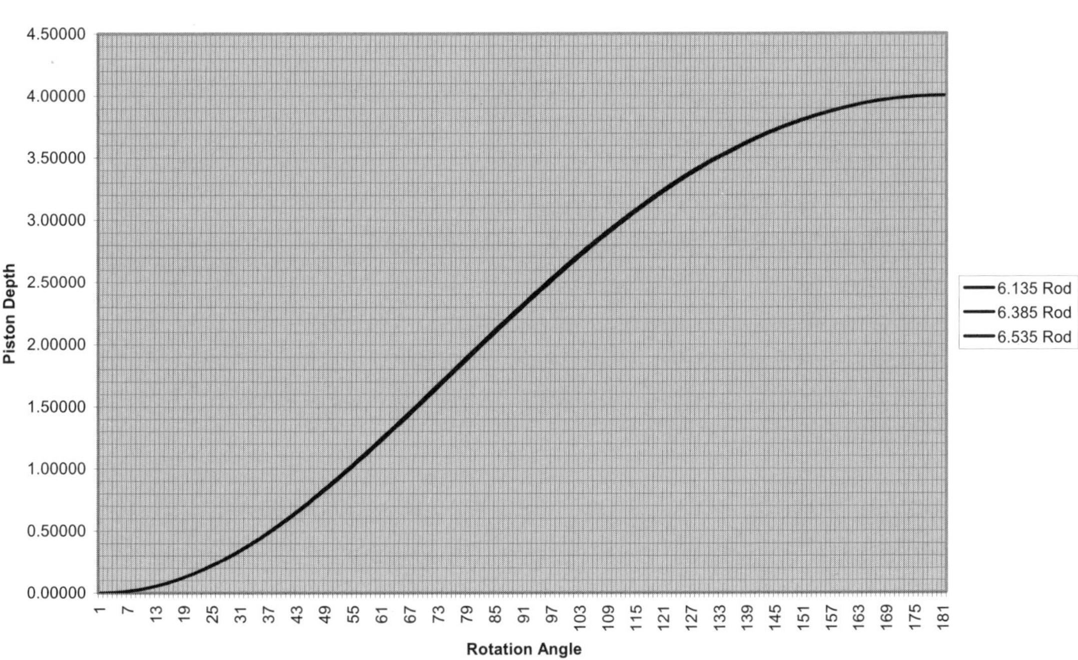

There are three traces on this graph, but they diverge so little at any point in the crankshaft rotation that they appear to be a single line.

At 10° ATDC (the time when the most pressure is present in the cylinder on a power stroke), the difference in piston location between the longest (6.535") and shortest (6.135") rod engine is only .0004" (four ten-thousandths of an inch). Even at 45° of crank rotation, the difference is only .01". This amounts to only .16 cubic inches per cylinder in a 502 CID engine. *Rod length and angularity have very little real impact on engine performance.*

Calculating Rod Length:

Total Deck Clearance - You should select a rod length that allows you to use lightweight pistons with a short CH (high pin location). The connecting rods grow with heat and stretch at high rpm's, so the length you choose must also provide the right *total deck clearance* for your engine. Total deck clearance is the deck clearance plus the thickness of the head gasket.

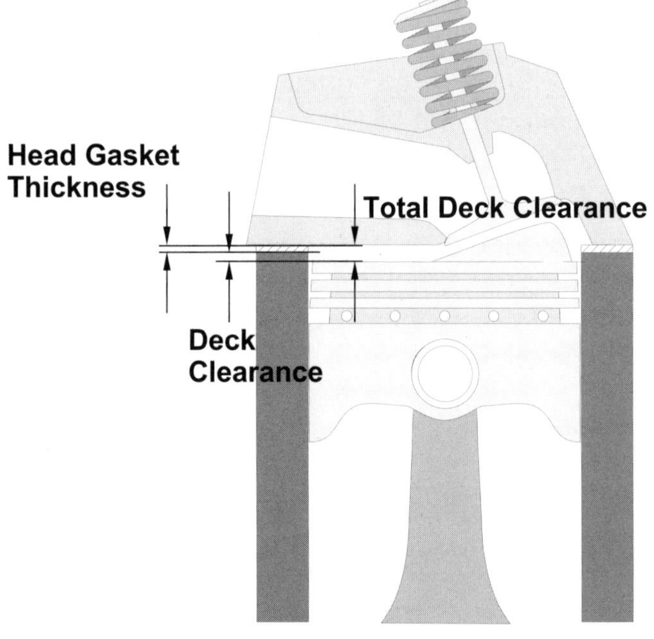

Total deck clearance is the sum of the deck clearance and head gasket thickness. You should choose a rod length that provides the required total deck clearance.

Total Deck Clearance = Deck Clearance + Head Gask. Thickness

If there is too little total deck clearance, the pistons will strike the cylinder heads at high rpm's. If you have excessive total deck clearance, compression is lost, and there is a reduced "squish/quench" effect from the cylinder heads. This can lower the horsepower output of the engine.

NOTE: The squish/quench effect is important because it helps control detonation and creates combustion chamber turbulence that mixes the air and fuel better.

The type of rod you choose has a lot to do with how much total deck clearance is necessary. Aluminum rods "grow" more in operation because aluminum has a much higher thermal expansion rate than steel and a higher modulus of elasticity. An additional .015"-.020" of total deck clearance is necessary anytime you build an aluminum rod engine. These are the total deck clearance specifications we use when building most of our racing engines:

- *Steel connecting rods - .040"-.050"*
- *Aluminum connecting rods - .055"-.070"*

Choosing a Head Gasket - The type of head gasket that is best for your application depends on the cylinder head/block combination and cylinder pressure levels. The vast majority of engines that we build have aluminum cylinder heads bolted onto ferrous blocks. Because of differences in the expansion rates of aluminum and iron, there are only two head gasket choices for this combination; composition or copper.

For medium horsepower applications, we usually use a .051" thick composition type head gasket. The new multi-layer shim gaskets are really amazing and work so well that we use copper head gaskets and O-ringed blocks far less frequently than we once did.

Copper head gaskets are available in thicknesses from .040" to .080". The thinner copper gaskets (.040"-.060") conform more easily and should be used if you have had your block O-ringed.

The compressed gasket thickness is often stamped on the top surface of custom head gaskets. If this information is not stamped on a copper or steel gasket, you can measure the thickness with a micrometer.

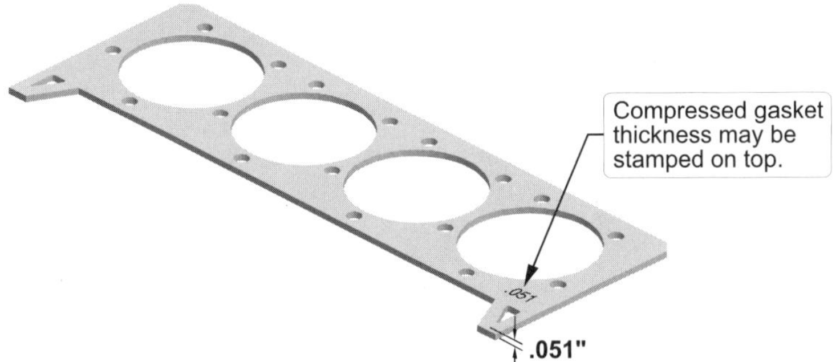

If the compressed thickness of a composition head gasket is not stamped on the top surface, it must be obtained from the manufacturer.

After you have determined the compressed head gasket thickness, use this simple formula to determine the deck clearance that you need for your engine:

Deck Clearance = Total Deck Clearance - Head Gasket Thickness

When we build a Pro Stock or other unlimited category racing engine, we really push the limits of safety by running minimal total deck and piston-to-valve clearances. Maintaining this degree of precision in machine work is time consuming, expensive, and leaves no margin for error. If you are on a budget and are building an engine for a sportsman category, we recommend that you err on the side of safety. Here is a good rule to follow when you are determining engine clearances.

There is always some error in any engine measurement or machining operation. Most engine failures result from clearances that are too tight. When in doubt, err on the side of looseness for engine clearances.

Unless you must find every last horsepower from your engine, aim for the middle to high side of the specifications for total deck clearance.

Example:

You are building a 502 cubic inch GM big block engine with aluminum connecting rods and aluminum heads. You will use a .051" thick composition head gasket. What must the deck clearance be to obtain the right total deck clearance?

The total deck clearance specification for an aluminum rod engine is .055"-.070". We will use a target clearance of .065" to allow a margin for error. Apply the formula to determine the desired deck clearance.

Deck Clearance = .065" - .051" = .014" (answer)

This engine needs a deck clearance of .014" to provide the desired total deck clearance of .065".

Stackup - You must determine the required *stackup* height before you can calculate the required rod length for your engine. The stackup is the combined height of the piston, rod, and crankshaft (at TDC).

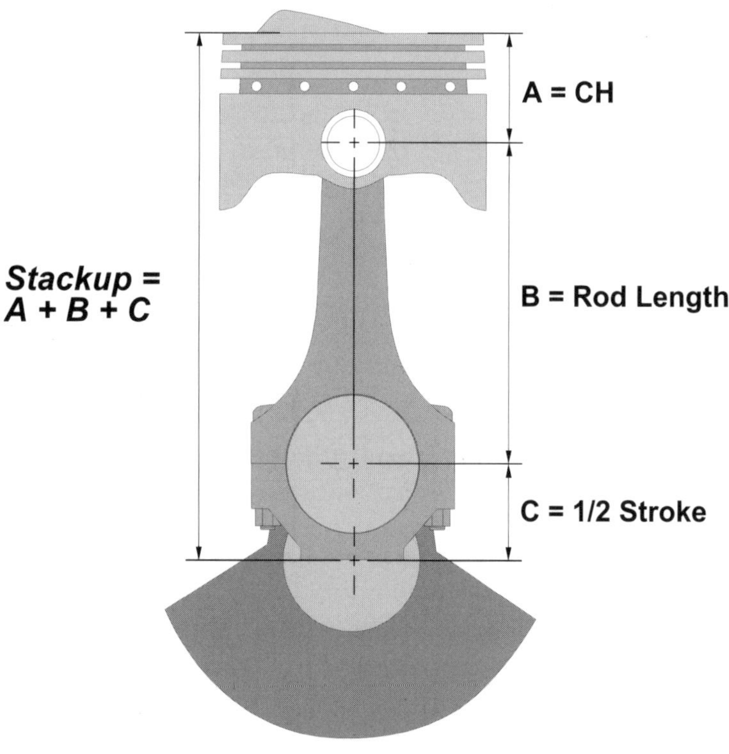

The stackup is the sum of the compression height of the piston (A), rod length, (B), and 1/2 the crankshaft stroke. The piston is at TDC for this calculation.

At this point, you should already know the piston compression height (A) and the stroke length of your crankshaft. Simply divide the crank stroke by 2 to determine variable (C) in the stackup.

The stackup that you need for an engine is the block deck height minus the deck clearance.

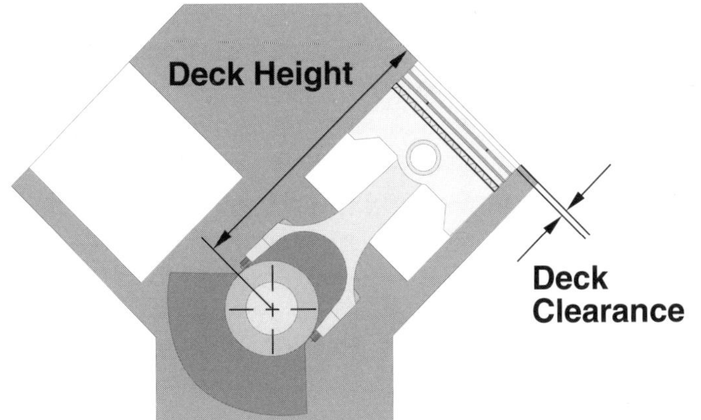

The stackup must equal the block deck height minus the calculated deck clearance.

Example:

You are building a 502 cubic inch aluminum rod GM big block engine. Calculate the required connecting rod length using these specifications:

- *Block Deck Height = 9.800"*
- *Deck Clearance = .014"*
- *Piston Compression Height (CH) = 1.250"*
- *Stroke = 4.00*

First, determine what the stackup height should be for this engine. Subtract the deck clearance (.014") from the block deck height (9.800")

Required Stackup Height = Block Deck Height - Deck Clearance

Required Stackup Height = 9.800" - .014" = 9.786" (result)

This engine needs a stackup height of 9.786, providing the desired total deck clearance of .065".

Calculate one half of the engine stroke:

4" Stroke ÷ 2 = 2" (half stroke)

The stackup height is the sum of the piston compression height, rod length, and half the stroke. Subtract the piston compression height (CH) and half the stroke from the desired stackup height calculation to determine the rod length for this engine:

$$\text{Req. Rod Length} = \text{Req. Stackup Height} - \text{Piston CH} - \frac{1}{2}\,\text{Stroke}$$

Req. Rod Length = 9.786" - 1.250" - 2" = 6.536" (answer)

The required rod length for this engine is 6.536"

> ***NOTE:*** When you assemble the short block to check clearances, you'll find that the piston measures about .003" farther in the hole than the above math would indicate. This is because of the oil clearances in the rod bearing and wrist pin (*bearing drop*).

We normally stock rods for GM big block V8 racing engines in 6.135", 6.385", and 6.535" lengths. The previous example problem called for a rod length of 6.536". This is only one thousandth of an inch (.001") longer than our standard 6.535" rod—a negligible difference that keeps the total deck height well within the desired range.

Connecting Rod Inspection:

Connecting rods should be checked for straightness and must be free from cracks. It's a good idea to have steel rods Magnafluxed. Aluminum rods can be checked for cracks with a Zyglo process.

Bent rods place side loads on the engine bearings, wrist pins, and pistons. Have your connecting rods checked by a qualified machinist from a reputable race engine building shop.

Connecting Rod Measurements & Preparation:

If the rods are free of cracks and are straight, perform the following measurements:

- Bore Diameters
- Deck Clearance
- Rod Side ("Cheek") Clearance

<u>Bore Diameters</u> - Correct rod bore diameters are very important to avoid piston and bearing problems. Measure the big and small ends of each rod with an inside micrometer or bore gauge. We prefer a rod bore diameter tolerance of ±.0002".

Check the big end rod diameter with a bore gauge. This measurement is critical to avoid spun bearing problems. If the rod bores do not meet the bearing manufacturer's specs, have them re-sized by an experienced machinist.

Bent rods should be discarded. If the big end of a connecting rod is the wrong size, it must be resized on a special rod reconditioning machine. The procedure is similar to align honing a block. Some material is removed from the cap parting line to close the hole. Then the cap is reinstalled and honed to the final bore diameter.

The machinist uses this special equipment to hone connecting rods.

If the pin bore is damaged, a bronze sleeve can be installed and honed to the original size. However, this procedure weakens the rod slightly and should only be performed as a last resort to save a valuable connecting rod.

This steel rod is being repaired by the installation of a press-fit bronze bushing.

Deck Clearance - Although you have made careful calculations and selected connecting rods that should provide the right deck clearance, the only way to be sure that everything is right is to perform careful measurements.

To measure the deck clearance, install the main bearings, crankshaft, and main caps. Be sure the parts are clean and well lubricated before you install them. Torque the main caps to specifications. Install the piston & rod assemblies and bearings. Use a dial indicator to locate the piston at TDC. (Refer to *pages 299-301* for procedure to locate TDC)

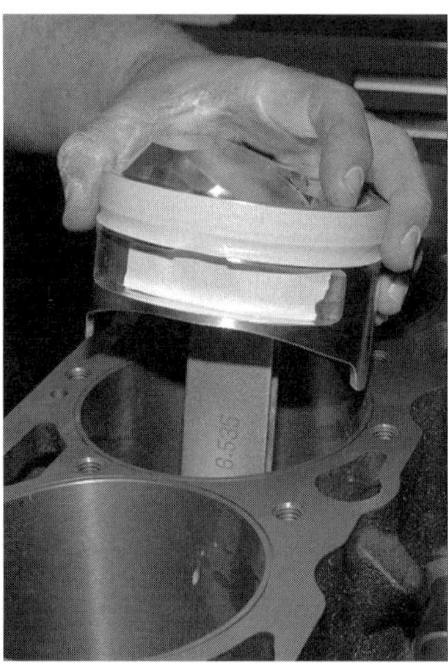

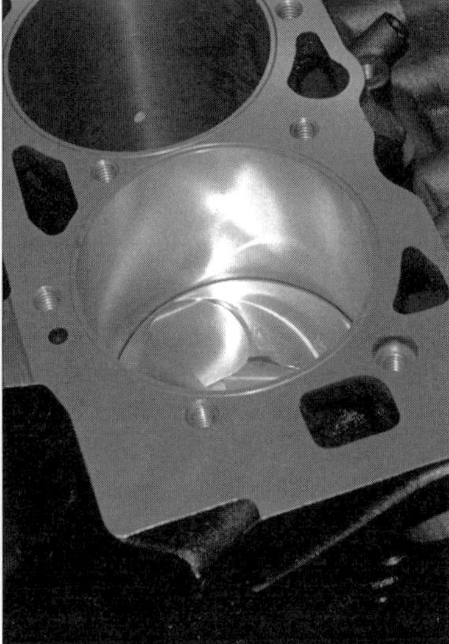

Install the piston & rod assembly into the bore. Install the rod cap & bearings.

NOTE: *It is unnecessary to tape the piston ring grooves if you are only performing a deck clearance measurement.*

To avoid measurement errors, we recommend that you measure the deck clearance with a dial indicator. First, zero the indicator dial. Rest it on the block deck with the plunger resting on the block deck surface. Rotate the dial until the needle points exactly on the zero mark.

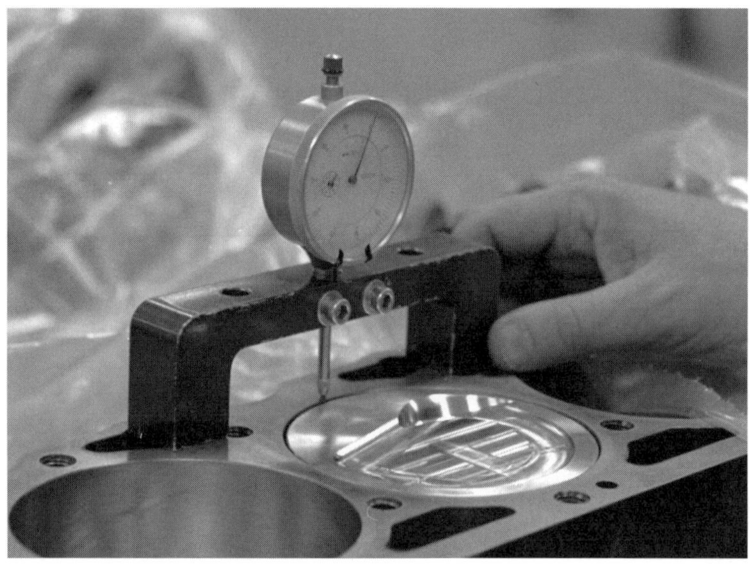

With the piston at TDC, place the deck dial indicator so that the plunger rests on the deck surface, then zero the dial.

Now, move the dial indicator so the plunger rests on the side of the piston closest to the lifter valley. Tilt the piston by pushing down on the near side of the piston. The dial indicator will read the amount deck clearance, minus the piston up-tilt.

> ***NOTE:*** Always position the dial indicator plunger as close as possible to the cylinder wall on the flat deck portion of the piston. Do not allow the dial plunger to rest on the dome or valve relief during this measurement.

With the dial plunger on the piston deck, rock the piston forward by pressing down with your fingers as shown. Write down the first dial reading.

Rock the piston the other way by pushing down with your fingers on the far side of the piston as shown below. The dial indicator will show the amount of deck clearance plus the piston down-tilt.

Rock the piston back by pressing down with your fingers as shown. Write down the second dial reading. Use the same pressure that you did on the previous measurement.

The actual deck clearance is the *average* the two tilted-piston measurements. To average the numbers together, add them and divide by two.

Example:

Average the two tilted-piston deck measurements below to find the deck clearance:

- *Measurement #1 (tilt-up) = -.010"*
- *Measurement #2 (tilt-down) = .018"*

Find the average deck clearance by adding the numbers together and dividing by 2

$$\textbf{Average Deck Clearance} = \frac{\textbf{measurement \#1} + \textbf{measurement \#2}}{2}$$

$$\textbf{Average Deck Clearance} = \frac{.010" + .018"}{2} = \frac{.028"}{2} = .014" \textbf{ (answer)}$$

The deck clearance for this engine is .014"

If the piston is below the block deck surface, the deck clearance is *positive*. If the piston is above the deck surface, the measurement is *negative*.

Positive Deck Clearance

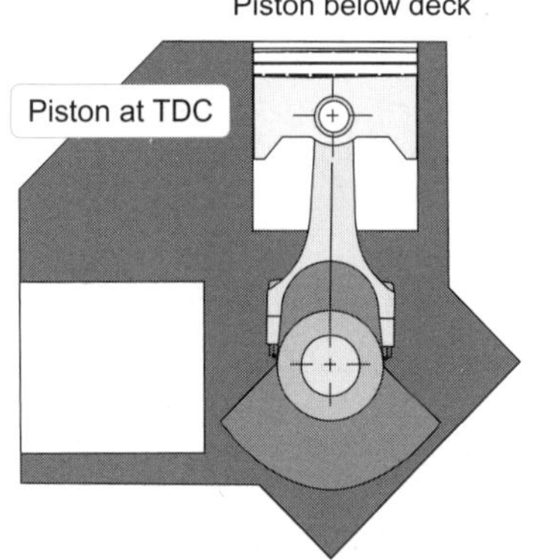

Negative Deck Clearance

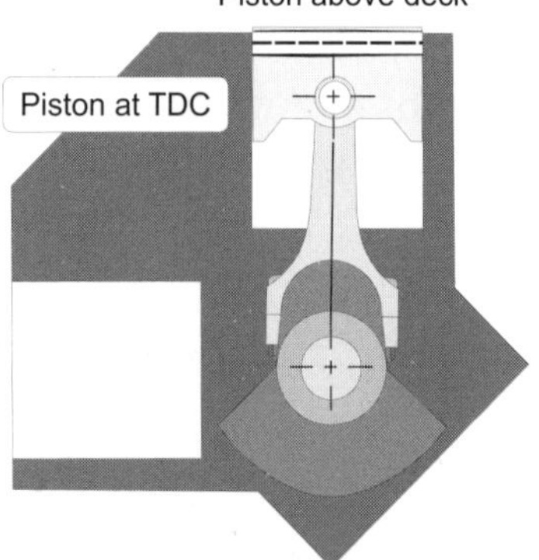

With positive deck clearance, the piston is below the block deck at TDC. Negative deck clearance means that the piston comes partly out of the bore.

It's a good idea to repeat the deck clearance measurement for all cylinders, or at the very least, the end cylinders. If the deck clearance measurements vary increasingly with each cylinder on a bank, the block deck is probably sloped. This can be corrected by having the block decks milled as long as you do not go below the minimum total deck clearance when you assemble the engine.

If the deck clearances are too small or slightly negative, you may be able to make up the difference with a thicker head gasket. If not, you may have to have the piston decks milled, use pistons with a lower compression height (CH), or buy shorter rods.

Rod Side Clearance - One often neglected aspect of rod preparation is the measurement and correction of *rod side ("cheek") clearance*. When the connecting rods are paired together on the crankshaft journals, there is a slight gap between them. This is called the rod side or "cheek" clearance.

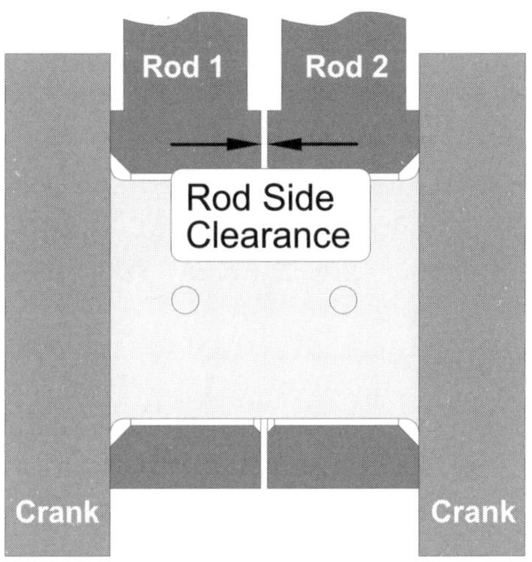

The rod side clearance is an important measurement. The size of this gap determines the rate at which oil is lost from the rod bearings and sprayed onto the cylinder walls and pistons.

Rod side clearance can be measured by subtracting the rod width measurements from the distance across the rod journals. Another way to make this measurement is to install the rods and use a feeler gauge to measure the gap between the rods.

IMPORTANT! One side of the connecting rods is deeply chamfered and the bearing is offset to clear the crankshaft fillet radius. Be sure that the rods are installed so that the deeper chamfer is toward the filled radius of the journal as shown below.

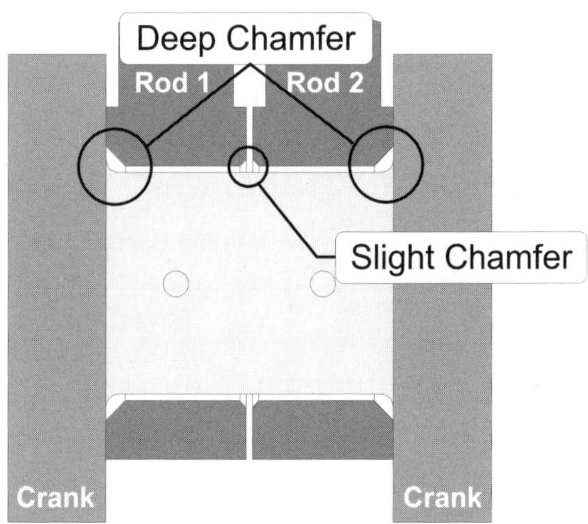

Make sure you orient the rods as shown here with the chamfered side toward the fillet radius. Use a feeler gauge to measure the side clearance (gap) between the rods.

We prefer to run .015"-.020" clearance with steel rods and .020"-.025" with aluminum rods. If the side clearances are too tight, have a machine shop grind the sides of the connecting rods to obtain the needed clearance.

Checking for Interference

The racing engines of today are built from components from many different manufacturers. This gives us the advantage of choosing from a very wide range of parts with a level of quality that couldn't have been imagined a few decades ago. However, because the manufacturers can't test all possible aftermarket parts combinations, there are often issues with rotating assembly component interference.

These problems become even more common in long stroke (*stroker*) engine applications. The pistons in stroker engines travel more deeply into the cylinder bores, the rods go through greater swing paths, and the crankshaft counterweights are very large. All of this can lead to mechanical interference that, if left unresolved, will result in catastrophic engine failure. It is the engine builder's responsibility to check and correct all rotating assembly interference problems.

Checking Crankshaft End Play Restrictions:

Crankshaft end play (thrust clearance) must be controlled *solely* by the thrust bearing acting against the smooth side surfaces of the crank thrust journal. On a GM engine, these are the polished surfaces at the front of the #5 main journal and the *thrust washer* at the rear. There must be no other mechanical contact within the lower engine assembly or the thrust bearing cannot do its job. The result of such end play restrictions can be catastrophic engine failure.

A good way to check for this problem is to install the four front (non-thrust) main bearings into the block only. Then push the crank toward the rear and try installing the thrust bearing. It should not be possible if the crank is moving far enough. Complete this check by pushing the crank as far forward as it will go. Again, if the crank is unrestricted, it should not be possible to slip the rear thrust bearing in place.

With the other main bearings in place, slide the crankshaft as far as it will go on one direction. The thrust bearing should be impossible to install unless something else is restricting crankshaft end movement. Side the crank in the other direction. It should still be impossible to install the thrust bearing.

If you find that the thrust bearing can be slipped in place with the crank pushed as far as it will go in one direction or the other, something else is contacting.

In this case, the crank was pushed as far as it would go in one direction, yet the thrust bearing can be slipped into position. This indicates a serious contact issue elsewhere within the bottom end assembly.

If the crankshaft thrust is being restricted, it can indicate one of several problems and you'll have to determine the cause. Crankshaft throws can be in contact with the block main webs or there may be some other issue with a mismatch of the crank journal radius and the main bearings being used.

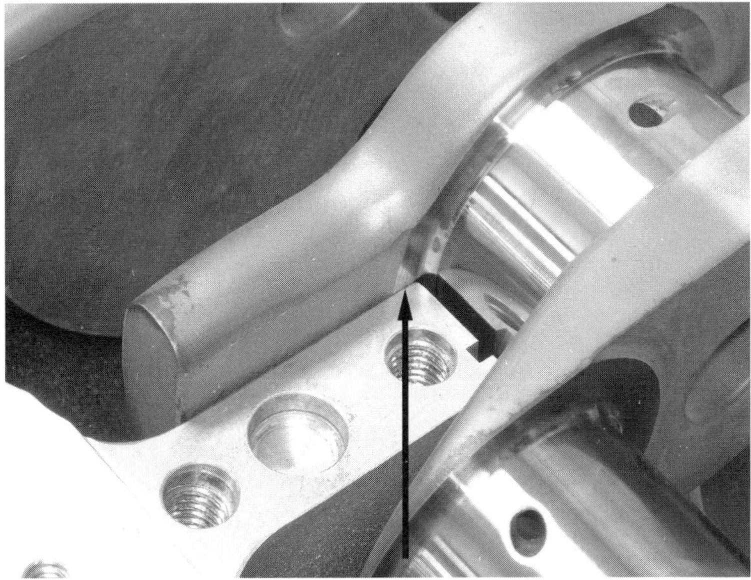

The problem has turned out to be contact between another main web in the block and a crankshaft counterweight. The crankshaft must be measured to be sure it has been machined correctly. If that's not the problem, additional relief will have to be ground into the side of the block main web.

Restricted thrust problems can require some very delicate machine work to correct the problem. This would be a good time to consult an experienced professional race engine machine shop for help.

Checking Rod to Wrist Pin Tower Clearance:

Aluminum rods are more bulky than steel rods. This can result in interference between the small (top) ends of the rods and the pin towers of the pistons. You must check to be sure there is adequate clearance and make the necessary modifications.

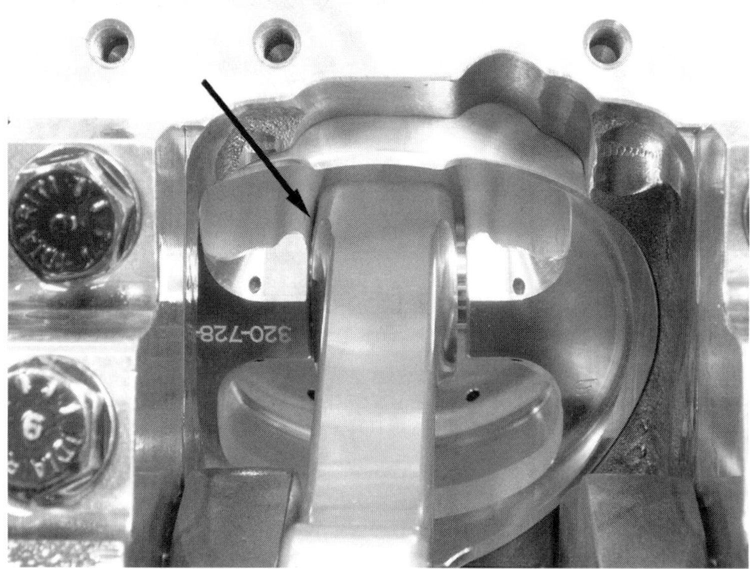

Aluminum rods often create interference with the wrist pin towers of the piston.

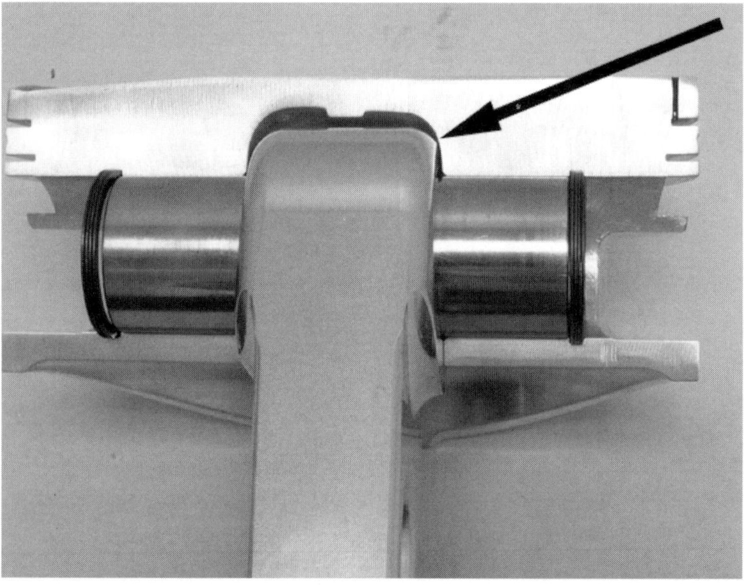

This cutaway piston helps show where the rod to pin tower interference can occur. The result if this is not corrected would be galling and metallic aluminum particles in the oil.

We order our aluminum rods with the small ends tapered a little to clear the top of the wrist pin towers. If the top of the rods interferes with the underside of the piston head, we remove a small amount of material at the top of the wrist pin towers with a vertical mill, being careful not to remove material from the bottom of the piston dome.

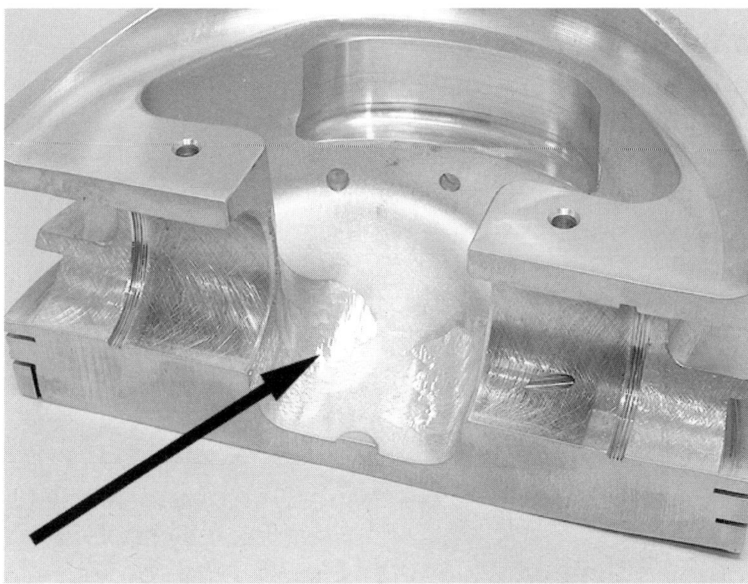

We use a vertical mill to create more clearance between the small end of the rod and the pin towers. Note the areas from which a small amount of material was removed. Don't thin the piston dome during this operation.

Checking Piston Skirt to Crank Counterweight Clearance:

The crankshaft counterweights may collide with the pistons, especially in long stroke applications. To make this check, first lubricate and install the bearings, crankshaft, and the piston and rod assemblies. You should not install piston rings at this time. Rotate the crankshaft slowly by hand as you check for interference. There must be at least .060" clearance between the pistons and crankshaft throughout the rotation. Use .060" diameter aluminum welding rod for this check.

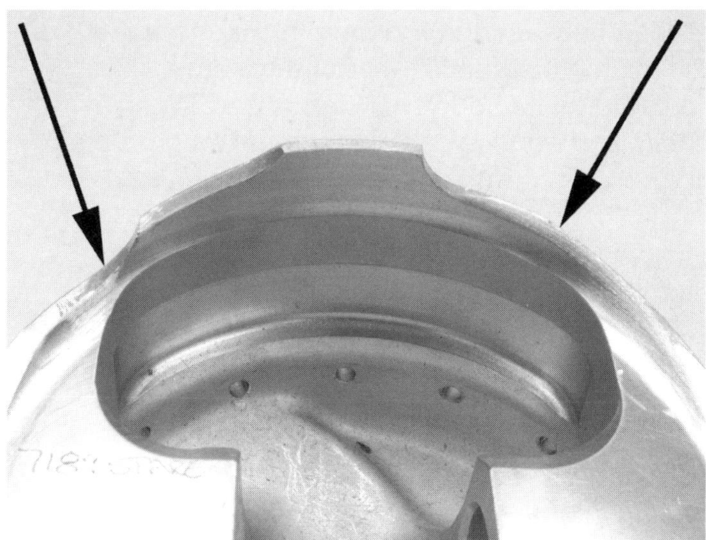

A very long stroke can result in collisions between the piston skirts and the crankshaft counterweights. If we find that that there is less than .060", we use a vertical mill to remove just enough material from the skirts to provide the needed clearance. Carefully deburr any sharp edges with Emory cloth or fine sandpaper.

Measuring Rod to Block Clearance:
Install the crank, rods, and pistons. It is not necessary to install piston rings at this time. Carefully rotate the crankshaft and look for interference between the rods and the engine block. If you find that there is not at least .060" clearance, mark the block and perform some careful relief work with a die grinder. Often, this means grinding away part of the oil pan rail area for clearance with the large ends of the connecting rods as shown below:

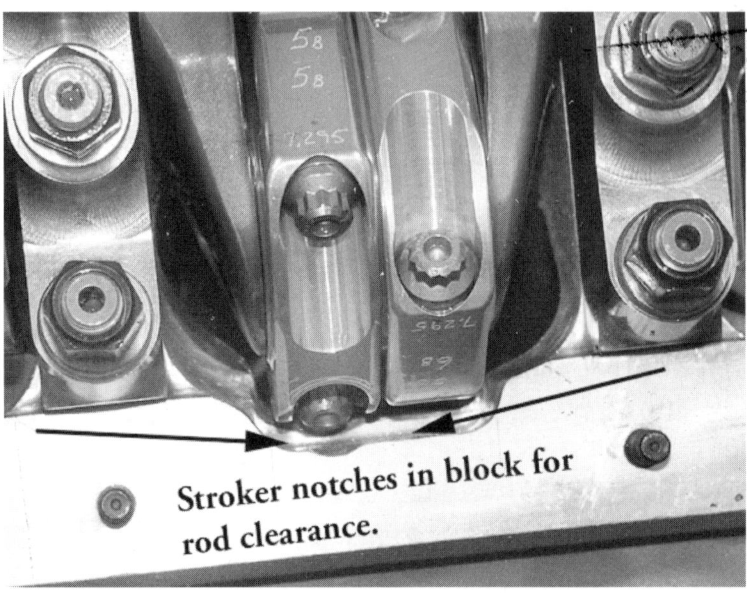

The rods in long stroke applications may contact the block as they go through their swing angles. It may be necessary to add some notches like these shown here on the oil pan rails.

There should be at least .060" clearance between the rods and block. Use .060" or larger aluminum welding fill rod to check the clearance. In some cases, a little chamfer added to the rod nuts will provide some additional clearance. When clearancing the block, use a die grinder and remove as little material as possible while leaving at least .060" clearance.

Use .060" aluminum welding rod to check for rod to block clearance. Rotate the crankshaft a small amount at a time to be sure there is adequate clearance in all rod positions.

You may also have to grind away part of the cylinder bores or sleeves in the case of aluminum blocks. Remove as little material as possible to leave at least .060" clearance with the rods. Be very careful not to scar the cylinder finish and smooth all sharp edges so that the notches do not scrape material off the piston skirts.

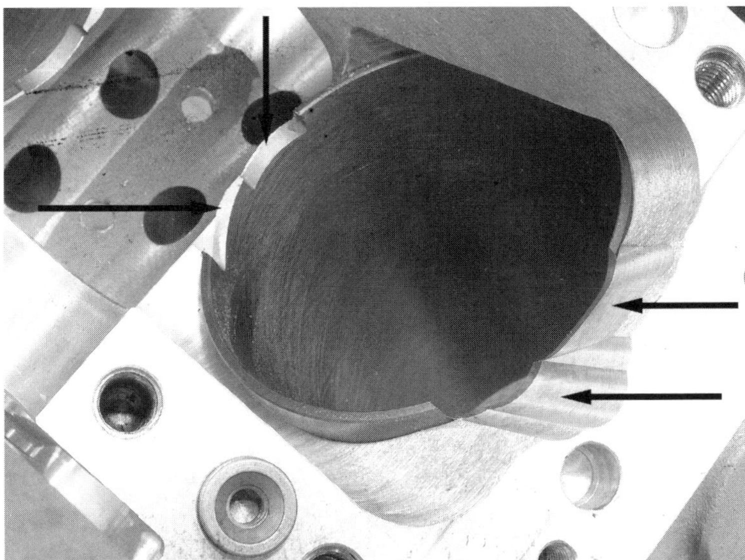

The cylinder bores usually require that some material is removed in long stroke applications. Removing material manually is a time consuming job, so we pre-clearance our common bore/stroke combinations with a CNC machine. This provides more consistent indexing and a better result.

Checking Rod to Camshaft Clearance:

Another common interference problem on long-stroke engines occurs between the connecting rods and the camshaft. As the rods swing through their elongated circles, they can collide with the camshaft lobes.

One way to resolve this issue is to special-order your camshaft with a reduced base circle diameter. However, smaller base circle cams also have smaller, weaker core diameters. This allows the camshaft to flex more, promoting erratic valve timing.

For this reason, we prefer to install a larger base circle cam, and then add clearance as needed by slightly modifying the rods. To do this, lubricate and install the camshaft, bearings, crankshaft, and cam drive assembly.

NOTE: It is extremely important to degree-in the camshaft so that it is in the correct orientation with the rods. Follow the steps described in *Unit VI - Short Block Pre-Assembly Measurements, Degreeing-In the Camshaft.*

Remember that the camshaft will flex during operation and change the running clearance. For this reason, we prefer a minimum of .060" to ensure that there will not be any contact between cam lobes and connecting rods.

Hold a .060" aluminum welding rod between a camshaft lobe and the rod. Rotate the crankshaft clockwise slowly through two full revolutions. This will ensure that the camshaft has gone through one full revolution. If at any point, you feel the welding rod pinch between the lobe and the rod, you have inadequate clearance. Repeat the check for each rod.

If you find there is too little clearance, it may be necessary to chamfer the rods slightly in the area shown below.

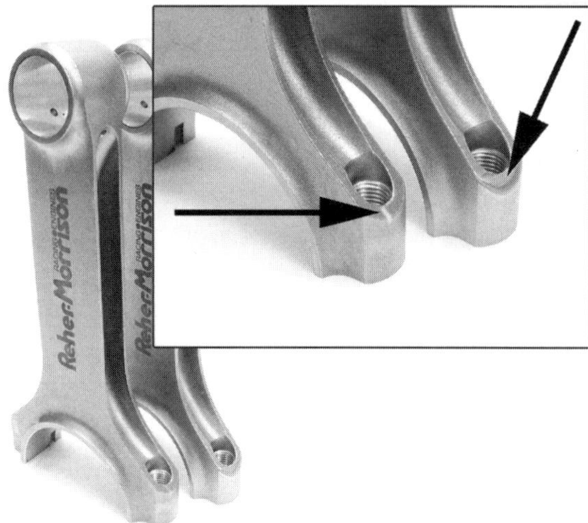

If there is inadequate (under .060") clearance between the rods and camshaft, you cannot remove material from the cam. The rods must be trimmed a little in the areas shown on the left. As always, remove as little material as possible and deburr any sharp edges.

Checking Rod to Crank Counterweight Clearance:

On some long stroke applications, it is necessary to machine counterweight clearance on the small end of the rods to avoid contact. The photo below shows the lower part of the pin boss on the rod where this contact may occur. As always, check for a minimum of .060" clearance and trim a little material from the rod as needed.

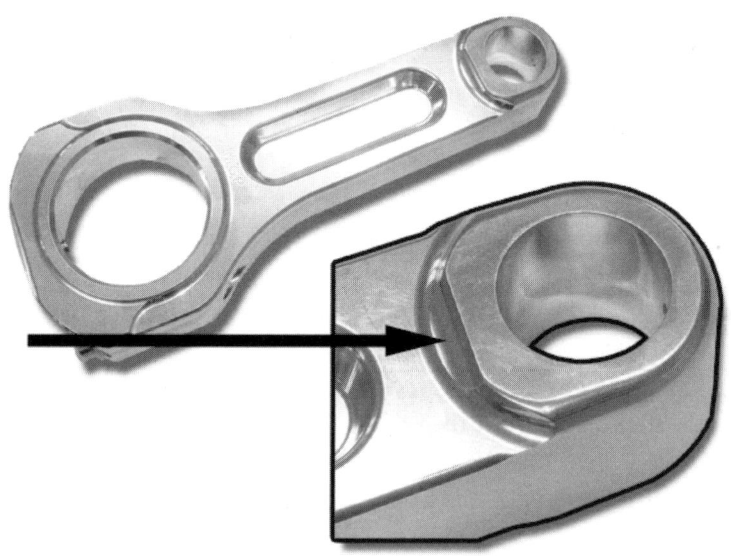

The very large counterweights of a stroker motor can contact the pin boss on the small end of the connecting rods, particularly in aluminum rod applications. It may be necessary to mill a small amount of the boss away to create adequate clearance.

Measuring Ring End Gap:

"File-fit" racing top rings are shipped with little or no end gap and must be ground before installing them in the engine. To avoid compression losses, end gaps on the top rings should be as tight as possible without risking butted rings.

A general rule of thumb is to allow .004" end gap per inch of bore diameter on the top ring. For example, a typical small block engine with a 4" bore may only require a .016" gap. However, the minimum required ring end gap also depends on the operating temperature range—the hotter that the engine runs, the greater the ring end gap must be.

We use an .018" ring gap for our naturally aspirated 500 CID Pro Stock engines. Nitrous oxide equipped engines have far higher combustion temperatures and require at least .030" ring end gaps. We recommend that you contact your racing engine builder or ring manufacturer for the minimum ring end gap specification for your engine.

Do not measure the ring end gaps until the cylinders have been bored and honed to the finished size. Use a ring squaring tool to be sure the ring is not tilted in the bore while making this measurement.

Ring squaring tools are available for all common racing engine bore sizes.

Install the ring, place the ring squaring tool into the bore, and then pull the ring up to the tool ledge with your fingers. This ensures an accurate ring end gap measurement.

After squaring a ring in the bore, measure the end gap with a feeler gauge.

Measure the end gap of each top ring with a feeler gauge as shown here.

If the end gaps of your rings are well over the specification, you must buy new rings. If the ring gaps are too small, grind the gap of each ring just enough to meet or slightly exceed the recommended minimum. This can be done with a file, but we use a special ring end gap grinding tool that saves time. It keeps the end gaps square and shows the amount of material that has been removed on a dial. After the correct gap has been achieved, be sure to carefully deburr the edges with a fine abrasive file.

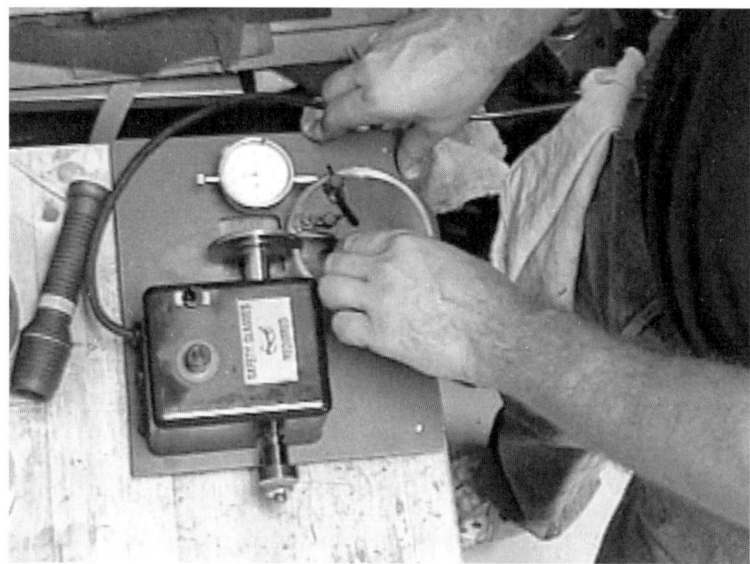

This technician is using a special machine to grind the ring end gaps to specs. This must be done very carefully to keep the ends square and avoid removing too much material.

Oil ring end gaps are far less critical than top ring gaps because they do not seal compression and are not subjected to extreme temperatures. Insert the rails squarely into the bore and make sure they have between .015"-.040" gaps. The expanders are compressible and do not require end gap measurements.

Checking Piston-to-Valve Clearance:

This measurement is of extreme importance to all racing engines. If pistons and valves collide in operation, the result is usually partial or total engine destruction. For this reason, racing pistons are cut with deep valve reliefs, but there are several factors that may still result in inadequate piston-to-valve clearance:

- *High Lift/Long Duration Camshafts* - The farther and longer that the valves are open, the more likely it is that the pistons and valves will collide.
- *Milled Cylinder Head or Block Deck Surfaces* - Either machining operation places the valves closer to the pistons.
- *High Rpm Engine Operation* - The combined mass of the lifter, pushrod, rocker arm, and valve causes the lifters to momentarily lose contact with the cam lobes at high speed. This is called *lifter loft* or *valve float*. There must be adequate clearance between the valves and piston to allow for this effect during high rpm engine operation.
- *Heat Expansion of Engine Parts* - Heat expands all of the train parts and changes clearances. However, aluminum cylinder heads grow at a greater rate than those made of cast iron and may actually increase piston-to-valve clearance slightly.

You may have heard an engine builder say that the intake valve "chases" the piston and that the piston "chases" the exhaust valve. Let's take a close look at what is happening.

Intake Piston-to-Valve Clearance - On the intake stroke, the piston pulls away from TDC as the intake valve opens. The intake valve is in effect "chasing" the piston down into the bore. So long as you have adequate static clearance between the intake valves and the pistons, the intake valves should never hit the pistons. This is because, at high rpm's, pushrod and rocker arm flex delay the rate of valve opening and can actually increase the intake piston-to-valve clearance as the engine is running.

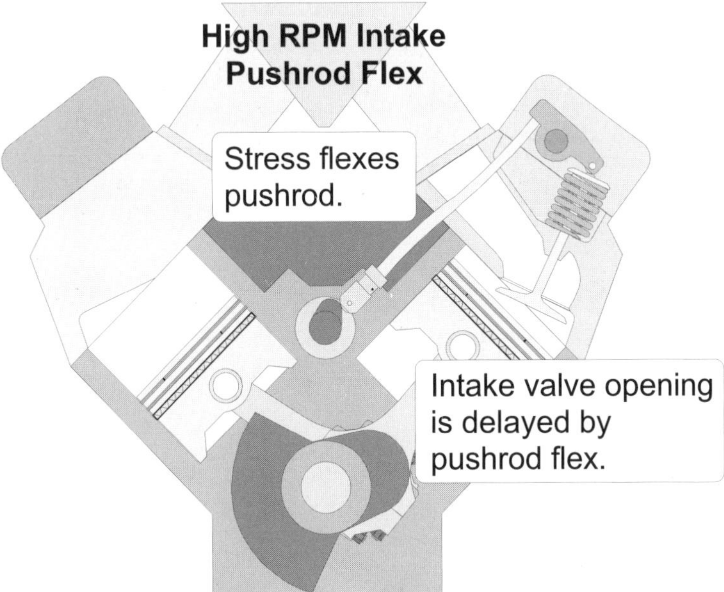

Pushrods and rocker arms flex while the engine is running, particularly at high rpm's. Because the intake valves "chase" the piston down, this flex can actually result in additional valve-to-piston clearance and reduces potential valve clashing problems.

As a general rule, intake piston-to-valve clearance should be a minimum of the total deck clearance plus .010" (see the *Calculating Rod Length* section of this unit).

Example:

A particular racing engine has been built to have a total deck height clearance of .050". Add .010" to find the minimum intake piston-to-valve clearance specification.

Min. Intake Piston - to - Valve Clear. = Total Deck Height + .010"

Min. Intake Piston - to - Valve Clear. = .050"+.010" = .060" (answer)

This engine must have at least .060" intake piston-to-valve clearance.

The majority of the racing engines we build have .060"-.065" intake piston-to-valve clearance. The valve reliefs must be cut on the same angle as the valves so that, should they ever meet while the engine is running, they will strike squarely. This minimizes the damage to valves, pistons, and cylinder heads.

The pistons can rock in operation and contact the side of the valve head. To avoid contact, there must be .050" to .060" radial valve clearance.

Intake Piston-to-Valve Clearance

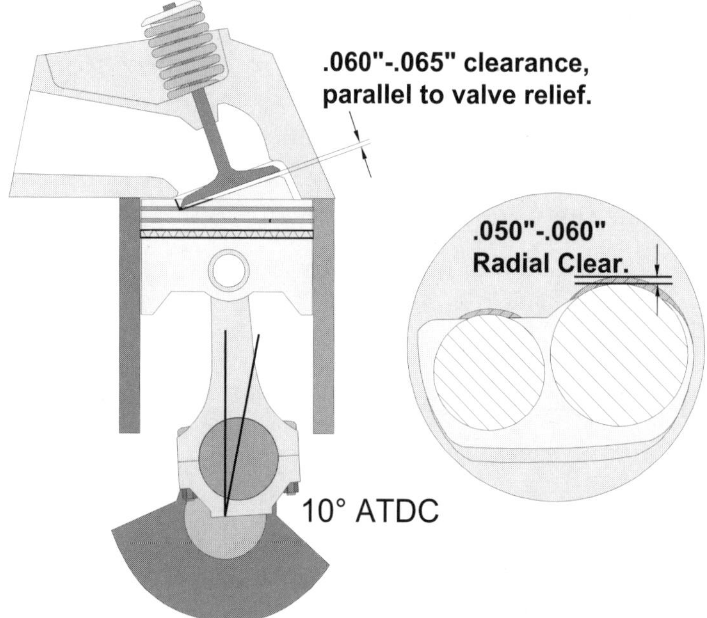

The intake valves must have at least .060" clearance when the piston is at 10° ATDC. The valve pockets must be cut to the same angle as the valves and there must be .050" to .060" radial clearance. Inexperienced engine builders often overlook these important aspects of proper piston-to-valve clearances.

<u>Exhaust Piston-to-Valve Clearance</u> - Adequate exhaust piston-to-valve clearance is especially important. Exhaust heat causes the valve stems to expand, making the valve longer and reducing clearance.

There are also mechanical reasons that exhaust valve clash is such a problem. On the exhaust stroke, the piston “chases” the exhaust valve near TDC. Any delay in valve closing reduces the exhaust piston-to-valve clearance. This happens when engine rpm’s begin to rise and the lifters start to lose contact with the cam lobes (float or loft). These problems are compounded if the valve springs are too weak or have harmonic control problems at certain speeds.

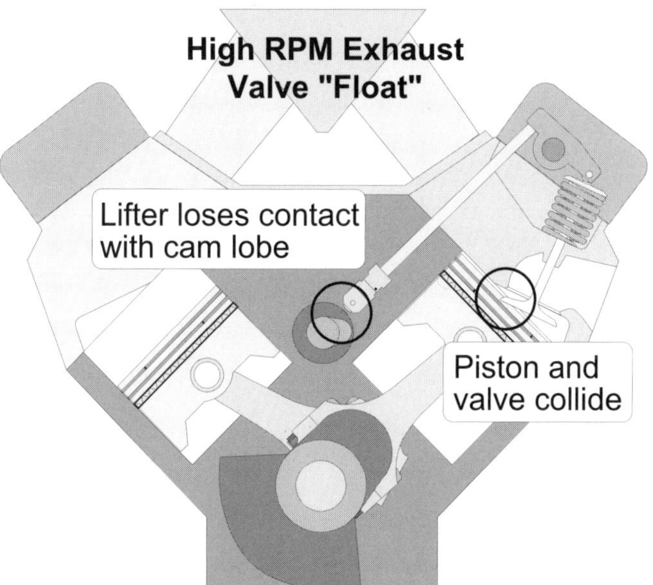

This engine was not built with enough exhaust piston-to-valve clearance. At high rpm’s, the exhaust valve spring is unable to maintain contact between the lifter and cam lobe. Lifter “float” or loft results in a collision between the piston and valve.

Additional static clearance is required to help ensure that the valves and pistons will not collide when the engine is running. A general rule of thumb for exhaust piston-to-valve clearance is to multiply the required intake clearance by 2.

Example:

The previous racing engine has .060” intake piston-to-valve clearance. Multiply this number by two to find a safe exhaust piston-to-valve clearance specification.

$$\textbf{Min. Exhaust Piston - to - Valve Clear.} = 2 \times \textbf{Intake Clearance}$$

$$\textbf{Min. Exhaust Piston - to - Valve Clear.} = 2 \times .060" = .120" \textbf{ (answer)}$$

This engine should have .120” exhaust piston-to-valve clearance.

The majority of the racing engines we build have a minimum of .120" exhaust piston-to-valve clearance. As with intake valve reliefs, the exhaust valve reliefs must be cut on the same angle as the valve heads. There must also be .050" to .060" radial clearance with the valve reliefs to avoid contact when the pistons rock.

Exhaust Piston-to-Valve Clearance

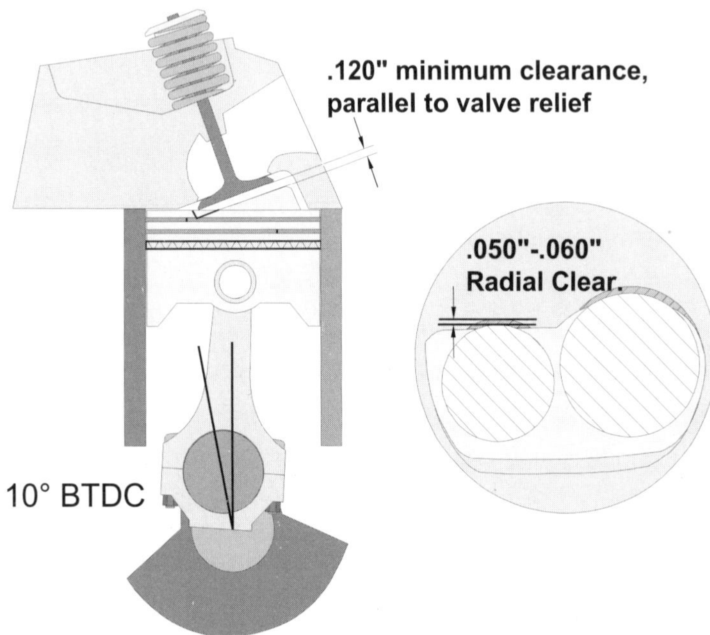

For our example engine, the exhaust valves should have at least .120" clearance when the piston is at 10° BTDC. The valve pockets must be cut to the same angle as the valves and there must be. 050" to .060" radial clearance.

Intake and exhaust piston-to-valve clearance must be measured before final engine assembly and after all engine machining operations have been completed.

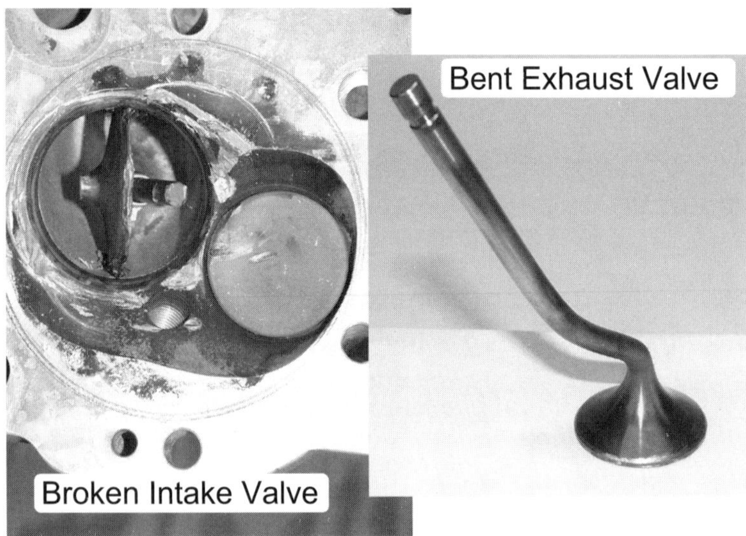

This is the reason for checking piston-to-valve clearance carefully. Unfortunately, the kind of damage shown on the left goes far beyond just the valves and heads.

Oiling System

A well-functioning oiling system is crucial to the longevity of any racing engine. Oil provides lubrication to nearly all of the moving parts in the engine and also helps to cool the pistons, valve springs, and other components. The main parts of the oiling system are:

- Oil Pump
- Pickup
- Pan & baffle
- Filter
- Passages
- Windage Tray

Oiling System Operating Principles:

Barring an oiling system failure, the camshaft or crankshaft journals never touch the bearing inserts while the engine is running. The journals ride on a layer of oil called a *hydro-dynamic wedge*.

Oil is pumped into the bearing in sufficient quantity and pressure to lift the journal off the bearing surface. As the journal rotates, a wedge of oil follows the journal and keeps the metal surfaces apart. Because there is no metal-to-metal contact, there is very little friction.

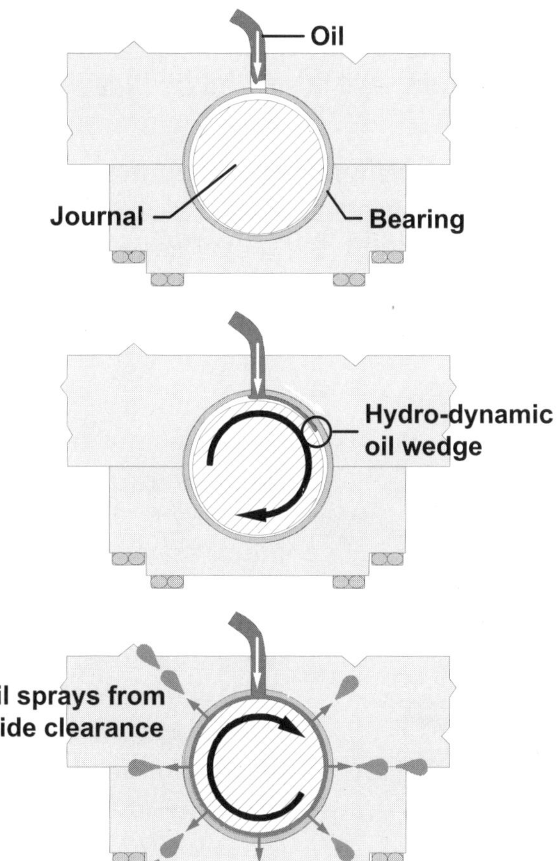

When you start the engine, oil flows through passages under pressure to the engine bearings.

As the crankshaft rotates, a hydro-dynamic wedge of oil "rolls" around the clearance between the journal and bearing. This separates the journal from the bearing.

Oil completely fills the space, and the journal spins freely on a cushion of oil. Excess oil sprays from the side clearance all the way around the journal.

Wet-Sump Systems - The *sump* is the deepest part of the oil pan. In a *wet-sump* system, the oil pump and pickup are submerged in oil inside the pan. The oil pump is driven off the camshaft through a gear and shaft in this system.

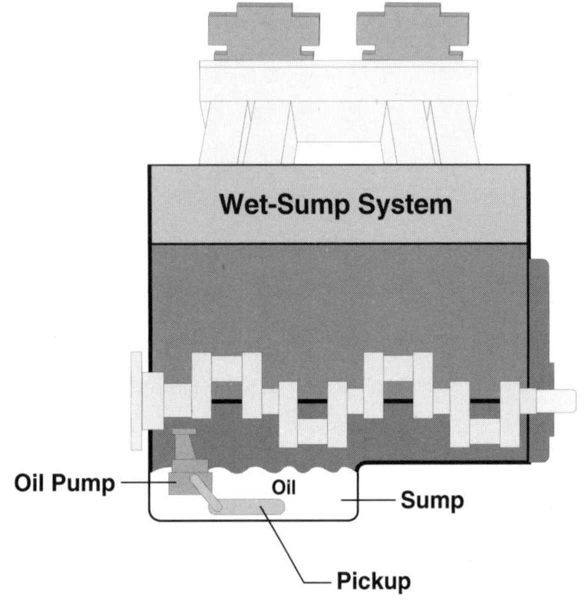

This is a wet sump oiling system.

When the engine is running, large amounts of oil spray from the engine bearings. The crankshaft acts like a blender, churning the oil and crankcase gases into windage. As the crankshaft cuts through windage, it is slowed by friction. This can rob 80 or more horsepower from the engine.

Oil Pan Design - As engine rpm's rise, the aerodynamic effects of the spinning crankshaft start to direct the oil spray to the right (passenger's) side of the engine. The more closely the oil pan shrouds the crankshaft, the more the oil windage interferes with crankshaft rotation. The best oil pan designs have a "kicked-out" section on the right side to provide a relief area.

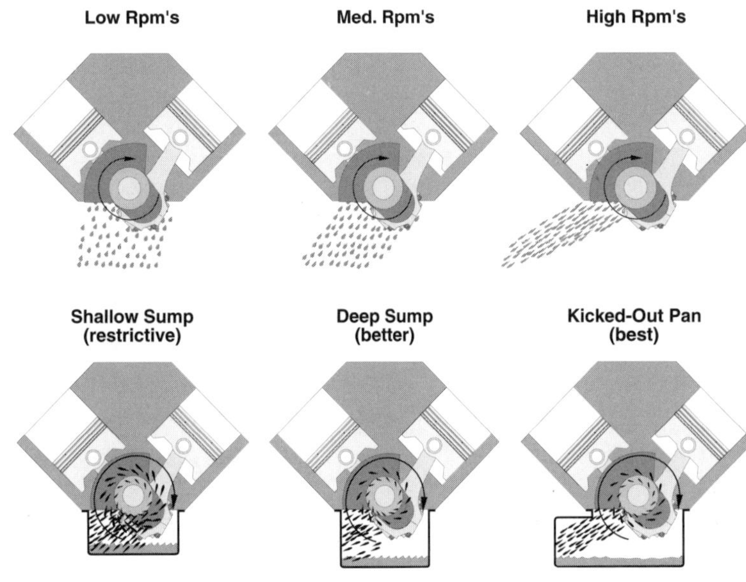

As engine rpm's climb, the oil spray is directed toward the passenger's side of the engine.

The oil pan design can have a lot to do with the amount of drag that results from oil windage. A kicked-out pan can reduce windage losses by 20 horsepower or more.

Most GM V8 engine blocks have the starter mounted on the passenger's side of the block. This location reduces the size that the oil pan kick-out can be.

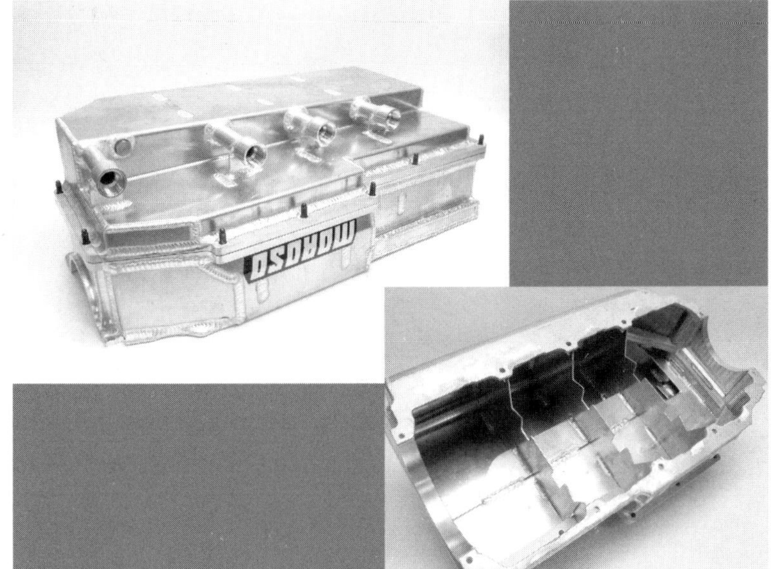

This aluminum racing oil pan has internal baffles to control the oil and reduce windage losses. Note the scavenging connections (inverted top photo) for a dry sump system.

NOTE: This is a two piece split pan for easier lower end maintenance.

On high-end racing applications, we often relocate the starter motor to the left (driver's) side of the block, then install a remote oil filter assembly. This allows the use of pans with larger kick-outs, further reducing horsepower losses from windage drag.

<u>Wet-Sump System Flow Path</u> - This is oil flow path in a standard wet-sump system:

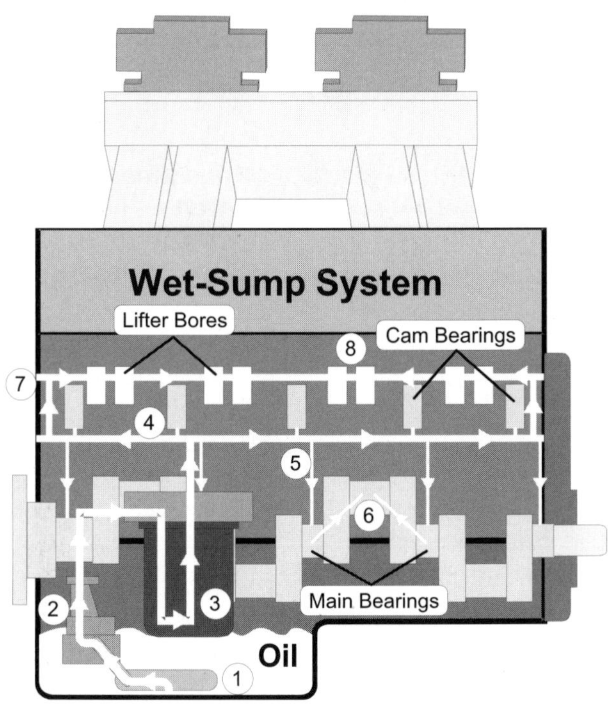

1. *Oil is drawn though the pickup screen into the oil pump.*
2. *The pump pressurizes the oil and delivers it to the oil filter.*
3. *The oil goes through the filtration paper or screen and exits to the main oil gallery.*
4. *The main oil gallery distributes oil to the main and cam bearings.*
5. *Oil travels through drilled passages in the block webs to the mains.*
6. *Oil travels from the main bearings to the rod bearings through drilled passages in the crankshaft.*
7. *Oil pressure from the main gallery fills the lifter galleries.*
8. *The lifters receive oil through holes in each lifter bore. The oil finally travels through the pushrods to the rockers (not shown).*

Dry-Sump Systems - In a dry-sump oiling system, a multi-stage pump is mounted on the outside of the engine and is driven by a cogged rubber belt. Dry-sump pumps have one oil pump section (usually at the rear) and multiple oil scavenging sections at the front.

A dry sump system uses a belt driven externally mounted oil pump. Note the many braided steel hose lines that are required for this system.

The oil pump section pulls oil from the reservoir and pumps it into the main engine oil galleries. With a five-stage system, there are four pickups in the oil pan. We use six-stage system in 762 CID and larger engines as well as our Pro competition engines. The extra stage scavenges oil from the lifter valley. This reduces windage drag, and also allows us to seal off the lifter valley area. If a valve train component breaks, the pieces are contained and there is less damage to the bottom end.

Dry-Sump System Flow Path - In a dry sump system, a multi-section oil pump is mounted on the outside of the engine and driven by a cogged belt. This is the flow of the dry-sump system:

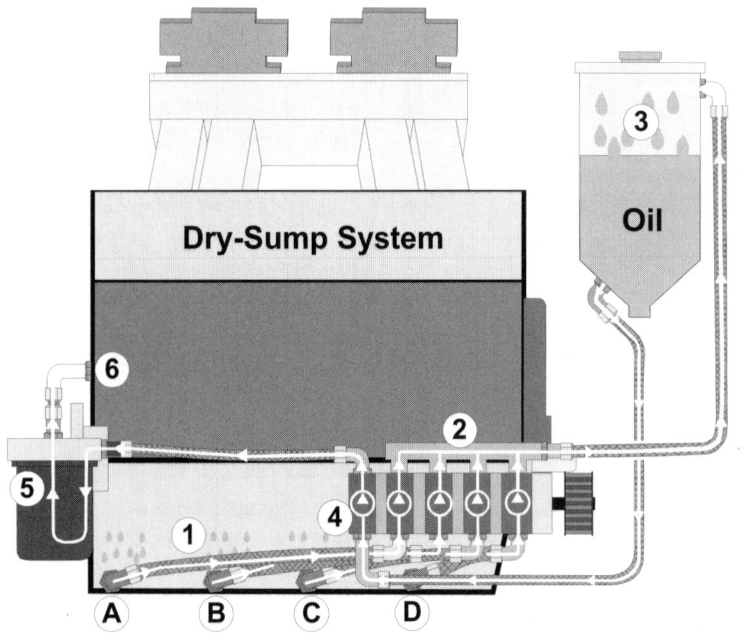

1. *Oil and windage are drawn (scavenged) from points in the oil pan (A, B, C, & D)*
2. *The oil and windage are collected by a manifold and sent through a single line to the top of the reservoir.*
3. *Gas separates and liquid oil settles into the bottom of the reservoir.*
4. *The oil is drawn into the oil pump stage.*
5. *The pump sends pressurized oil to the filter.*
6. *After filtration, oil travels to the main oil galleries.*

The photo below shows how all the hardware looks on a 762 Super Series engine with a 6-stage dry-sump system:

1. *Oil reservoir (tank)*
2. *Oil scavenge lines from the oil pan and lifter valley*
3. *Oil pump scavenge sections*
4. *Oil pump section*
5. *Oil filter*
6. *Oil return line*

A good dry-sump system is expensive, but offers many advantages for high-horsepower applications including:

- Reduced Crankcase Windage Losses - With less gas in the crankcase, there is little or no medium in which the oil spray can mix. Instead of being suspended in a churning froth, the oil sprayed off the crankshaft just deflects off the internal engine surfaces and runs down into the pan to be scavenged by the pump. Also, there is far less windage pumped back and forth by the pistons. The reduction in windage losses can mean 20 or more horsepower to a racing engine at a crankcase vacuum of 18-20 inches mercury.
- Insurance Against Loss of Oil Pressure - With a wet sump system, the oil pressure gauge will indicate "0" if the pickup becomes uncovered under high G-forces. This often happens in a drag car when the driver hits the brakes at the end of the quarter mile. Even a momentary loss of oil pressure can harm the engine bearings and crankshaft. A dry-sump system has a large external reservoir that maintains a steady supply of foam-free liquid oil to the engine. This extra volume provides a greater safety margin and helps cool the engine oil.
- Smaller Oil Pan Dimensions - The short dry-sump oil pans provide more ground clearance and allow the engine to be mounted lower in the race car.
- Reduced Camshaft Load - Wet-sump oil pumps are driven off the distributor gear and camshaft. This can twist the cam and upset normal valve timing.

To install a dry sump system, you must make your own braided steel hose lines. It is very important to use the right type of hose and fittings and to cut the lines with a special tool that provides a clean, straight cut. If you wish to install a dry-sump system, we recommend that you talk to an experienced racing engine builder and the dry-sump system manufacturer to get the right pump, drive speed, and installation & pressure adjustment procedures. Be sure that you can make everything fit and work correctly before you make your purchases.

Oil Splash Lubrication:

Many engine components are lubricated and cooled by oil splash or spray including:

- Cylinder Walls & Pistons
- Piston Pins
- Timing Chain or Gears (not Belt)
- Cam Lobes
- Distributor & Oil Pump Gears
- Rocker Arms
- Valve Springs
- Valve Stems & Guides

Splash-Oiled Components - Oil that is thrown off the crankshaft lubricates the cylinder walls & pistons, piston pins, timing chain, cam lobes, and the distributor & oil pump gears. Roller cam bearings (if equipped) also receive their lubrication from splash.

Pushrod-Oiled Components - Oil that is pumped into the lifters is released through the hollow pushrods to lubricate the pushrod ends, rocker arms, and valve stems & guides. High pressure valve springs get extremely hot in operation. The oil that sprays out of the pushrods also provides critically important cooling of the valve springs.

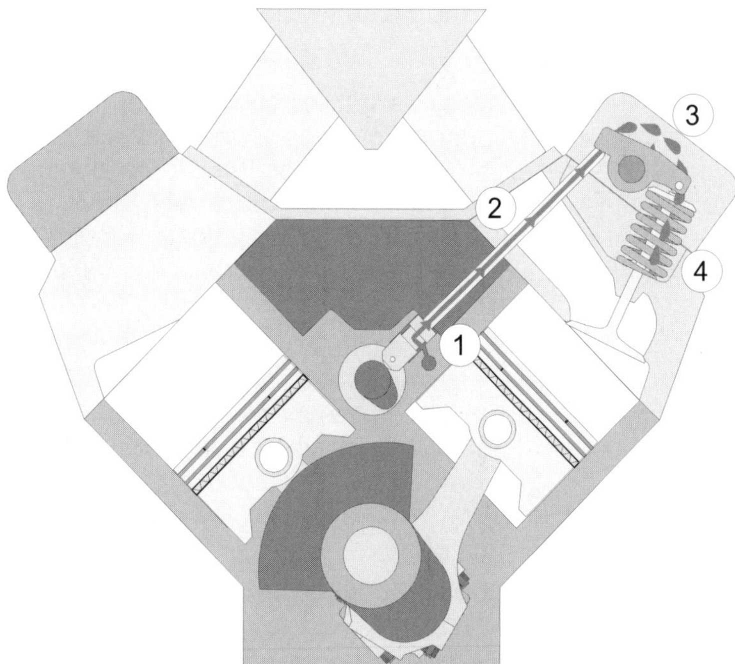

1. *Oil pressure from the lifter gallery enters a hole in the side of the lifter, filling it with oil.*
2. *The oil flows up the pushrod.*
3. *Oil spurts out the top of the pushrod through a small hole in the rocker arm. This lubricates the rocker arm and pivot.*
4. *Oil runs down the valve spring and valve stem, cooling the spring and lubricating the stem & guide. The oil then returns to the crankcase through large holes located at the ends of the cylinder head.*

Valve guide seals may be required in stock or endurance applications where part throttle operation creates strong intake manifold vacuum. This vacuum tends to draw excess oil through the clearance between the intake valve stems and guides, contaminating the combustion process. Various types of seals are available to prevent this from happening. Drag racing engines that are well maintained and operate almost exclusively at wide open throttle usually do not require valve guide seals.

Most flat tappets are designed to deliver pushrod oiling in spurts. Oil flow is controlled by pressure on a shim inside the lifter. When the lifter rides up on the cam lobe and begins to open the valve, it must do so against valve spring pressure. When the lifter is back on the base circle of the cam, *lash* (looseness) allows oil to flow around the shim and lubricate the components. This is how it works:

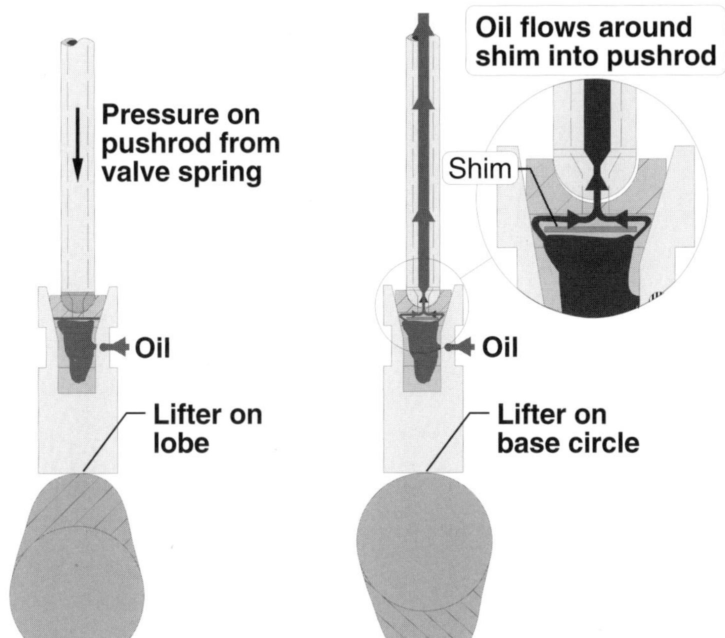

When the valve is open (left diagram), valve spring pressure on the shim seals off oil flow.

When the valve is closed (right diagram), lash allows oil to flow around the shim and into the pushrod.

NOTE: Roller lifters have almost completely replaced flat tappets, even in stock applications and are superior in nearly every way. Only use flat tappets in a racing application if they are required by your race sanctioning organization.

Lubrication System Performance:

Several factors affect the performance of the lubrication system including:

- Oil Pressure & Volume
- Bearing Oil Clearances
- Oil Types & Properties

<u>Oil Pressure and Volume</u> - In a passenger car engine, 30 or 40 psi (pounds per square inch) of oil pressure is usually enough to maintain good engine lubrication. By comparison, racing engines place much higher loads on the crankshaft and camshaft journals. Engines that operate above 7000 rpm's require higher oil pressure to maintain separation between bearings and journals. Most of our medium to high horsepower racing engines run 50 to 60 psi oil pressure or higher, depending on the application.

Oil flow rates also depend on the application, but generally range from 8 to 12 gpm (gallons per minute). The oil pump must be able to maintain pressure at this flow rate to avoid bearing-to-journal contact and engine failure.

As the crankshaft and camshaft spin faster, the rate of oil loss from bearings increases. If the pump cannot keep up with the volume demand, oil pressure will drop off rapidly. In order to maintain adequate oil pressure throughout the engine rpm operating range, you must have a pump that can deliver at least 8-12 gpm.

Maximum delivered oil pressure is determined by the spring pressure against the relief valve. Any time pump pressure exceeds the limit, the relief valve lifts off a seat inside the pump and allows the excess oil to return to the suction side.

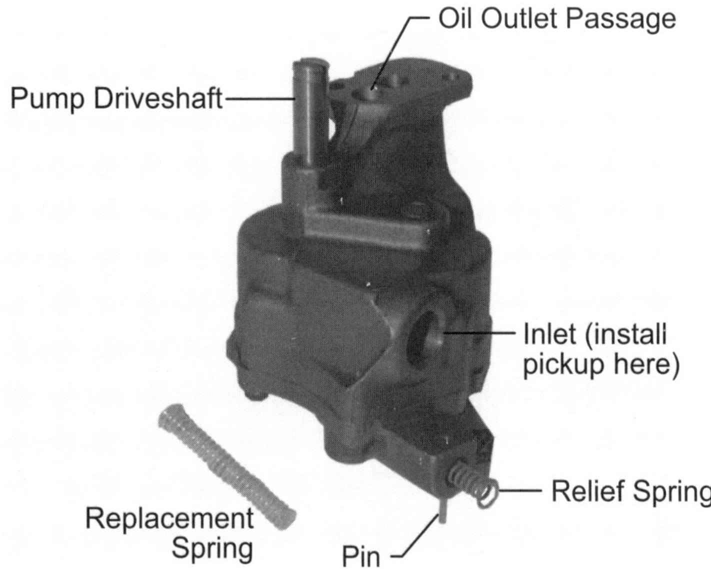

Adjust the maximum regulated oil pressure in a stock-type wet-sump oil pump by changing or shimming the relief valve spring. The pickup tube will be positioned and installed in the oil inlet hole later.

We made our own bench testing device to check the pop-off pressure on the relief valve for wet-sump oil pumps. We seal the rubber end of an air blow gun to the oil outlet passage on the pump, then release air pressure until the relief valve opens. The gauge shows the pop-off pressure (maximum regulated oil pressure).

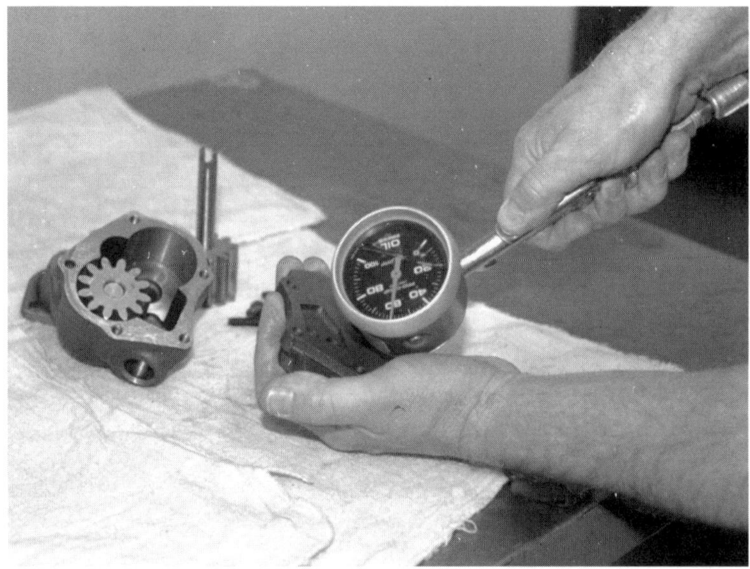

We built this simple device to test the pop-off pressure on wet-sump oil pumps. Note that the dial shows a pop-off pressure of 60 psi. This is adequate for most racing applications.

If the pop-off pressure is too low (below 60 psi for most applications), we either replace the spring or shim the existing spring to increase the pressure. If the pop-off pressure is too high (above 80 psi), we install a weaker relief valve spring.

On a dry-sump oil pump, the relief valve spring pressure can be adjusted while the engine is running. The relative size of the drive pulleys determines the pump speed. This affects the oil flow and scavenge rates. Follow the manufacturer's recommended procedure for setting the pump speed and pressure for a dry sump pump.

A dry sump pump like this 6-stage version can be adjusted for both pumping rate and maximum oil pressure.

<u>Bearing Oil Clearances</u> - Engine bearing oil clearances have a lot to do with oil pump volume requirements. If the clearances are too loose, oil sprays from the bearings faster. The pump may not have enough capacity to keep up with the flow demands. If this happens, oil pressure will drop.

Another reason to pay close attention to engine bearing oil clearances is that the oil that sprays from the crankshaft journals winds up on the cylinder walls. If the cylinders are flooded with too much oil, the rings may not be able to scrape it away fast enough. The extra oil raining down from the interior engine surfaces becomes an additional source of windage drag for the crankshaft.

Make sure you measure all engine bearing oil clearances and rod side clearances accurately. Replace or re-machine the internal engine parts as required to maintain these critical clearances in your engine. This is one of the best ways to ensure long racing engine life.

Oil Types & Properties:

There are important differences between motor oils that are formulated for passenger cars and those made for racing applications. The API (American Petroleum Institute) sets a number of standards for passenger car motor oils. They work closely with automobile and motor oil manufacturing companies to establish minimum requirements and testing standards for various motor oil grades. The motor oil in a passenger car remains in the crankcase for many thousands of miles. It contains detergents, anti-oxidants, pour point depressants, and other additives to cope with these demands.

The type and quality of motor oil that you choose can have a lot to do with engine life and power output.

Racing engines operate almost exclusively in a high-temperature, high-load environment. In these engines, the motor oil is drained and replaced frequently, often after every race. In racing engines, we are less concerned with the ability of the oil to last for long periods and more concerned with its ability to lubricate and reduce power losses. The detergent additives in many stock motor oils only serve to promote foaming at high rpm's and are not usually part of the additive package in a racing motor oil.

Oil can be divided by type into two categories, *synthetic* and *non-synthetic*. Synthetic motor oils are created from petroleum products and chemicals. Non synthetic motor oils are refined from crude oil that is pumped out of the ground.

Racing synthetic motor oils have important qualities that make them desirable for use in most racing applications. Synthetic oils can reduce engine friction and are very thin, thus reducing pumping losses (viscous drag). They can handle very high temperatures without scorching. Synthetics tend to burn cleaner when compared to most non-synthetic oils. These qualities usually lead to a measurable increase in horsepower output.

IMPORTANT! Synthetic motor oils lubricate so well that they can prevent a newly-assembled engine from ever achieving a good ring seal. We use non-synthetic oil on the cylinder walls and in the crankcase at the time of assembly, then drain the oil and install a high quality synthetic racing oil after the break-in period.

Viscosity is another important oil characteristic that influences performance. Viscosity means thickness. It is measured and rated by a standardized numerical system developed by the SAE (Society of Automotive Engineers).

Anyone who has ever changed oil in a hot engine knows how thin oil gets at higher temperatures. Oil viscosity is closely related to its temperature. Engine motor oil absorbs a lot of heat from the engine block, cylinder heads, pistons, and other engine parts. As the oil thins, it pours out of bearings faster. This reduces oil pressure and can increase oil volume requirements.

Thin oils are rated in "weight" numbers under 20. Thick oils range from 30 weight to 50 weight. Some oils can exhibit the properties of both thin and thick oils. These are called *multi-viscosity* motor oils. The letter "W" follows the first number in a multi-viscosity motor oil. This stands for "winter" and indicates the tested viscosity of the oil at 0° F. The second number is the viscosity of the motor oil at 210° F. Here is one type of multi-viscosity racing motor oil:

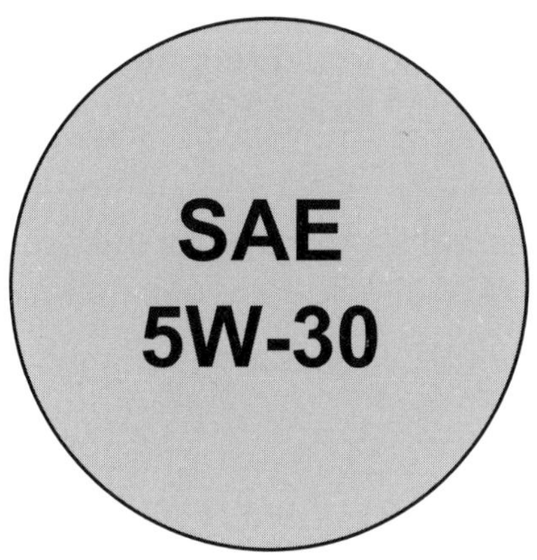

The first number (5) in this multi-viscosity motor oil indicates that it is the same thickness as a straight 5 weight motor oil at winter temperatures (0° F). The second number (30) indicates that it will thin no more than straight 30 weight at 210° F.

Multi-viscosity motor oils are able to perform better with varying temperatures, so we prefer to use them in all high performance applications.

Many synthetic racing motor oils have a very low viscosity—usually around zero weight. A different and more sensitive metric scale called *centistokes* is now being used to rate the viscosity of these oils. Thin synthetic racing motor oils require an increased flow rate through the engine. Despite this drawback we recommend the use of synthetic motor oils for most racing applications after the initial assembly and break-in periods.

Review Questions

1. What is a "ferrous" block? What are some advantages and disadvantages of using a ferrous block for a racing engine? What are most non-ferrous blocks made of? What are some advantages and disadvantages of using non-ferrous blocks?

2. What is a "seasoned block"? What are some advantages and disadvantages of using a new block instead of one that has been seasoned?

3. Why is it important to clean the engine block before you make measurements? How do you clean the oil galleries? What should you do to prevent rust formation after cleaning the block?

4. Name five things that you should check for when inspecting an engine block. What is "Magnafluxing", and what kind of block would require this process? For what type of material would you use the Zyglo® process?

5. Why is it important to inspect the cylinder walls? What type of damage may be visible on the cylinder walls? How do you spot evidence of a blown head gasket?

6. What problem is indicated in the photo below? How should the block appear?

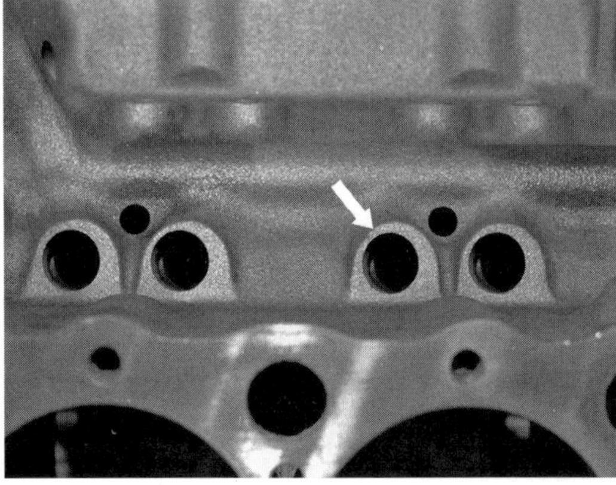

7. Name six important block measurements.

8. What is "deck height"? What other components and relationships are affected by the deck height of the block?

9. What tools may be used to measure bore diameter, cylinder out-of-round, and taper? Describe how each of these is measured.

10. How do you measure main bore diameter? How is main bore alignment measured? Why is correct main bore alignment important? What is the maximum allowable main bore misalignment? How can excessive bore misalignment be corrected?

11. Why are cam bore alignment and diameter important measurements? What are the tolerances for cam bore diameter and misalignment? How can you have cam bore misalignment corrected?

12. Name nine important block machining operations. How can you tell good machine work from bad machine work?

13. Describe main bore and cam bore align boring procedures. How are cam bearings removed?

14. Why is it a bad idea to have a cylinder block sleeved? What effect does overboring an engine have on engine displacement and compression?

15. What is the purpose of cylinder honing? What is a torque plate? Why is it important to use a torque plate when honing the cylinder walls? What is a crosshatch pattern? What creates this crosshatch pattern? What determines the particular cylinder wall finish that is required?

16. What is the purpose of lifter bore honing? How can worn or damaged lifter bores be repaired?

17. What is the purpose of milling the engine block?

18. What is an "O-ringed block"? How do O-rings create a reliable cylinder seal? What type of head gaskets should be used with an O-ringed block?

19. Why is it a good idea to deburr the block after machining operations? What is crankcase "windage"? Why is it helpful to smooth sharp edges in the crankcase area? What is "thread chasing"? Why is it important to chase the threads? What tool is used for this?

20. What are two types of engine bearings? Describe the construction of an engine bearing. What is bearing crush and why is it important? What is bearing spread? How does bearing spread make engine assembly easier?

21. What is the purpose of the oil hole in one bearing insert? Does the insert with the oil hole go in the block or the cap? What will happen if you put the inserts in the wrong way?

22. How do you choose between roller and babbitted cam bearings? What are some advantages of roller cam bearings?

23. How are undersize main and rod bearings identified? How can you match main bearing inserts to obtain a difference of .0005"?

24. What is the purpose of pinning a rod bearing insert in an aluminum rod?

25. Name three types of crankshafts, and explain how to identify them. What are the advantages and disadvantages of each for use in racing engines? Why are there counterweights on the crankshaft? What is the purpose of a rounded leading edge on the crankshaft counterweights?

26. Why are the edges of crank journals radiused? Why are there holes drilled from the main journals to the rod journals? Why should you never use a cross-drilled crankshaft in a high-rpm racing engine? How can you tell if the crankshaft has been cross-drilled?

27. Explain how to inspect a crankshaft. How can you check crankshaft straightness? How do you measure crank journal diameter and out-of-round? How do you measure crank journal taper?

28. Why is it important to chamfer the oil holes after regrinding a crankshaft? What is the purpose of polishing a crankshaft? How is this done? Why is it important to pay attention to the direction of rotation when polishing a crankshaft?

29. Why is proper engine balancing important in a racing engine? Explain the difference between internal and external balancing. What parts must be weighed to balance the engine? How is weight removed from a crankshaft counterweight? How can weight be added?

30. What type of pistons must be used in racing engines? Identify the piston features in the photo below:

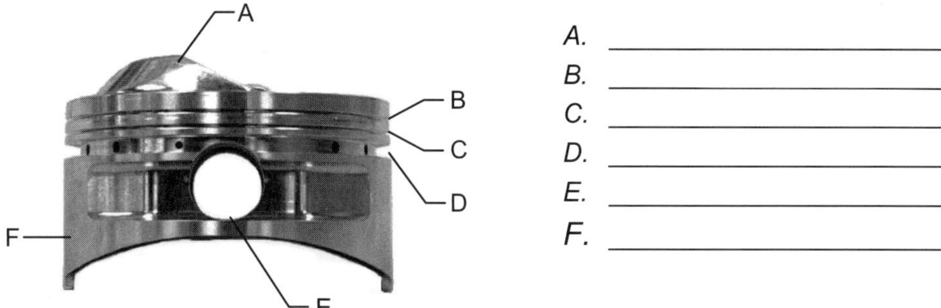

A. ____________________
B. ____________________
C. ____________________
D. ____________________
E. ____________________
F. ____________________

31. Why is a piston cam ground? Why is a piston tapered? What is piston compression height (CH)?

32. Name three ways that the piston pin may be retained in a racing piston. What is a “full floating” piston pin? How is the pin retained in a full floating design? What are three types of lock rings that are used to retain piston pins?

33. In a typical racing ring package, how many top rings are there? How many pieces make up the oil ring? What are these pieces called?

34. What is blow-by? Name five things that affect the quality of the ring seal.

35. What functions do the compression rings serve? What is the purpose of the chamfer (bevel) in the inside edge of the ring? Which way should the chamfers go on the top and 2nd rings? What is the purpose of an accumulator groove between the top two rings? What are gas ports, and how to they work?

36. Describe the function of the oil ring. What is the best way to choose a ring package for your application?

37. Why is a ring “break-in” period necessary? How long does this usually take?

38. What are the purposes of the ring end gaps? What is a “zero end gap” ring? What causes ring flutter?

39. Name seven piston and ring measurements. Why should racing pistons be as lightweight as possible? How does piston compression height (CH) affect piston weight? Calculate the compression height (CH) for the piston below:

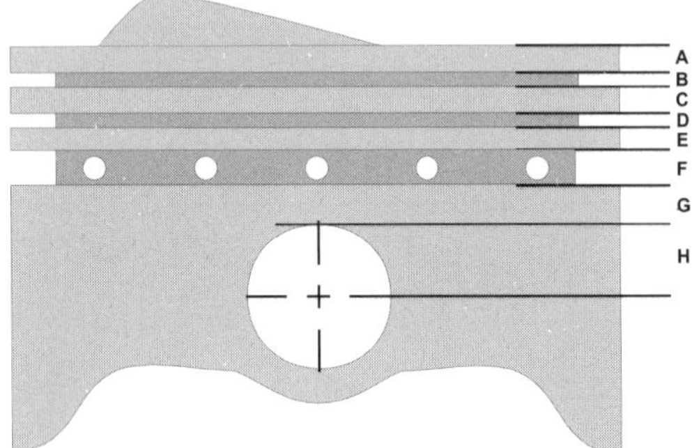

A. .250"
B. .044"
C. .150"
D. .044"
E. .120"
F. .126"
G. .045"
H. .395"

40. What is the normal tolerance for piston-to-wall clearance in a racing engine? How do you measure piston-to-wall clearance?

41. Why are ring groove depth and vertical clearance important? How do you check for proper ring groove depth? How can you measure ring groove vertical clearance?

42. How do you measure ring end gap? What is a general rule for determining the minimum compression ring end gap? What is a good way to square the ring in the bore? What do you do if there is too little end gap?

43. Why is it so important to have adequate piston-to-valve clearance? What are some things that can cause pistons and valves to clash in a racing engine? When are the valves most likely to hit the pistons? What are the minimum piston-to-valve clearances for intake and exhaust valves?

44. Name four types of connecting rods. What are the advantages, disadvantages, and uses for each type?

45. Identify the features in the photo below:

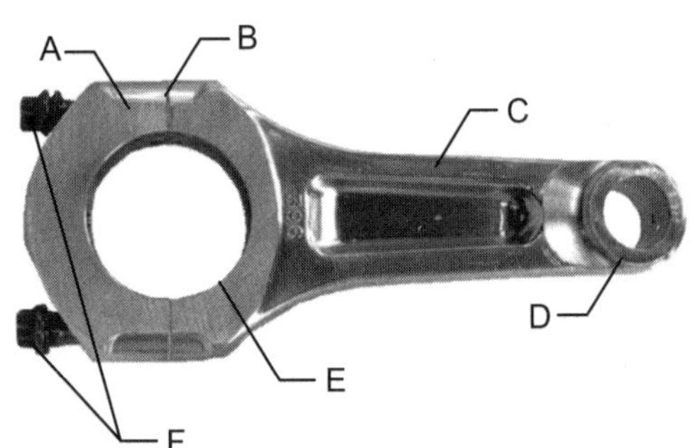

A. ____________________

B. ____________________

C. ____________________

D. ____________________

E. ____________________

F. ____________________

46. How is rod length measured? How does rod length affect rod angularity? Is this a critical concern in a racing engine?

47. What is total deck clearance? Why is the required clearance different in an engine with aluminum rods than it is with steel rods? Why is the thickness of the head gasket important?

48. What is piston & rod "stackup height"? How is it related to block deck height?

49. Calculate the required stackup for an engine with these specifications:
    - Block Deck Height = 9.800"
    - Deck Clearance = .010"

50. Calculate the required rod length for an engine with these specifications:
    - Block Deck Height = 9.800"
    - Deck Clearance = .010"
    - Piston Compression Height (CH) = 1.405"
    - Stroke = 4.00"

51. What should you inspect on connecting rods? Name three important rod measurements. How do you measure the rod bore diameters? How do you measure deck clearance? How do you measure rod side clearance?

52. How must the chamfers be positioned when installing rods and measuring side clearance? What is a normal rod side clearance tolerance for a racing engine?

53. What should control crankshaft end play (thrust clearance)? How do you check for end play restrictions? How do you measure the wrist pin to pin bore clearance? What should that clearance be? What do you do if there is already too much clearance? How do you measure wrist pin to lock clearance? What should that clearance be?

54. Why is it important to measure wrist pin to pin tower clearance? What type of rods make this more of a problem? How do you add additional clearance? How do you check the piston skirt to crankshaft counterweight clearance? What do you do if there is inadequate clearance?

55. What is the minimum clearance between the big end of the rods and the engine block? If the rods contact near the oil pan rails, how can you create the necessary clearance?

56. How much clearance is required between the rods and the camshaft? How do you make this measurement? What can you do to the rods to provide the needed clearance? At what location do the small ends of the rods sometimes interfere with the crankshaft counterweights? What can be done to modify the rods for the correct clearance?

57. What is a wet-sump oiling system? Describe the oil flow path in a wet-sump oiling system. What happens to the oil spray as engine rpm's climb? How does this affect oil pan design? What is the best wet-sump oil pan design?

58. What is a dry-sump oiling system? Describe the flow path in a dry-sump oiling system. What are some advantages of a dry-sump system?

59. What components are oiled by splash? Describe the pushrod oiling system.

60. What are three factors that affect the performance of the lubrication system? What is the normal range of oil pressure for a racing engine? How is the maximum oil pressure regulated? What happens to oil volume requirements as engine speed increases? How is maximum oil pressure adjusted on wet and dry-sump oil pumps? How do bearing oil clearances affect oil pressure and volume requirements?

61. What are some differences between oil formulated for passenger cars and racing motor oils? What is the relationship between oil temperature and viscosity? What is multi-viscosity motor oil?

62. What is synthetic motor oil? What are some advantages and disadvantages of synthetic motor oils over non-synthetic motor oils? What is wrong with using a synthetic racing motor oil on cylinder walls during engine assembly? When should you install a synthetic racing motor oil?

Championship Engine Assembly

Unit IV - Upper End Component Selection

When selecting upper engine assembly components, a lot of thought must be given to the specific requirements of a particular racing engine. The selection must also be based on your budget constraints.

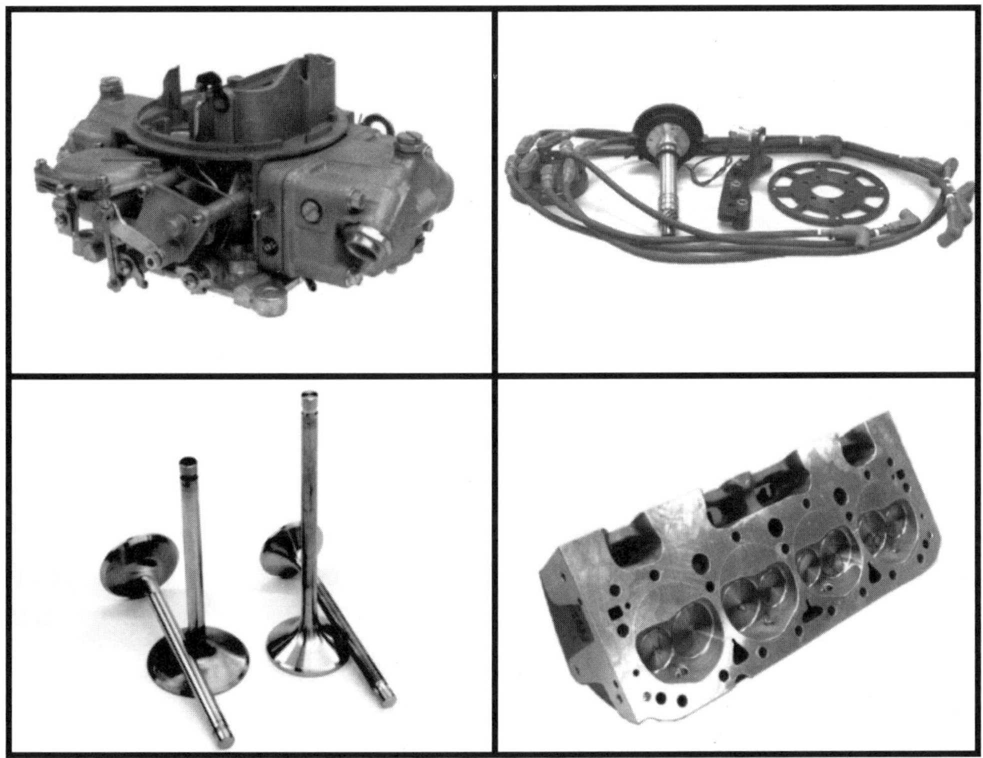

Cylinder Heads

No other areas of racing engine development hold as much potential for increased performance as cylinder head selection and preparation. The horsepower difference between a short block assembled by several different racing engine builders may be as little as 3-5%. This translates into about 25 horsepower in an 800 hp engine. By contrast, the horsepower difference between a poorly prepared set of cylinder heads and a really good set may be several times greater—perhaps a hundred horsepower on the same 800 hp engine.

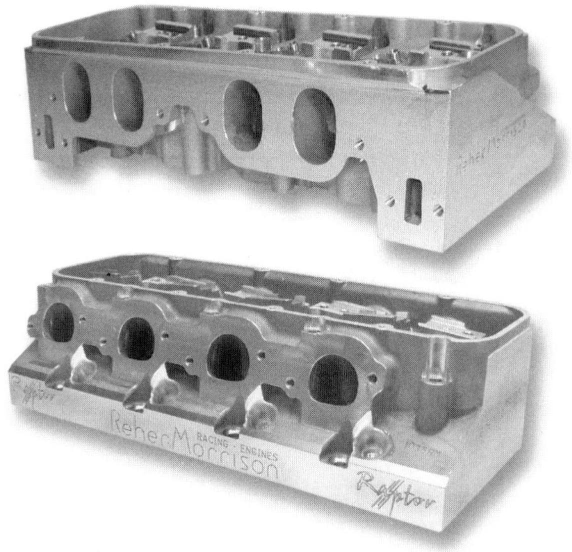

With the right combination of engine parts, these RM Raptor® high performance cylinder heads can be worth a couple of hundred horsepower over stock models. Careful preparation can result in even greater efficiency and power.

Cylinder head selection and preparation are important because the engine breathes through the ports and burns the intake mixture in the combustion chambers. A great cylinder head design allows a lot of air and fuel into the cylinders and burns the mixture very efficiently.

A few years ago, we had to make do with heads that were designed primarily for high performance street applications. These stock heads required a lot of work to get them ready for use on a racing engine. Today, we have many great racing cylinder head choices from both original equipment and aftermarket manufacturers.

Cylinder Head Types:

Cylinder heads can be categorized by the metal from which they are cast and by the combustion chamber/valve layout. However, the type of cylinder head that may be used is usually tightly restricted by your race sanctioning organization. Always read your rulebook before you make any cylinder head purchases or modifications.

Cast Iron Cylinder Heads - Cast iron heads have nearly disappeared from the racing scene. They are very heavy and extremely difficult to modify or repair. In theory, cast iron heads should be able to produce more power than aluminum heads because they draw off heat from the combustion chambers more slowly. However, cast iron is so difficult to work with that you could probably never realize these gains. The only real advantage cast iron heads offer is their relatively low cost.

This stock cast iron head should only be used on a racing engine if required by the rules for your class.

Stock Cast Iron Head

Aluminum Cylinder Heads - If rules permit and you can afford the extra cost, it's hard to beat aluminum cylinder heads. They have several important advantages over cast iron heads that can mean a lot in a racing application.

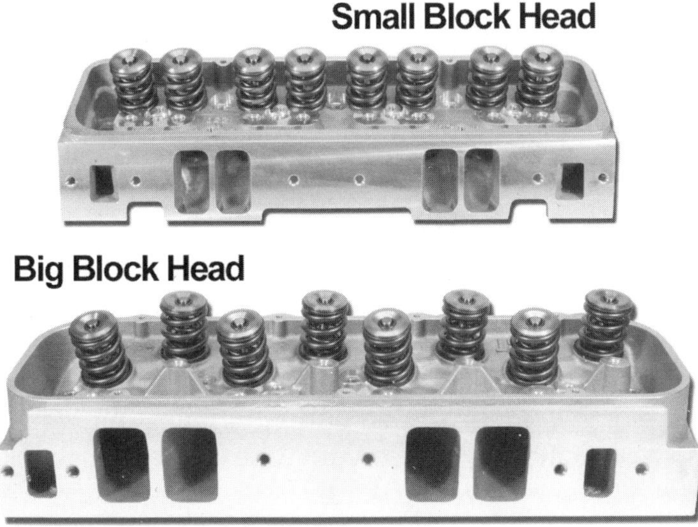

Aluminum cylinder heads are a great choice for building serious horsepower in small and big block racing engines.

Weight - Most aluminum heads weigh about half that of their cast iron counterparts. This weight savings can be important to the performance of a race car. The heads we use on our Pro Stock engines are extremely tall and have very thick walls. After machining, they're still rather heavy—around 40 pounds each. If these heads were cast out of iron, it would be like putting a couple of anvils under the hood of the car.

This aluminum semi-finished Pro Stock cylinder head is a couple of inches taller than stock and has a lot of extra material around the ports and combustion chambers.

Modifications/Reparability - Aluminum is soft and can be easily machined and re-contoured. This really saves time and reduces the cost for custom port work. A TIG welder can be used to build up material as needed or to perform repairs. This allows the head porter almost unlimited freedom to make modifications within the rules of the race sanctioning organization.

This aluminum head developed a crack between two rocker bosses. A TIG welder was used to make the repair. Minor repairs like this often can be performed provided that the head is not overheated.

NOTE: Large repairs or modifications to aluminum heads may result in "heat-soak" problems. This makes the head soft and the relationship between the valve guides and seats is lost. After extensive welding work has been performed, you should have the head re-heat treated and re-machined. Before you have this done, check the cost of replacing the head—it is almost always the more cost-effective way to go.

Valve/Combustion Chamber Layouts - The vast majority of naturally aspirated gasoline racing engines are either a *wedge* design or have *splayed (canted) valves*. The figure below shows the difference between these two designs.

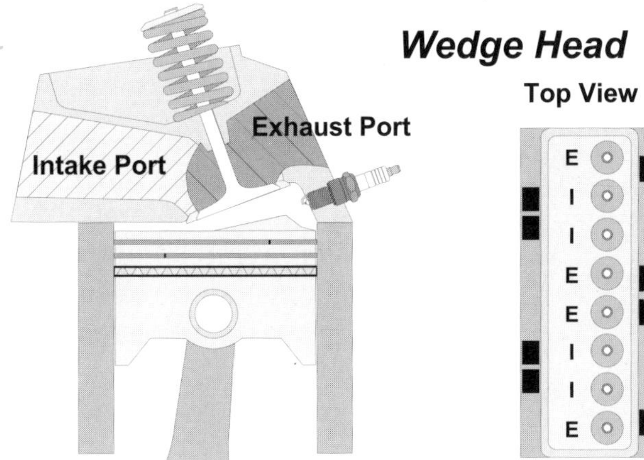

In a pure in-line wedge engine, the valves are arranged in a straight row.

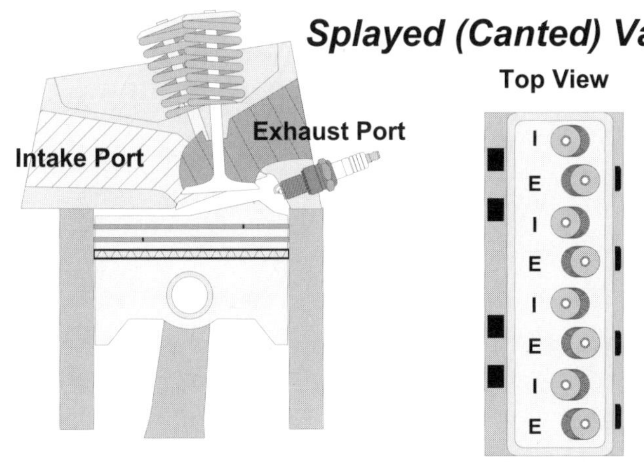

In the splayed or canted valve design, the intake and exhaust valves are lean toward the ports in compound angles. The head is cast wider to accommodate the angled valve springs.

Wedge style heads are very compact and lightweight. The main disadvantage of this design is a somewhat reduced breathing capacity. This is because of the sharp turn that the exhaust gases must make as they exit the exhaust ports.

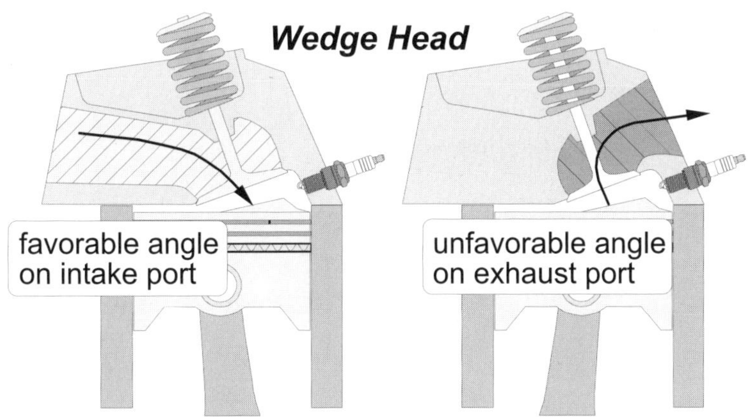

The exhaust gases must make a very sharp turn in an in-line wedge design. This causes some exhaust flow restriction.

The splayed valve design has a somewhat better approach to the exhaust ports, but the heads are a little wider and heavier. The squish/quench pad region may also be a little smaller on a splayed valve head.

Splayed (Canted) Valve

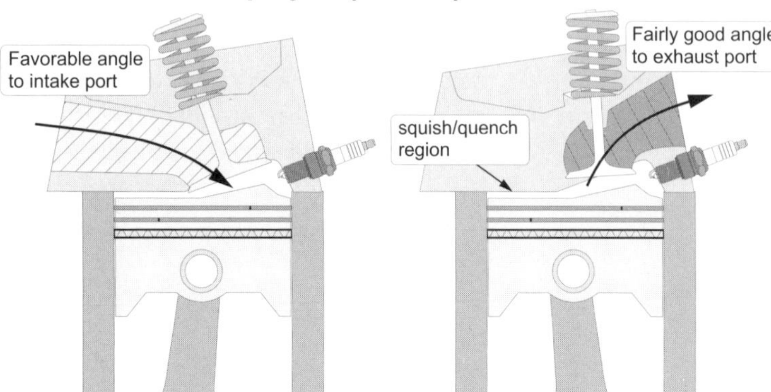

The splayed (canted) valve arrangement is a good compromise between breathing and combustion efficiency for naturally aspirated gasoline racing engines.

Nearly all GM big block V8 racing cylinder heads are of the canted valve design. Although most GM small block V8 racing engines are still built with standard wedge heads, the new canted valve small block heads are starting to provide some impressive results in high-horsepower applications.

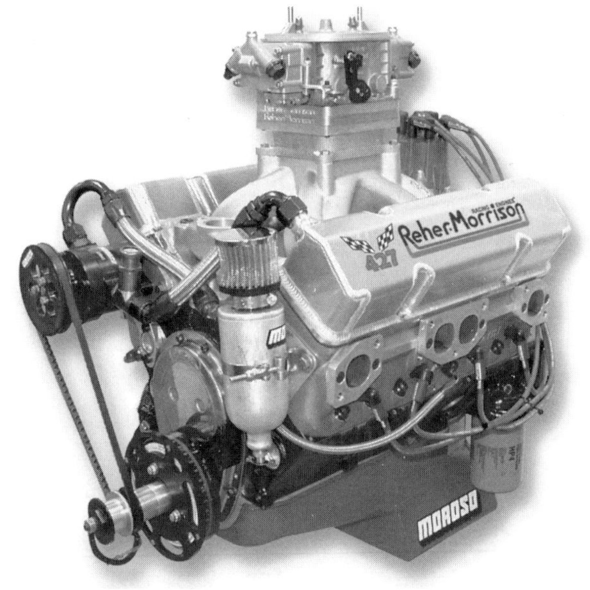

This RMRE Super Series 427 CID small block engine uses 15° wedge cylinder heads and produces a whopping 840 HP with a single four barrel carburetor on racing gasoline.

Combustion Chamber Designs:

Open vs. Closed Chambers - The shape of the combustion chamber also affects how well the gases flow into the cylinder and the combustion efficiency. The original design (1965-1968) GM big block V8 cylinder heads were of the *closed chamber* design. The chambers were oval shaped with a volume of about 107 cc's. It was learned that this design shrouded the valves causing a small flow restriction.

In 1968, GM reworked the Mark IV cylinder heads with an *open chamber* design. The chamber is opened to the spark plug side giving it a triangular shape. These heads have a combustion chamber volume between 110-118 cc's.

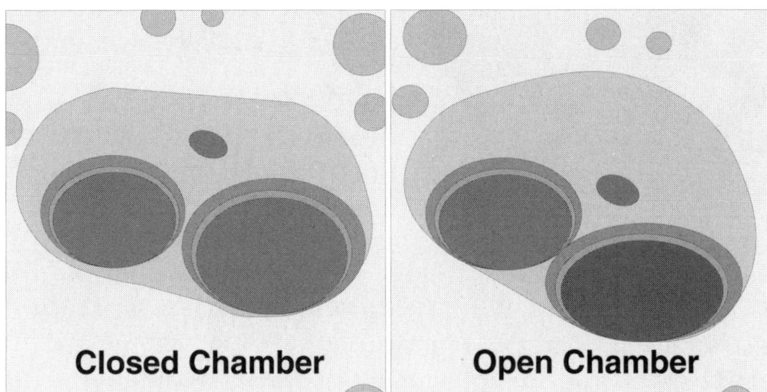

The open chamber design un-shrouds the valves and offers somewhat better breathing characteristics than the closed chamber style.

Combustion Chamber Volume - The static compression ratio of the engine is largely determined by the relative volumes of the piston domes and the cylinder head combustion chambers. The rules for many race car classes strictly control the maximum allowable compression ratio and the minimum combustion chamber volumes. Be sure to consult your rulebook and check the listed combustion chamber volume the cylinder heads before you make your purchase.

Combustion chamber volume is equally important if you are building a street engine. If you wind up with a compression ratio much higher than 9:1, you may not be able to operate the engine on standard unleaded pump gasoline. Aluminum heads dissipate heat faster than cast iron, allowing a higher (about 10:1) compression ratio on pump gasoline.

GM Performance Parts offers small block V8 cylinder heads with listed combustion chamber volumes from 28 cc's to 76 cc's. Their big block V8 heads range from 60.4 cc's to 118 cc's. Don't make any cylinder head purchase until you know what piston configurations will work with your heads to give you the desired static compression ratio and if they are legal for your class.

Custom Chamber Design - Creating one-of-a-kind heads from raw or semi-machined castings is a very expensive and time consuming process. The photo below shows some of the steps involved in making a prototype Pro Stock head.

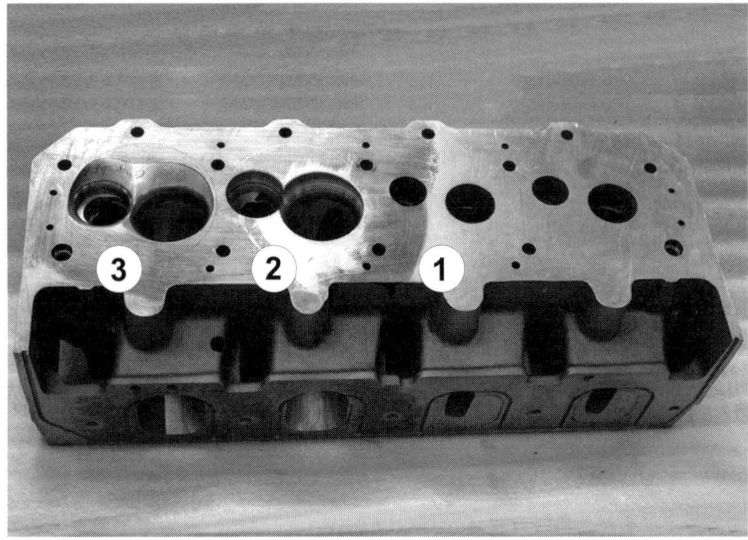

1. *This is how the semi-machined casting looks before the combustion chambers and valve seats are cut.*
2. *We locate and bore the valve guide holes, then cut the valve seats.*
3. *We hand-cut and contour the combustion chamber to the desired shape.*

If the design performs well in flow bench testing, we duplicate the machine work on a CNC machine. Spark plug holes, valve spring pockets, and numerous bolt, water, and pushrod holes must be added before the gasket mating surfaces are milled.

The larger the volume of the combustion chamber, the larger the volume of the piston dome must be in order to achieve a high compression ratio. The problem with big chambers and high piston domes is that they tend to shroud the valves and increase the distance the flame must travel.

A recent trend in cylinder head design is a heart-shaped chamber with a very small volume. Breathing is improved because the valves open into the cylinder. The small chamber volume (usually around 49 cc's) means that a high compression ratio can be achieved with a piston that has a flat top. The squish/quench areas are larger. This improves turbulence and creates a more rapid and complete burn.

This is the latest thing in combustion chamber design. The very small heart-shaped combustion chamber un-shrouds the valves and uses a piston with a nearly flat top. There is a lot of squish/quench pad to increase turbulence.

Because of the large number of cylinder heads that are available, you really have to pay attention when you select pistons. Often, the dome interferes with the combustion chamber and modifications are necessary.

For cylinder heads with custom-made combustion chambers, we have special pistons manufactured with plenty of extra material around the piston domes. After the dome has been shaped to fit the chambers in the heads, we back-cut the pistons to make them lighter.

We mill our own pistons from semi-machined blanks for custom applications. This work is time consuming and very expensive.

Unless you are trying to run a competitive Pro Stock operation, we strongly recommend that you use readily available cylinder heads and pistons. Your money can be more wisely spent in other places that offer higher returns for the investment.

Valve Angle and Valve Tilt:

Valve Angle - Standard GM small block V8 cylinder heads have a valve angle of 23°. Several years ago, some racers realized that they could improve (flatten) the approach angle of the valves by *angle milling* their heads. These "rolled-over" heads sometimes outperformed the stock heads.

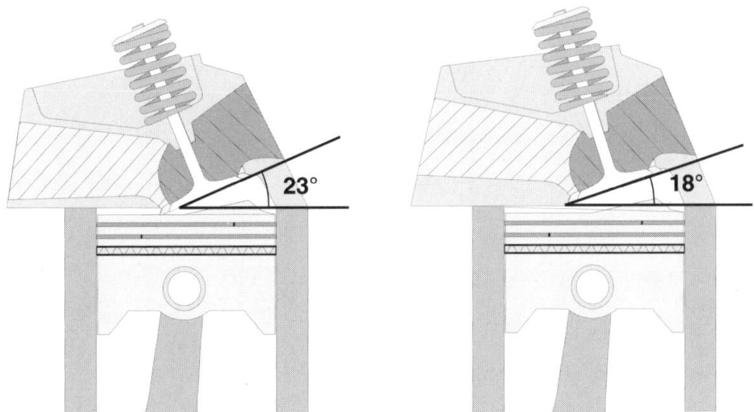

This is a comparison between a 23° angle head and a "rolled over" 18° head. Note that the 18° head offers a more vertical approach to the cylinder and also raises the angle of the intake port.

Another reason racers sometimes angle-mill heads is to increase the static compression ratio. Angle milling removes more material on the deep side of the combustion chamber wedge and can significantly reduce the chamber volumes.

If your heads have already been flat milled, a lot of material is already gone and you may not be able to roll the heads very much. Angle milling changes the angles of every gasket mating surface and bolt hole in the head. You may have to make a custom intake manifold and exhaust headers, or modify your existing pieces significantly to restore the fit. Angle milling should only be attempted if you can withstand the higher time and money costs.

GM Performance Parts and other aftermarket manufacturers offer small block cylinder heads that are designed with 18° and 15° valve angles. These heads require no special procedures to correct alignment problems, but do require the use of special parts including pistons, valves, rockers arms, pushrods, intake manifolds and exhaust headers. Special components made for rolled-over heads are usually much more expensive than those used with the standard 23° small block heads.

Splayed valve heads have one angle for intake valves and another for exhaust valves. There are several small block cylinder heads with different valve angles that are available from GM Performance Parts and aftermarket suppliers.

Valve Tilt - The exhaust or intake valves may also be "tilted" (usually 4°) off the centerline of the cylinder. The purpose of valve tilt is to get the valve away from the cylinder wall so that it is un-shrouded and breathes better.

Splayed Valve Small Block Head, GM #24502517

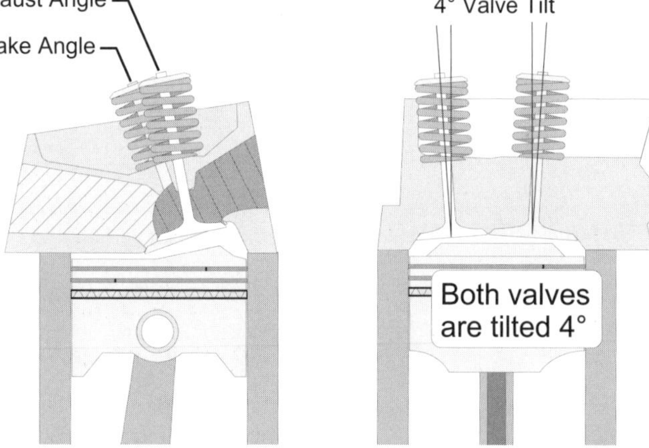

On splayed valve small block cylinder heads, the intake and exhaust valves are tilted toward the cylinder centerline. This un-shrouds the valves and promotes better breathing.

To accommodate the valve tilt angle, the rocker arm bosses on the head castings are also tilted to the same (4°) angle. Independent shaft rocker arms keep the rocker arm operating in the same plane as the valve.

Port Design:

Here are three factors other than valve size that affect flow rates in the cylinder heads:

- Port Shape & Size
- Port Bend Radius
- Interior Surface Texture

Port Shape & Size - Most horsepower improvements to a naturally aspirated racing engine relate directly to intake and exhaust port velocities. High velocity intake and exhaust gases pack a lot of inertial energy and continue to move into and out of the cylinder long after the pistons have reversed direction.

There is a direct relationship between the shape & size of ports and the gas velocities created. All other things being equal, a port with a larger cross section can flow more gas than a smaller one. Port flow must meet the demands of the engine for the best performance. Generally, the larger the engine displacement and the higher the rpm range of the engine, the larger the ports can be.

It is possible to select heads with ports that are too large for your application. The lost velocity leads to reversion problems at low rpm's and kills low end engine power. Here is a great general rule that can be applied not only to port size selection, but nearly every choice that you make for an induction system component:

The smaller you can make induction system components without reducing the horsepower output, the better your race car will perform.

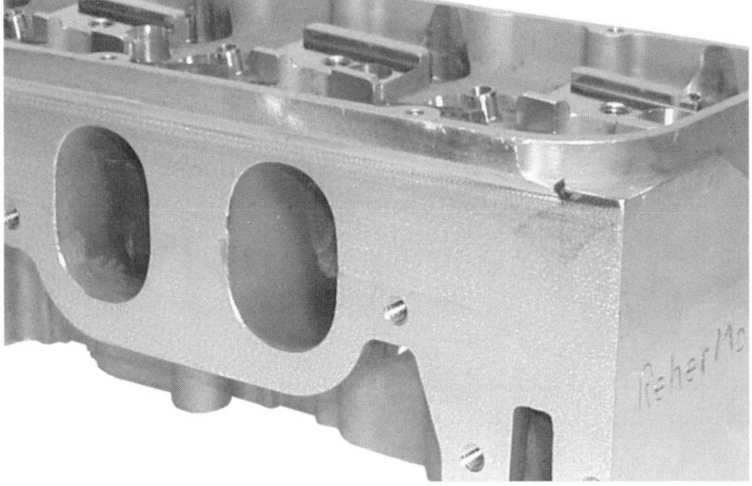

These large oval intake ports on our Raptor® cylinder heads result in tremendous power output when used on an engine with enough displacement to handle them.

Inertial forces cause the gases to hug the long radius (top) of the port. This is why the contour of the high side of the ports is important.

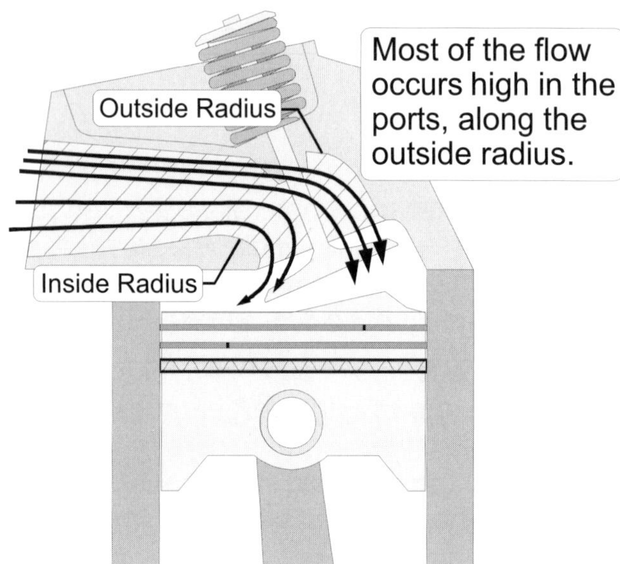

Unequal flow rates and other factors may influence the port shape that works best in a racing engine.

Intake ports are usually rectangular or oval in shape. Most exhaust ports are round or D-shaped.

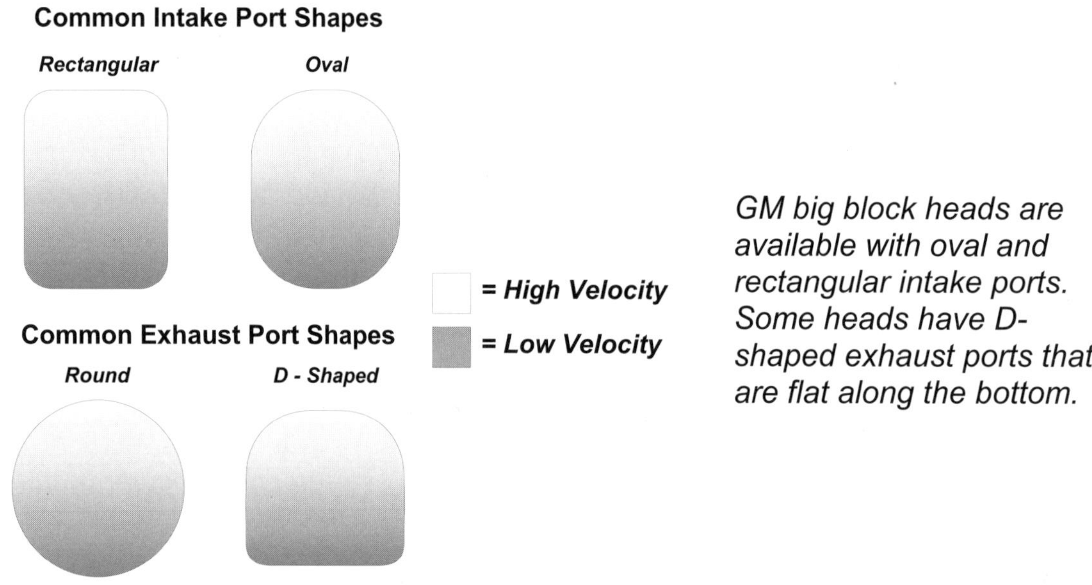

GM big block heads are available with oval and rectangular intake ports. Some heads have D-shaped exhaust ports that are flat along the bottom.

Exhaust gas velocities are many times higher than intake velocities and really hug the top (outside radius) of the port. D-shaped exhaust ports are somewhat flat along the bottom to fill in some of the low velocity area.

Port shape becomes extremely important near the valve seat. Cylinder head porters often refer to this as the venturi area. It must be carefully shaped to "set up" the intake gases so that they can bend around the valve. The angles of the valve seat also have a lot to do with how well the port flows.

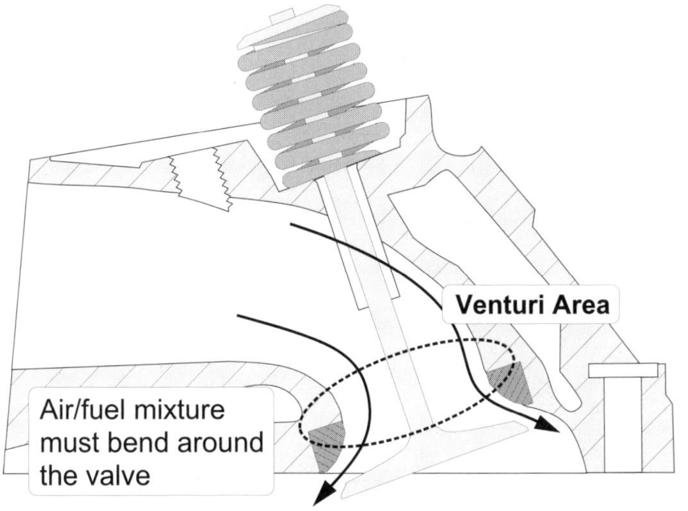

No other part of the port is as important as the venturi area. The head of the valve partially obstructs the flow, so the shape of the port must set up the gases to make the bend.

WARNING! If you incorrectly alter the shape of the venturi or even open it up only a few thousandths of an inch too much, the gases may begin to pile up at the back of the valve and obstruct flow. It may look pretty, but the head is probably ruined. Only qualified head porters should modify this important area!

Port length is another important consideration. The combined length of the head and manifold ports must be "tuned" to the reversion waves that back up through the system. Long ports tend to improve torque at low rpm's and short ports work best at high rpm's.

Exhaust ports tend to be very short to allow access to the head bolts. Many heads show improved exhaust flow rates when the port length is extended by about ½ inch. This is why we often add an *exhaust port intermediate plate* between the heads and the header exhaust flange. These plates are installed after the head bolts have been torqued.

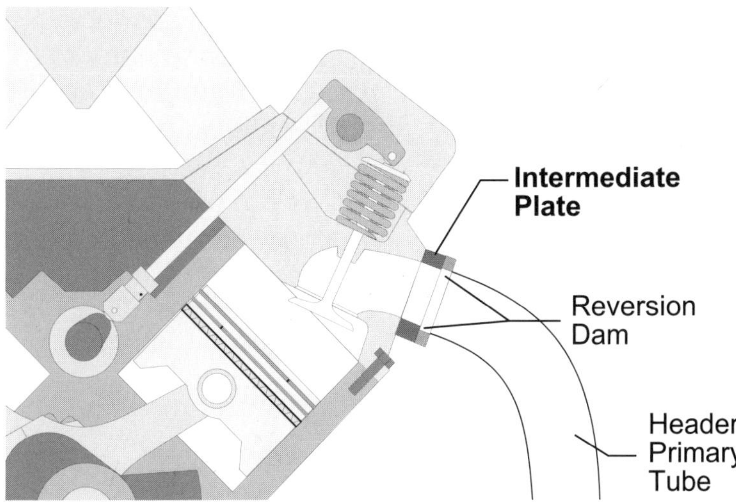

This intermediate plate improves the exhaust flow by adding length to the port. The opening in the plate is made a little smaller than the header tube to create an exhaust reversion dam.

The intermediate plates are first cut and bolted to the exhaust ports as shown in the photo below. Then we machine openings to the OD of the exhaust port.

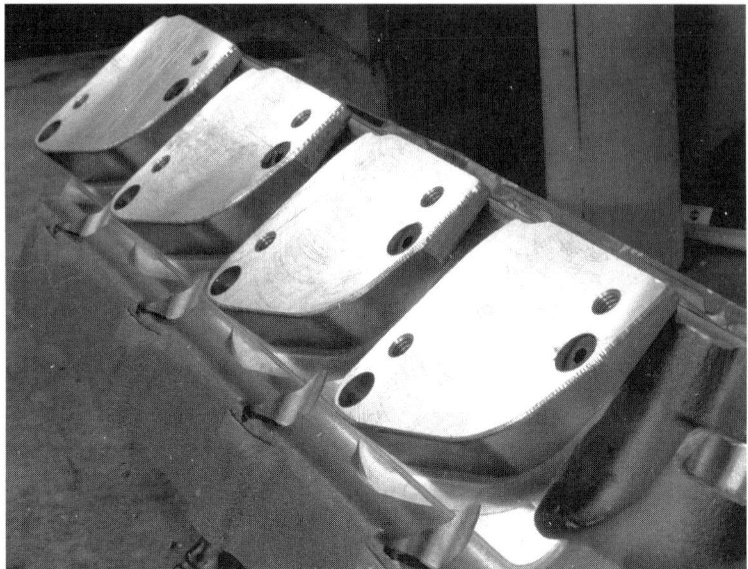

The intermediate plates are shaped and drilled to fit the heads. We use our CNC machine to mill the port close to the OD of the exhaust port, then hand-blend them with a grinder.

Mapping Ports - During cylinder head development, we try many different port shapes. The best ones usually test with higher flow rates at maximum valve lift on the flow bench. To further improve the performance of the port, we measure, or "map" the air velocities by testing the pressure at different points in the port.

With the flow bench on, we insert a small tube into the port. This tube connects to the manometer (pressure gauge) on the flow bench. High air velocities create low pressure. "Dead" areas of the port (those with relatively low velocities) show less pressure drop on the manometer. When we find a dead area, we can fill it to improve port velocities and engine performance.

Mapping the Port

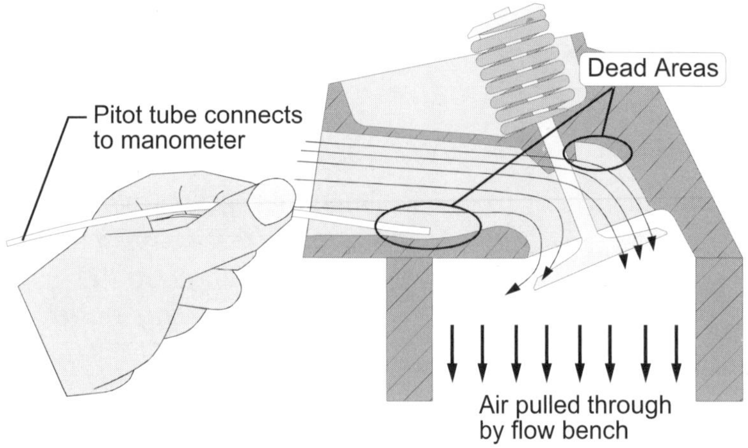

We insert a small tube into the port that is connected to a water manometer to map "dead" areas. These regions should be filled in to keep the velocity as high as possible throughout the entire port cross section.

Port Bend Radius - Inertia causes the gases flowing through intake and exhaust ports to resist changes in motion. This brings up an important rule about intake and exhaust port design:

The less you make the gases bend, the better the flow will be.

An important goal in port design is to create the straightest possible path from the carburetor barrel to the valve. The ports must bend vertically to get around the spring pockets and valve guides. Once the bend has been made, the port can be turned or angled as needed to aim at the carburetor barrels.

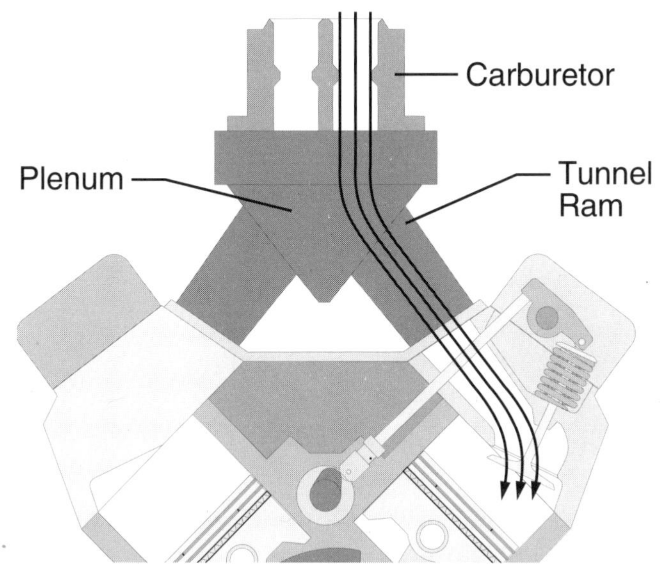

We aim the intake runner at the carburetor barrels to provide the straightest possible path for intake gases into the engine. A short-deck block also helps bring the cylinder heads closer together and allows an even more direct path.

High port heads (also called *raised runner* or *raised port heads*) provide a straighter approach angle from the carburetor. Here is a comparison between low port GM small block cylinder heads and high port designs:

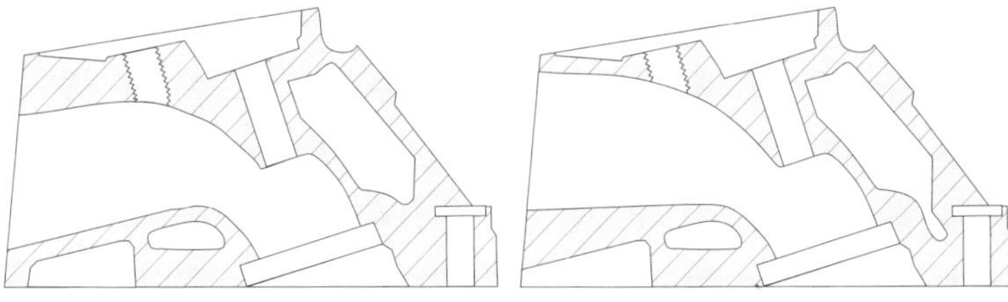

High port heads offer improved flow because of the steeper approach angles between ports and valves.

NOTE: High port heads require the use of special intake manifolds and exhaust headers.

Surface Texture - Two decades ago, racers routinely had their stock cylinder heads "ported & polished" by specialty shops. It was discovered some years later that all this work to create a glossy surface was actually making matters worse on the intake side of the engine. Slick surfaces have a very thin *boundary layer*. The boundary layer is the gas that is in contact with the port surfaces. It moves much more slowly than the rest of the gases and promotes the separation of fuel droplets from the air stream.

The best interior finish for intake ports is one with small grooves or scratches that run perpendicular to the flow path. It is believed that this works better because the grooves capture a boundary layer of air that spins in tiny, circular flow paths called *vortices.* These tiny, tornado-like currents keep the fuel droplets mixed with the air and act as "roller bearings" for the gases.

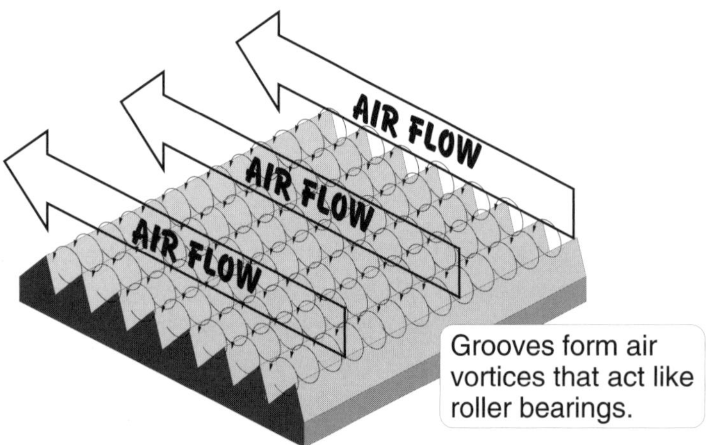

A textured surface with grooves perpendicular to the air flow path works best for cylinder head ports.

You should create a surface texture using a sand roll and grinder so the scratches are perpendicular to the flow path. CNC (Computer Numerical Control) machined heads are usually shipped with the characteristic tooling grooves still in the ports.

Note how the CNC textured finish is perpendicular to the flow path. This need not be removed.

Choosing Cylinder Heads:

Normally, about a quarter of your entire racing engine budget will be expended on the cylinder heads. Before you make your final choice, we highly recommend that you rely on the experience of a racing engine builder. These folks have tested a number of engine/cylinder head combinations and can help you choose heads that are right for your budget and racing application.

Be sure to read your rulebook thoroughly. Cylinder head selection has an enormous impact on engine performance, so there may be a number of restrictions for cylinder head types and modifications for your class.

You'll need to read all the applicable rules and regulations for your class before you choose the cylinder heads. Rulebooks are automatically sent to paid members of the racing associations.

If you are building an engine for NHRA Stock or Super Stock categories, you will also need to obtain a *Stock Car Classification Guide* and *Blueprint Bulletins* from the NHRA. These list the engines that are acceptable for use in these classes and have exacting specifications for cylinder head configuration and modifications. Other categories like Super Comp and Super Gas may not have any restrictions on the type of heads that you may use.

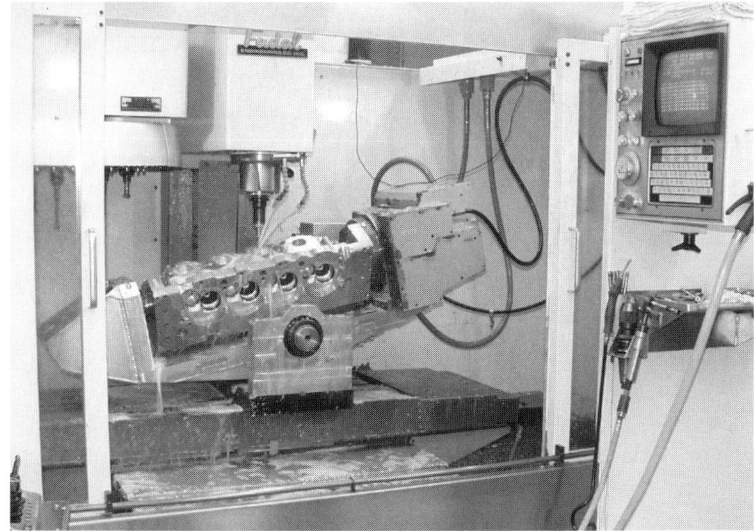

The CNC technology of today has made it possible to produce a wide variety of cylinder heads for any application and at affordable prices.

If you are going to purchase new cylinder heads, insist on *flow bench* data for your set. Flow testing is the best way to determine the breathing characteristics of cylinder heads and can help you make many other engine and race car component choices. If you already own a set of heads, take them to a reputable engine builder or cylinder head specialist to have them flow tested.

A flow bench passes air through the ports at various rates and valve lifts. The *manometer* on the bench measures the reduction in flow rate caused by port and valve restrictions as inches of water. This pressure measurement can also be expressed as a flow rate in cfm (cubic feet per minute).

We spend thousands of hours each year testing cylinder head port and valve configurations on our flow bench.

If you want serious horsepower, you'll need a great set of heads. Experienced engine builders know that horsepower development means cylinder head development.

Valves & Valve Springs

To many novice engine builders, valves are like any other metal engine parts—just put in the biggest ones that fit, bolt on the heads, and go racing. We have found that valve selection is one of the most important decisions that you will make when planning your engine.

Valve Features:

The angles on the valve must be carefully chosen for the particular application. Intake and exhaust gases do not slow down or become turbulent so long as the transition from one valve or seat angle to another is no greater than 15°.

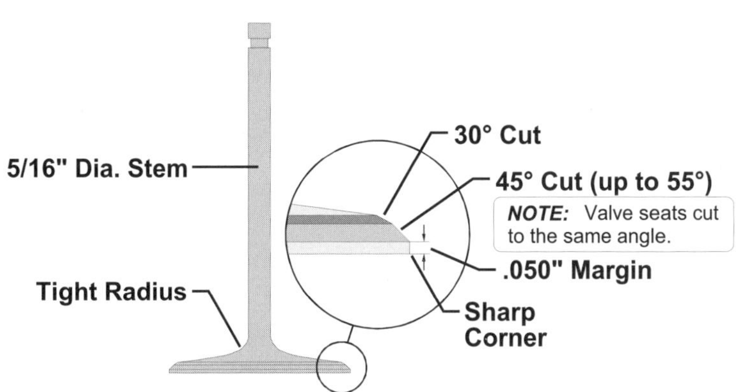

The intake valve should have a tight radius to avoid restrictions at partial valve openings. A good seal is created with the valve seat in the 45°-55° cut. The 30° cut helps smooth the transition to the seat. A sharp corner on the valve head helps reduce intake reversion flow.

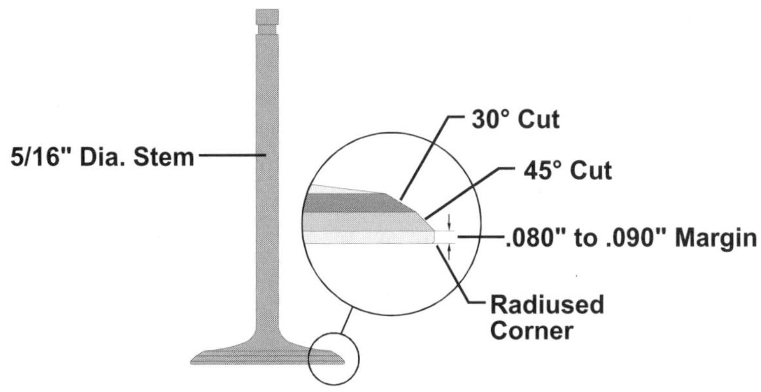

The exhaust valve has the same cut angles as an intake valve but requires a narrower seat and wider margin. The radiused corner helps smooth gas flow around the valve head.

Narrow exhaust seats help the valves cut through carbon buildup and maintain a tight seal. However, the margin cannot be too small or it will develop hot spots that shorten valve life and promote pre-ignition problems in the engine.

Always have your valve and cylinder head machine work performed by an experienced racing engine builder or cylinder head specialist. They have the necessary experience to create the correct angles, seat widths, and metal finish.

Valve Sizes:

The valves are a flow restriction in a racing engine. Large diameter intake valves usually flow better, but the bore diameter of the cylinder limits how big the valves can be. Intake gases must be "coaxed" into the engine with cylinder vacuum, so the intake valve is the larger of the two. Our experience has shown that the intake valve needs to be about 52% of the bore cylinder bore diameter to work best.

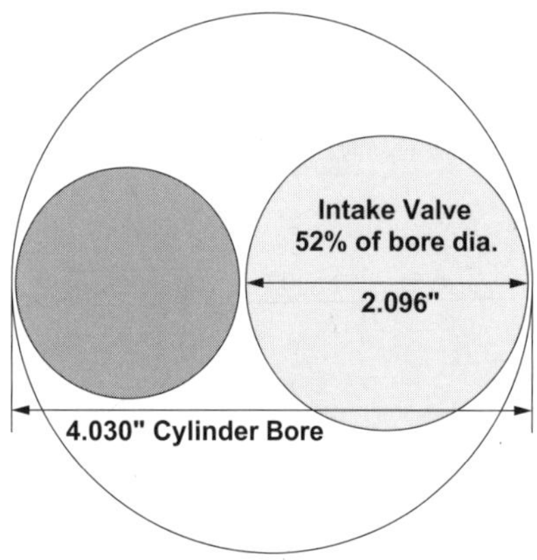

Normally, we select an intake valve that is about 52% of the cylinder bore diameter.

The exhaust valve diameter usually ranges between 72% and 76% of the intake valve diameter, but bigger is not always better. When the exhaust valve opens into the bore, it is shrouded by the cylinder. Sometimes, an exhaust valve that is a little smaller than the largest that would fit winds up flowing better because it is farther from the cylinder wall. This is also the main reason that the newer small block "splayed valve" heads have a 4° valve tilt (see the *Valve Angle and Valve Tilt* section of this unit).

Valve Materials:

Racing engine valves must be lightweight, hard, and durable. Most racing valves are made of stainless steel or titanium alloys. Stainless steel valves are suitable for low to medium performance engines, but titanium valves deserve serious consideration if you can work them into your budget.

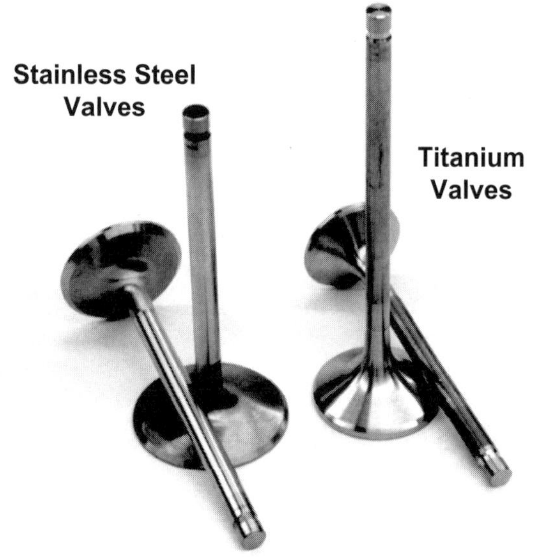

We firmly believe that titanium valves will save money in the long run with lower maintenance costs and better engine performance.

Because they are so much lighter, titanium valves have less inertia to overcome than do their steel counterparts. This has a very positive effect on the performance and longevity of many engine components. Titanium valves allow the use of camshafts with higher valve acceleration rates and greater lift (see the *Camshaft & Lifters* section of this unit for more information).

At a given rpm, light valves do not require as much valve spring rate as heavy valves. This means less stress on the rocker arms, pushrods, and lifters. An engine with titanium valves is more durable and has fewer problems with valve train wear, flex, and harmonics.

IMPORTANT! Titanium valves require the use of bronze valve guides in the cylinder heads. They must also have coated stems (usually molybdenum) so that they will not gall against the guides. The valve stem tips must be mechanically protected from galling with steel *lash caps* or steel inserts.

Valve Springs:

Valve spring performance is enormously important to the operation of a racing engine. Valve spring rates and their harmonic characteristics have a lot to do with how well the valve train components are controlled. The springs you select have a direct effect on power output and valve train life.

Common Misconception

Some racers believe that very stiff valve springs stress the valve train and add a lot of drag to the engine. Neither is true. Often, damage to a racing engine valve train can be directly attributed to weak valve springs. Very little drag is actually added by stiff springs because there are always the same number of lifters closing valves as there are opening valves.

The energy consumed when a spring is compressed is largely returned to the system when that force is released. If you rotate the crankshaft in an assembled engine (with no spark plugs to eliminate compression losses), you can feel the offsetting effects of springs that are closing valves versus those that are opening the valves. While it is true that higher spring rates do add some friction to the moving valve train parts, this small loss is more than offset by the horsepower and part longevity gained by controlling lifter loft and valve bounce.

IMPORTANT! Never rotate the crankshaft on a racing engine with a breaker bar. The extreme valve spring rates can cause it to suddenly rotate with great force. Always use a ratchet that will overrun if the crankshaft suddenly turns.

It is extremely important to choose the right valve springs and check them frequently. All too often, an engine teardown will reveal the devastating effects of inadequate valve spring rates. The valve job has been destroyed with seats that are beaten and worn, and the valve faces show fretting (tiny surface fractures). If you have roller tappets, stiff valve springs actually extend the life of your valve train.

At different points in the rpm range, all valve springs will encounter harmonic problems. This adversely affects valve spring rates and valve control. Racing engines have multiple springs on each valve that help dampen spring harmonics. By combining several springs together with different resonant frequencies, the springs tend to dampen one another. Multiple springs also offer some additional margin of protection by sharing the spring rate burden among the separate springs.

One fairly recent development is the "beehive" valve spring. It has coils of diminishing diameter as they approach the top of the spring. This sets up a variation in harmonics which provides a dampening effect and creates additional clearance to valve train components. The beehive spring also reduces coil bind problems in application requiring very stiff wire diameters for high lift camshafts.

Comparison of a standard and "beehive" valve spring

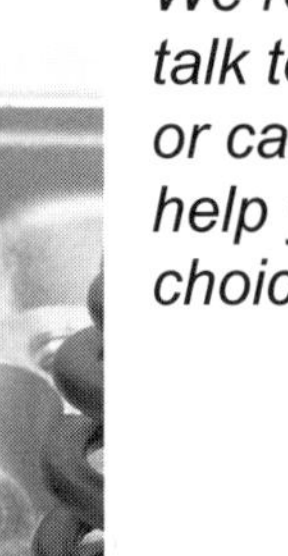

Bee hive valve spring installed on head

Do you need standard or beehive valve springs? We recommend that you talk to your engine builder or camshaft supplier to help you make the right choice for your application.

The material from which springs are made also influences their dampening characteristics. In some high-end engines, we find that titanium springs do a better job of dampening spring harmonics and help the car get through the entire operating rpm band.

It makes sense to buy only premium quality valve springs and check them often as part of your regular engine maintenance program. Don't assume that the springs that are supplied as part of a matched cam kit are all you'll need. Talk to your racing engine builder and make sure you have plenty of valve spring pressure.

Retainers & Keepers:

A "dropped valve" is one of the most destructive things that can happen to a racing engine. Don't skimp when it comes to the valve spring attaching hardware. This includes the retainers and keepers (split locks).

The diagram below details the valve spring and hardware that attach the spring to the valve stem.

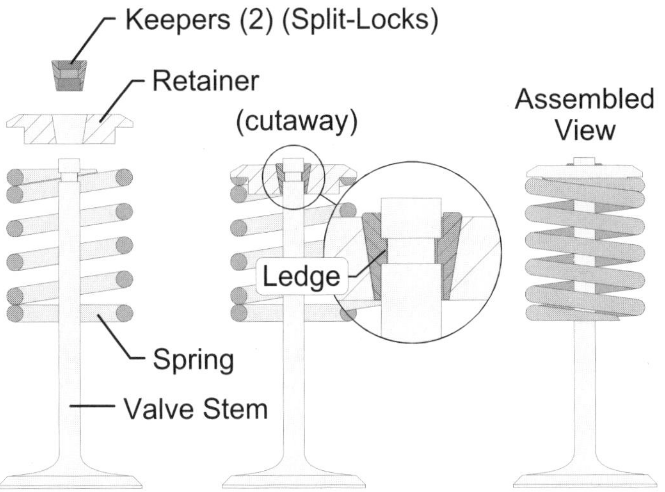

The valve stem is attached to the retainer by two keepers (split locks). The taper in the retainer hole applies clamping pressure ("collet effect") that keeps the tang in the keepers from slipping out of the groove in the valve stem.

Retainers - Stock steel retainers are fine for low rpm street engines, but add too much mass to work with the valve velocities at high rpm's. Aluminum retainers are light, but not strong enough for a true racing engine. Although the titanium retainers cost more, we feel the high strength and weight savings are well worth the added expense.

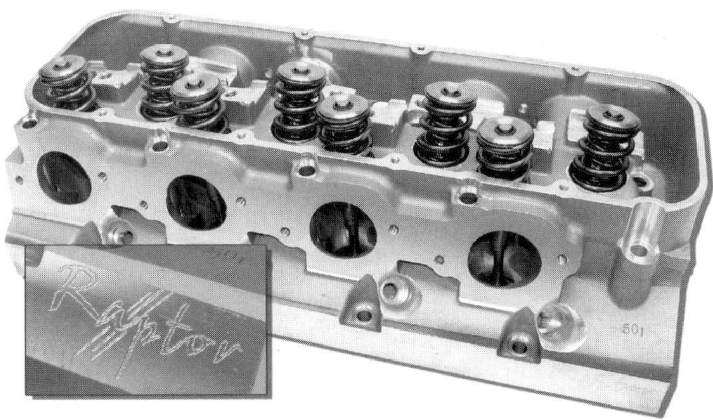

We use quality titanium retainers on all of our racing engines. They are very light and can handle the pounding from high lift racing camshafts.

NOTE: Some race sanctioning organizations have very strict rules for stock and hobby classes. Before you purchase titanium retainers, be sure they are allowed for your class.

The retainers must have the diameter right and number of steps for the springs. Check with the valve spring manufacturer to be sure you are using compatible retainers. Never assume you have the right parts—always check the fit of the retainers and valve springs before you assemble the cylinder head.

Keepers and Lash Caps - The standard angle for keepers (spilt locks) is 10°. Some engine builders prefer a smaller 7° angle that applies more clamping force to the valve stem. However, 7° keepers really wedge into the retainers and stick, making it very difficult to disassemble the heads. For this reason, we recommend high quality heat-treated chrome-moly racing keepers with a 10° taper angle that matches the 10° angle in the titanium retainer.

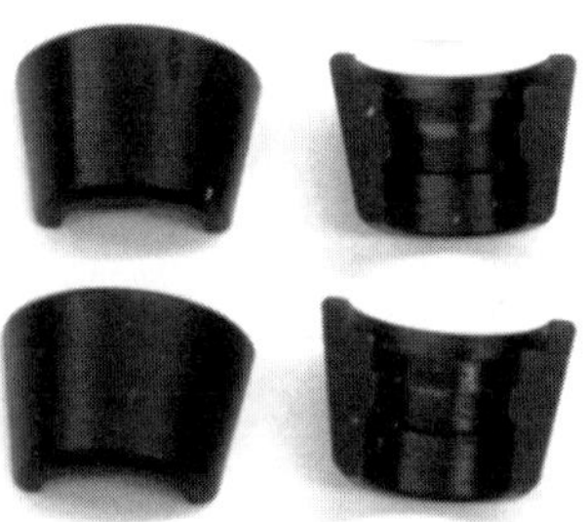

Don't skimp on the quality of the attaching hardware on your racing engine! The keepers must have the right taper angle and quality to prevent the devastation caused by a dropped valve.

Titanium valves that do not have steel tip inserts require the use of hardened steel lash caps on the valve stem tips to prevent wear between the rockers and valve stems.

Be sure to install special hardened steel valve stem caps and the undercut keepers if you have titanium valves. We prefer the "bead-lock" styles that have rounded grooves. They eliminate stress risers (sharp edges) in the valve stem groove to help prevent destructive valve stem breakage.

It is very important that the keepers do not touch the hardened caps. Always check to be sure the parts you are using provide at least .020" clearance.

Standard-Type

.020" min.

Shelf-Type

.020" min.

The caps may be designed to work with standard keepers or those with a machined shelf. Both types must have at least .020" clearance with the caps.

Camshafts & Lifters

Correct camshaft and lifter selection are crucial to getting the most out of a racing engine. If the valves open just a few degrees too early or too late, power output is affected or piston to valve contact may occur. The camshaft must also be compatible with the type of *lifter* (tappet) that is used.

Lifter Types:

There are two main lifter (tappet) types; flat and roller. Either is available in a "solid" design that has no adjusting mechanism, or a "hydraulic" design that uses oil pressure to self-adjust while the engine is running.

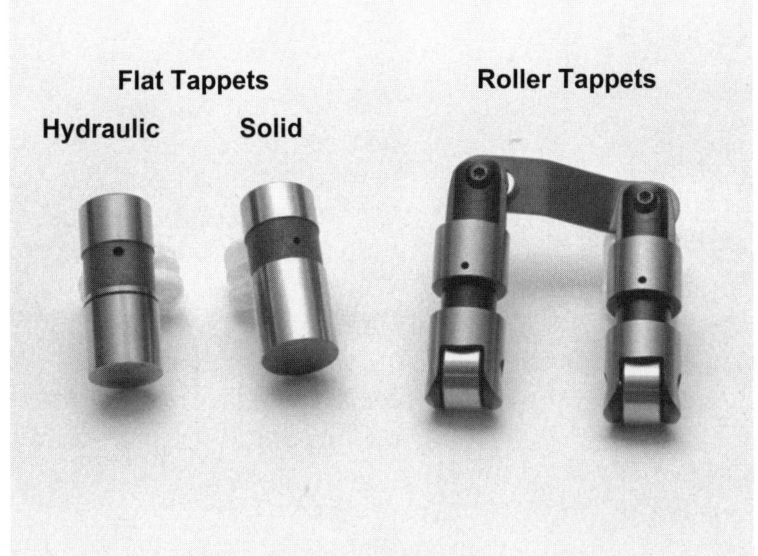

Older passenger cars usually had hydraulic flat tappets. Over the last few years, roller tappets have become very popular in both street and racing applications.

Hydraulic Lifters - In the late 1950's, *hydraulic lifters* became popular for use in passenger car engines. A hydraulic lifter is very similar in outward appearance to a solid lifter, but has an internal plunger, spring, and ball check mechanism that uses engine oil pressure to self-adjust.

The problem with using hydraulic lifters in a racing engine is that the internal parts gain inertia and "pump-up" (increase in height) at high rpm's. This causes the valves to "float" (remain open), killing engine power and possibly causing pistons and valves to collide.

Hydraulic lifters usually pump-up and float the valves at speeds around 6000 rpm's—far too low for true high performance racing engines. Even special high performance hydraulic lifters cause valve float at speeds above 7000 rpm's. We recommend hydraulic lifters only for street applications unless rules require them for your race car class.

Solid Lifters - *Solid lifters* have a fixed operating height with no moving parts that can upset the opening and closing times of the valves. Because they do not self-adjust, solid lifters require frequent valve lash adjustments. Most racers check and adjust the valve lash between every round of racing to be sure nothing in the valve train has worn, bent, or stretched.

Racing solid lifters are hollow inside to reduce the mass (weight). This reduces the inertial forces and helps ensure lifter to cam lobe contact at high rpm's. When the engine is running, the lifter cavity fills with motor oil under pressure. This oil is metered into the pushrods to lubricate and cool the upper valve train parts.

The end of a new solid lifter appears flat, but actually has a slight (about .0005") crown. This crown helps the lifter break in properly with the cam lobe.

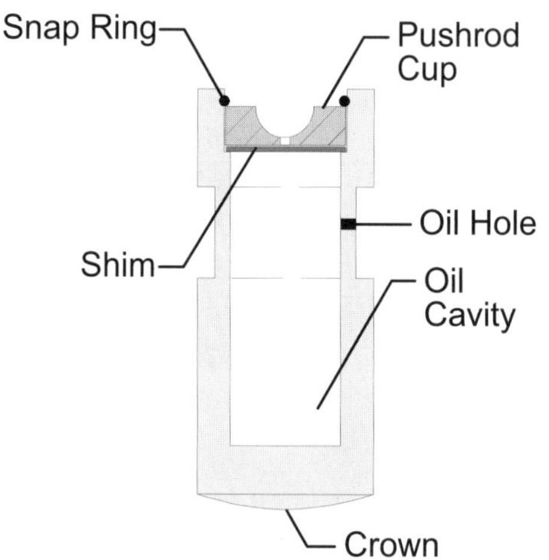

The pushrod cup supports and centers the pushrod. It is retained by a snap ring. Oil pressure enters the oil hole and fills the oil cavity. The slight crown helps the lifter mate with the cam lobe properly during the break in. The shim controls oil flow into the pushrod.

The cam lobe is ramped (sloped) to make the lifter spin in operation and to keep the camshaft from walking out of the block. Spinning reduces the sliding friction between the lifters and cam lobes.

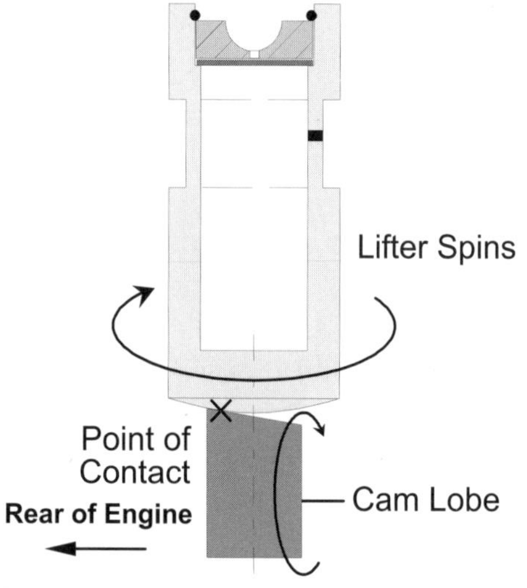

The ramp on the cam lobe causes an off-center point of contact with the lifter. This makes the lifter spin in the bore. It also helps to keep the cam pushed back into the block (thrust control).

<u>Roller Tappets</u> - A *roller tappet* (lifter) has a small steel roller that follows the cam lobe. The roller adds extra mass, but it reduces friction between the lifters and cam lobes. This allows the use of very stiff valve springs that can control engine valves at higher rpm's. The roller also keeps the edge of the tappet from dragging on a steeply sloped lobe. Much more aggressive cam profiles with faster valve opening and closing rates are possible when you use roller tappets.

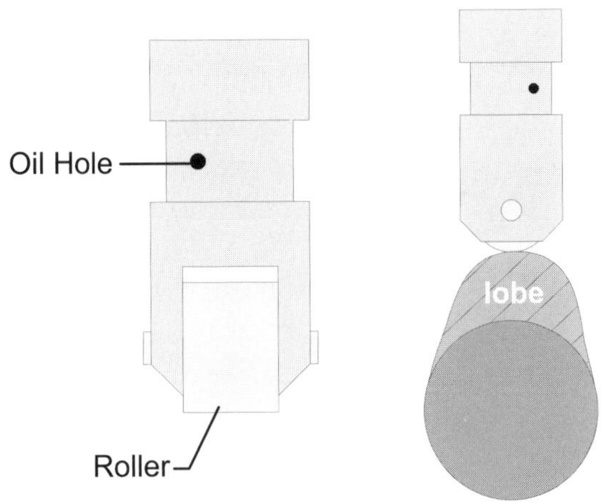

The roller reduces friction between the lifter and cam lobe and allows the use of radical racing camshaft profiles.

Roller tappets must not be allowed to turn in relation to the cam lobe. There are several different systems used to prevent roller tappet rotation, but most use a link that connects the lifters together in pairs.

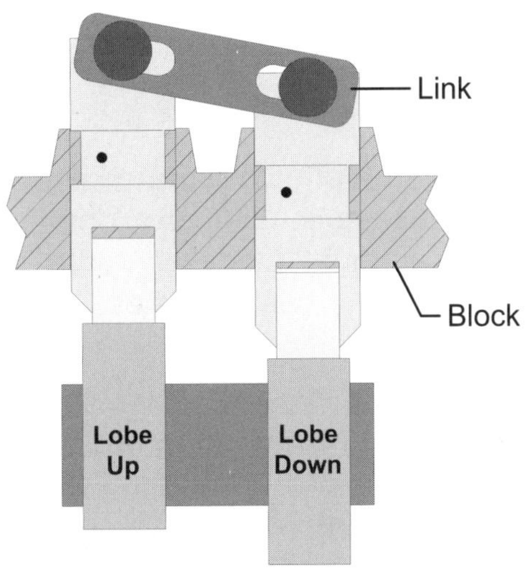

The lifter link can pivot and slide as necessary to allow independent lifter operation while controlling unwanted rotation.

Because the rollers ride on level cam lobes, a roller camshaft must also have some type of thrust control system to keep it from moving in or out of the engine block. Despite these problems and the initial high cost, we recommend that you purchase a good roller tappet camshaft and kit for your engine if permitted by your race sanctioning organization.

Choosing a Camshaft Profile:

More is not always better when choosing a camshaft. A radical racing camshaft may increase or decrease horsepower, depending on the particular requirements of your engine.

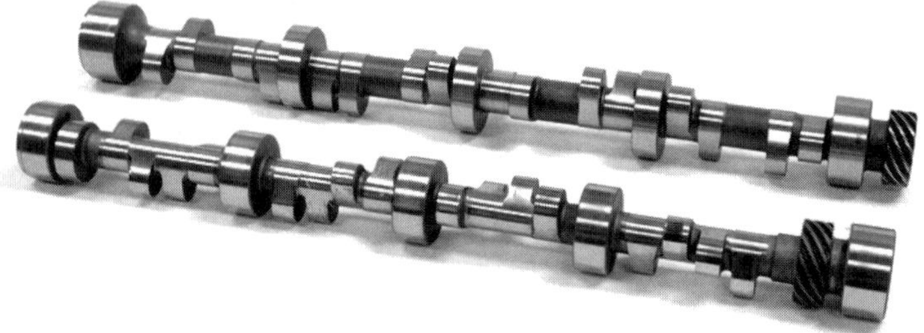

The camshaft profile is one of the most important choices you must make to get the most out of your racing engine.

When choosing a camshaft profile, it is important to consider the following:

- Rpm Operating Range
- Budget Constraints
- Engine Breathing Characteristics
- Mechanical Limitations

Rpm Operating Range - Camshaft profile has a large effect on the engine torque and horsepower curves. The goal in camshaft profile selection is to find one that maintains adequate intake and exhaust velocity across the operating rpm range of the engine. Generally, the more lift and duration that a camshaft has, the faster the engine must run to make it work.

One of the most common mistakes made by a novice racer is to install a radical racing camshaft into an engine with a stock passenger car bottom end or high vehicle gearing. The engine will not operate at high enough speeds to create the high gas velocities that make a radical cam profile work.

IMPORTANT! Very often, just slipping a high lift/long duration cam into an engine creates serious mechanical problems like inadequate piston-to-valve or valve spring bind. Have the valve springs checked by a reputable shop with a lot of racing cylinder head experience and measure the piston to valve clearance.

Engine Breathing Characteristics - Engine breathing is a function of engine size, exhaust system efficiency, intake and exhaust port flow characteristics, manifold design, and carburetor size. Long stroke, large displacement engines tend to produce high velocities and usually need a cam profile with high lift and long duration. Small, short stroke engines will not tolerate as much camshaft lift and duration.

Racing camshafts usually have a lot of overlap. Valve overlap requires a free-flowing and efficient exhaust system to scavenge low pressure in the combustion chamber. Mufflers and long exhaust systems create exhaust back pressure that destroys the scavenging effect. These vehicles usually require camshafts with less overlap (a larger lobe center angle).

If the engine has small, efficient intake and exhaust port designs that create very high velocities, it will benefit from long duration, high lift cam profiles. However, if the velocities are not high because of large ports, manifolds, and carburetors, the intake gases will turn around and head the wrong way in the intake manifold. Intake reversion reduces the amount of air & fuel in the cylinders, disrupts normal carburetor operation, and destroys intake manifold vacuum.

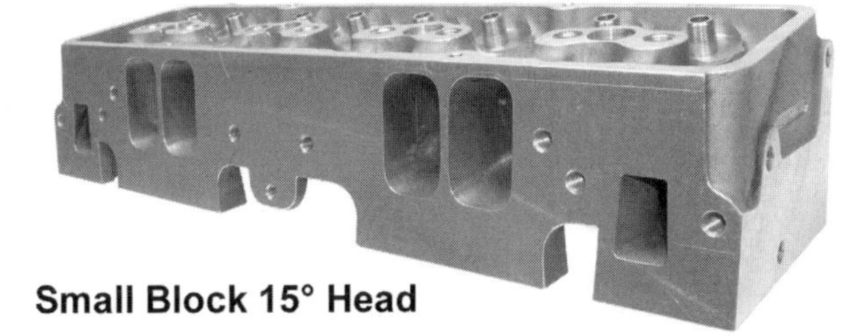

Small Block 15° Head

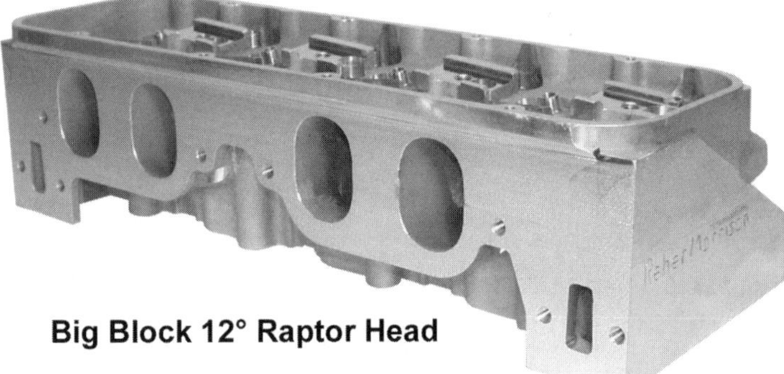

Big Block 12° Raptor Head

The huge intake ports and valves in these racing cylinder heads can mean a ton of horsepower, but only when used with the right cam profile and engine combination.

Good port design is critical to the success of a racing engine. We map our ports looking for dead areas, and then fill them in to maintain velocity throughout the cross section of the port. If the ports in the cylinder heads flow very efficiently, the engine may actually need *less* camshaft.

Budget Constraints - High lift, long duration camshafts and high rpm engine operation place enormous stresses on nearly every engine component. Even if the parts are more than strong enough to resist short term breakage, the demands of racing inevitably cause metal fatigue and failure at an accelerated rate.

The higher the horsepower output of the engine for its displacement, the shorter the parts replacement cycles tend to be. The parts needed to make a lot of power generally cost more as well.

All too often, racers expend too much of their budget purchasing exotic engine components only to find out that they can't keep up with the costs in money and time to maintain the engine. The very stiff and exotic valve springs required to handle the extreme valve acceleration rates in a modern Pro Stock drag racing engine are a good case in point. It is not uncommon for a competitive NHRA team to run up an annual bill of $40,000 or more just in valve spring replacements alone!

These expensive triple-wound valve springs have compressed rates well over 1000 lb. They allow us to use cam profiles and rpm's that would have been unthinkable just a couple of decades ago. However, the frequent replacement cycle adds a lot to the cost of running a race car.

One key element to consider when you choose a camshaft profile is the mass of the valves. If you can fit them in your budget, titanium valves are the way to go.

NOTE: For more information about valve selection, see the *Valves & Springs* section of this unit.

Don't just look at the initial purchase price of the parts when you build your racing engine. Be sure to talk with an experienced racing engine builder about the costs of maintaining your engine with the cam and kit that you select.

Mechanical Limitations - Even when money is no object, there are limits as to what can be done with a racing camshaft profile. There are mechanical limitations to how far and long engine valves can open and practical limits beyond which the costs in time and money outweigh any potential gains.

More lift means that the valves have to be opened and closed faster. High valve velocities really add to the stress on pushrods, rocker arms, and valve springs. The valve springs tend to be the weakest link in the system.

Twenty years ago, racers found it impossible to run cam profiles with much more than .750" lift. At lifts higher than that, the springs would coil bind or could not maintain lifter-to-cam lobe contact because of valve float or harmonic problems. Recent developments in valve spring technology have allowed cam grinders to produce profiles with .900" lift, or higher.

Even with titanium valves and the best springs, there are limits as to how far cam duration may be pushed. Engines are particularly sensitive to intake closing time. The best flowing heads will not tolerate intake valve closings much later than about 75 or 80 degrees after bottom dead center (ABDC). The highest duration cams today have about 290° intake and 324° exhaust duration (crankshaft degrees @ .050" checking height).

There are also limits to how soon the valves may open and the range of lobe centerlines that will work. Valve timing limitations do not mean that there can be no further improvement in camshaft profiles. Two camshafts with the same lift, duration, and lobe center specifications can still perform quite differently in a racing engine.

A better way to look at the effective degree to which the camshaft opens the valves is by examining the *area under the curve*—a graphical way to show the true breathing potential of a particular cam profile.

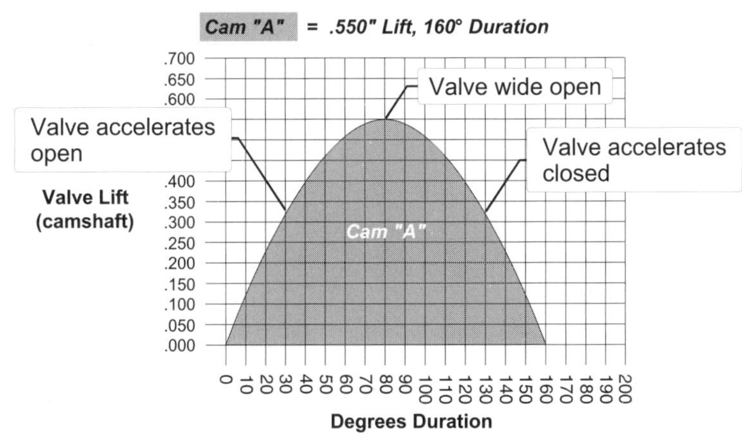

Area under the curve is not a silhouette of the cam, but a graphical representation of valve operation.

Two camshafts can have exactly the same lift and duration specifications, but one may have more area under the curve. This is possible by changing the slope of the cam lobe so that the valve opens and closes faster.

The figure below shows two camshafts with the same lift and duration. Camshaft "B" may make more power because it has greater area under the curve.

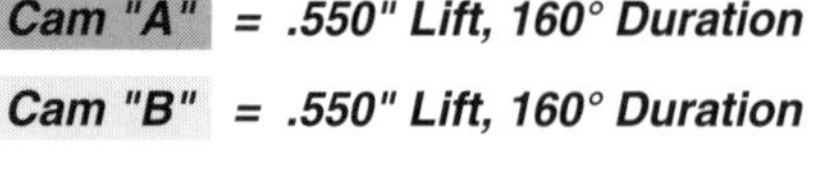

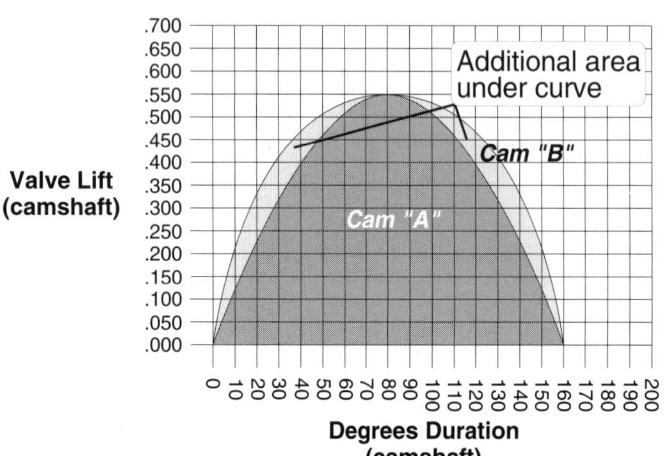

Cam "B" accelerates the valve open and closed faster than cam "A". This results in more area under the curve. Cam "B" has greater potential for creating more horsepower.

Racing engine builders and camshaft grinders are still finding ways to reshape the cam lobes so that they create more area under the curve. This has been an important factor in horsepower development for many professional racing categories.

Roller tappets can withstand very high forces, allowing steeper opening and closing ramps. This results in more area under the curve, but it also means higher valve velocities and inertial forces. The high level of stress on valve train components requires stronger and more expensive parts.

One of many problems faced by high performance camshaft designers is how to control flexing and twisting of the camshaft under the extreme forces developed in a racing engine. To make a high lift lobe, the base circle must be cut down in size. This weakens the core of the camshaft.

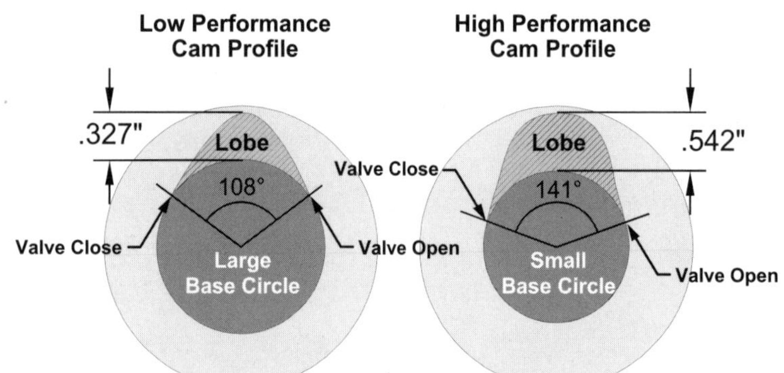

The additional lift and duration of a racing camshaft come from a reduced base circle diameter. This weakens the core of the camshaft.

To help overcome cam flexing problems and to allow even more radical camshaft profiles, the trend in professional racing has been to use new blocks that have a larger camshaft tunnel. This permits the use of large-journal camshafts that are much more rigid.

High performance engines require extremely stiff valve springs to prevent valve float at high rpm's. The combination of stiff valve springs and high inertial forces bends the camshaft between the bearing journals.

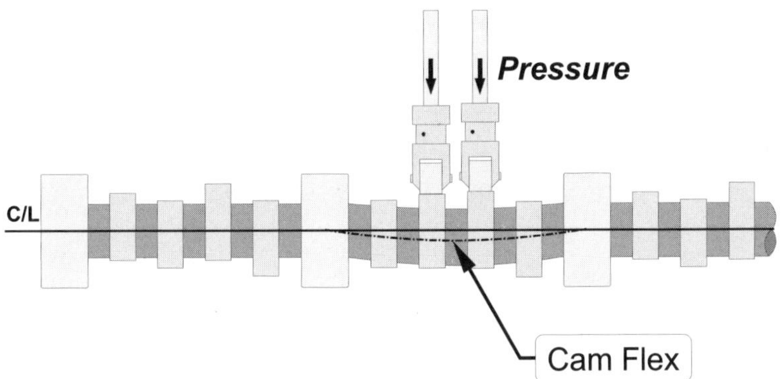

Inertial forces and high-rate racing valve springs place hundreds of pounds of force on the camshaft—enough to cause some bending of the camshaft.

The friction caused by high valve spring pressure and drag from operating the oil pump can cause torsional twist in the camshaft. To control flex and twist, camshafts must be made from of strong, stiff steel alloys.

One way to increase high performance camshaft core strength is to design the engine with a larger cam bore. The diameter of these cams is typically 55 mm, 60 mm, or 65 mm. A larger base circle provides and a bigger cross section through the core of the camshaft that resists flexing. This allows for faster opening rates and higher lift.

The trend in Pro Stock racing had been to large-bore camshafts. The larger journal allows a bigger base circle and more rigid camshaft core.

There is one tradeoff when using a cam with a large base circle—it creates higher speeds between the lobes and lifters. The results are a small increase in frictional drag and potentially shorter lifter roller life. When using large-bore cams, it's a good idea to also use lifters with a correspondingly larger roller diameter.

Street Use of HP Camshafts:

There are a number of problems with using a high performance camshaft in a street driven vehicle. Racing camshafts cause low speed intake reversion that kills intake manifold vacuum. Mufflers, catalytic converters, and restrictive exhaust systems compound this problem. This means that manifold vacuum-operated devices like power brakes will lose their power assist and will not function properly.

High-overlap camshafts cause hydrocarbon emissions. For this reason, many state and federal laws restrict the use of high performance camshafts in street driven vehicles. Always check with your state licensing agencies or highway patrol for applicable regulations before you install a racing camshaft in a street-driven vehicle.

This radical racing camshaft may not be legal for street use. Always check state and federal laws about engine modifications before you make your purchase.

The only way to really know what camshaft will work best in a given application is to test many different profiles, but this is usually not an option for the average racer. Instead, we recommend that you rely on the advice of an experienced racing engine builder and the camshaft manufacturer. They can help you make a sensible choice that provides you with the best opportunity to realize the potential of your engine combination.

NOTE: Remember to degree-in your camshaft and measure piston-to-valve clearance. For these procedures and additional information about camshaft and drive assembly selection & operation, see *Unit VI, Short Block Pre Assembly Measurements, Degreeing-In the Camshaft.*

Camshaft Drive Assemblies

The camshaft drive assembly must turn the camshaft at exactly half the crankshaft speed. This 2 to 1 turning speed ratio is necessary because the valves operate only once for every two revolutions of the crankshaft in the 4-stoke cycle.

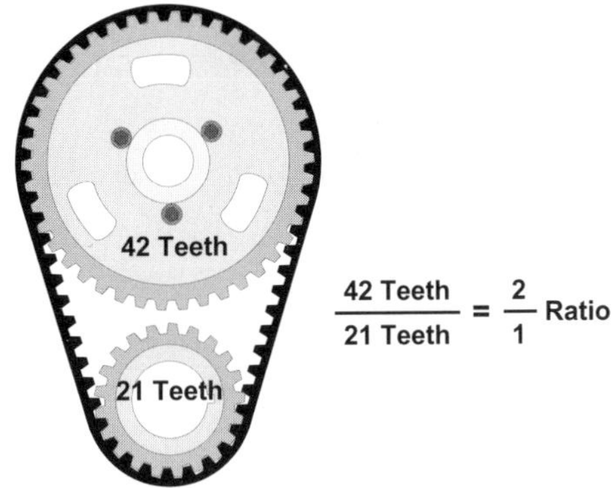

The cam sprocket, pulley, or gear always has twice as many teeth as the one on the crankshaft. This creates the necessary 2 to 1 turning ratio between the crankshaft and camshaft.

On a typical high-horsepower Pro Stock racing engine, the valves and pistons may clash with as little as 2° valve timing variation. To prevent failure and maintain correct valve timing, racing engine camshaft drive components must be much stronger and more durable than those designed for passenger car applications.

Chain & Sprockets:

A quality racing chain & sprocket assembly is a very reliable and effective way of driving the camshaft for most applications. Racing sets feature high strength steel sprockets and a seamless roller chain with thrust-control hardware..

This heavy-duty timing chain set includes a double-roller chain with large .250" diameter seamless rollers, steel billet crank and cam sprockets, a cam sprocket thrust bearing, a needle bearing thrust button, and a locking plate with cam bolts.

When choosing a chain camshaft drive, it is important that the chain has large diameter (.250" OD) seamless pins or rollers. The cam sprocket must have the side that faces the block machined to accept a thrust bearing so that the block doesn't become worn. A needle bearing thrust button is needed to limit forward camshaft movement. We prefer that the clearance between the camshaft thrust bearing button and the timing cover is between 0" to .010". Be sure the timing cover you choose is very stiff so it won't flex to maintain the correct camshaft thrust clearance.

Belt Drives:

Although they cost more than chain and sprocket assemblies, we prefer belt drive systems for some of our high-horsepower racing engines. A quality racing belt drive is very durable and maintains precise valve timing. With the front cover plate and oil seal located behind the belt, the drive mechanism is exposed. This allows the racer to make very quick camshaft or cam phasing (timing) changes.

This cogged belt drive kit is complicated and expensive, but has several advantages over a chain and sprocket cam drive system.

Most camshaft belt drive systems come from the manufacturer with detailed installation instructions. It's important to read through this information to be sure the system is installed right. We do a few extra things to extend the service life of the belt drive system. Because of variances between block manufacturers it may be necessary to machine the cover side of the crank pulley.

We machine the inner chamfer of the crank pulley (right arrow) to provide a minimum of .020" clearance between the pulley and the cover. To extend seal life, we also polish the seal surfaces of the crank pulley (left arrows). When it's time for final installation, apply a bead of RTV silicone to the inner chamfer.

Special modifications are often needed when using a belt-drive camshaft drive system with roller cam bearings. We have found that you if you try to run cam thrust washers alone with roller cam bearings, the block side of the thrust washer often wears excessively. To solve this problem, we install a roller-style cam thrust bearing between the cam hub and the cover thrust plate.

We machine the cam hub to accept the roller style thrust bearing. We also install a thrust washer between the other side of the cam hub and the block. When running the roller-style thrust bearing, it may be necessary to machine the back of the cam spider for seal and stud nut clearance.

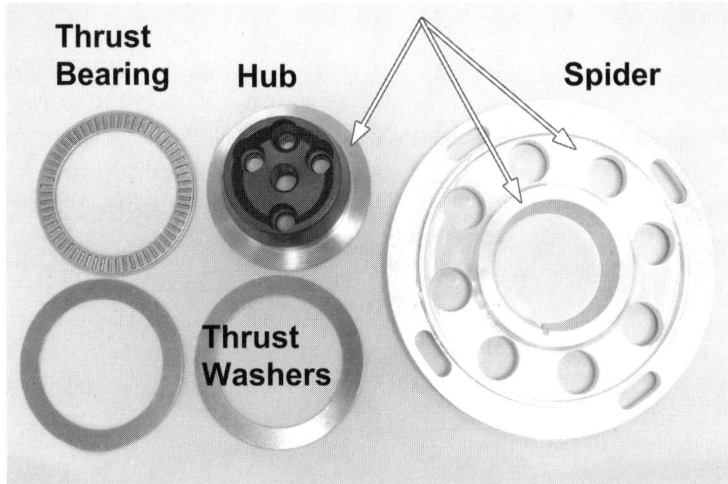

The arrows on the left point to the places that we often machine to install a roller-type thrust bearing on a belt drive system. This includes cutting the thrust surface of the hub and the spider for seal and stud nut clearance.

Gear Drives:

Gears are the most positive and reliable camshaft driving system, but are very noisy and expensive. Gear drive systems are primarily used in supercharged applications because they can handle the drag of the high pressure/high volume mechanical fuel pumps.

This gear drive system is noisy and expensive, but more reliable for use in supercharged engines.

Racing engine builders find that installing a gear drive system robs the engine of about 15 horsepower. When we take apart gear drive engines, we often find that the cam bearings are worn on the top side as the gears try to separate from each other in operation. Gear drives are the best choice in unlimited fuel applications where the engine has more than enough horsepower and strength and reliability are the primary considerations.

Pushrods & Rocker Arms

Just having the right camshaft for your engine is not enough to ensure top performance. Racing engines place enormous forces on other valve train components including the pushrods, rocker arms, and valve springs.

Pushrods:

We have found that the pushrods are one of the most important "tuning" components in the valve train of a racing engine. As the lifter climbs the cam lobe, the pushrods must overcome not only valve spring pressure, but also inertial forces in the rocker arms, valves, and valve spring hardware. Exhaust pushrods receive even higher loads than intake pushrods because they must push the valves open into extreme cylinder pressures. This can create a significant amount of flex that has direct effects on valve operation and valve train life.

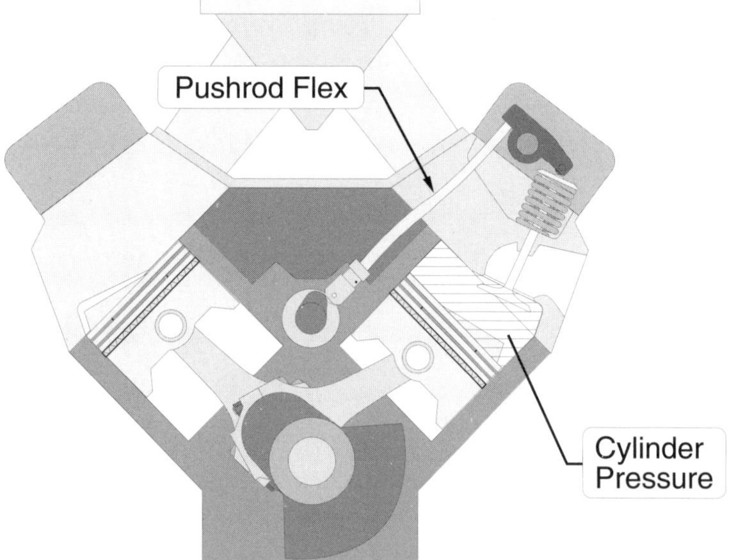

At high rpm's, compressive forces on the exhaust pushrods are so great that they flex, becoming "S" shaped.

A racing engine needs extra side clearance around the pushrods. We've seen evidence of pushrod-to-block contact in engines that have the wrong pushrods even with a full half inch of side clearance! Pushrod length, material, diameter, and wall thickness must be carefully matched to the rest of the valve train to work properly throughout the rpm range.

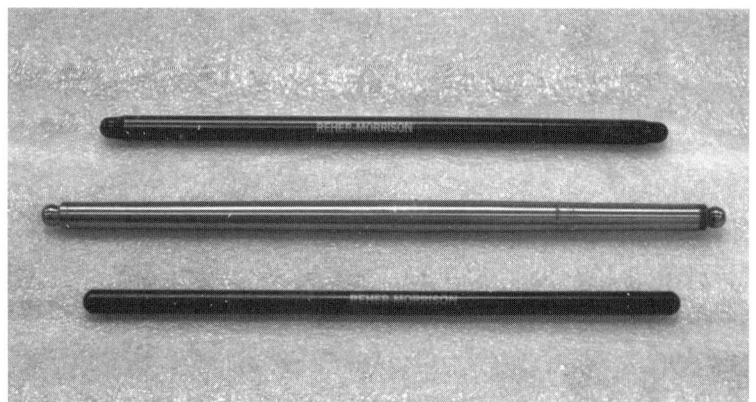

We custom-cut our own pushrods, usually from .080" to .160" wall chrome-moly stock. Diameters range from 3/8" to 9/16", depending on the application.

High-strength steel alloy pushrods are the best available for racing engines. The pushrods are hollow to reduce weight and provide a passageway for oil to the upper valve train components.

Pushrod Length - Pushrod length is very important in a racing engine. The pushrods have to be the right length in order to maintain correct rocker arm geometry. Good geometry minimizes problems with side thrusting of the valve stem, excessive roller travel, and eliminates any binding of the rocker arms.

Many rocker arm manufacturers prefer the roller to be on the valve stem centerline (fig A) when the valve begins to open. As the rocker arm moves to mid-travel, the tip rolls slightly off the centerline (fig B) and imparts some side loading to the valve stem. When the valve is wide open, spring pressure is high and the roller should once again be on the stem centerline (fig C).

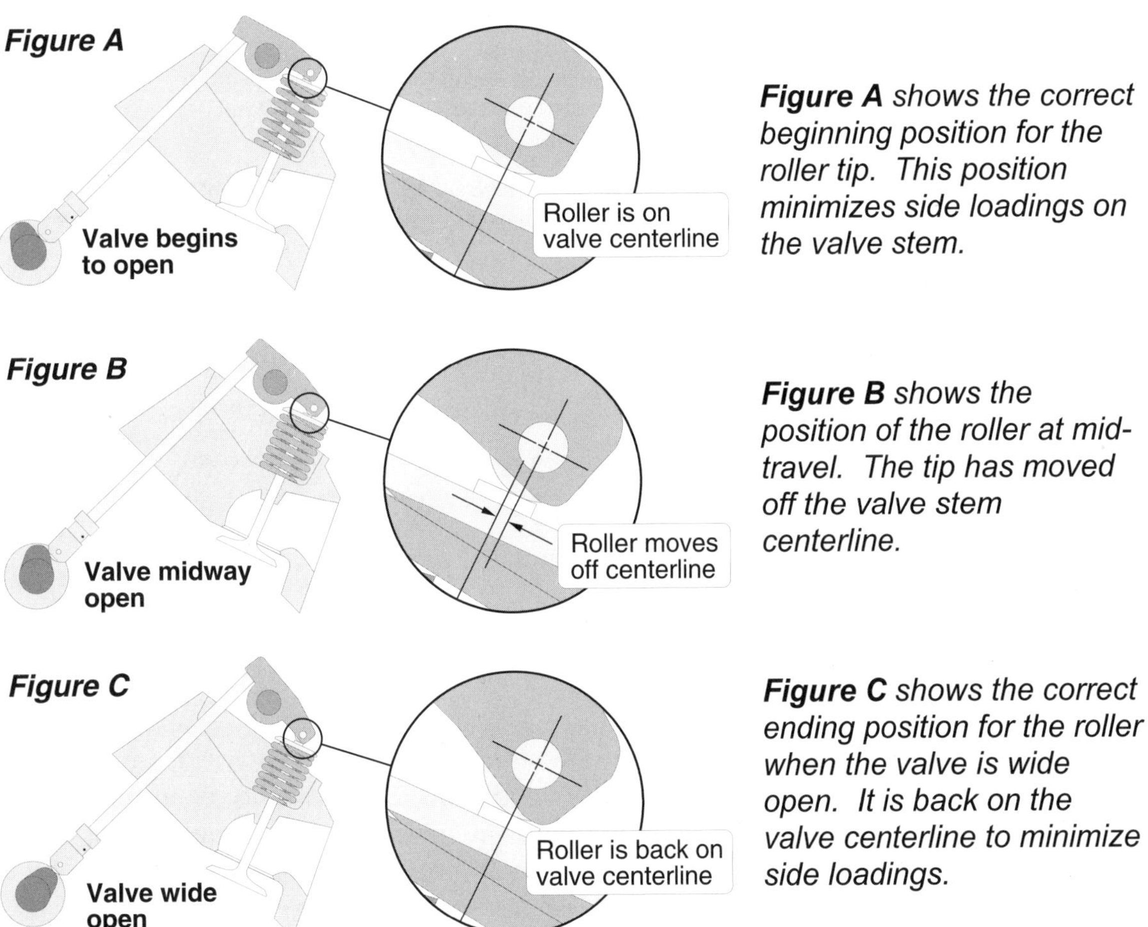

***Figure A** shows the correct beginning position for the roller tip. This position minimizes side loadings on the valve stem.*

***Figure B** shows the position of the roller at mid-travel. The tip has moved off the valve stem centerline.*

***Figure C** shows the correct ending position for the roller when the valve is wide open. It is back on the valve centerline to minimize side loadings.*

NOTE: This description represents ideal rocker arm action. However, variations in the design of different valve train components may make it difficult or impossible to achieve the exact results shown above. In these cases, make the needed compromises that provide rocker operation that most closely resembles the desired goal.

Rocker binding problems can also result if the pushrods are not the correct length.

Pushrod Length Correct

Valve Closed Valve Open

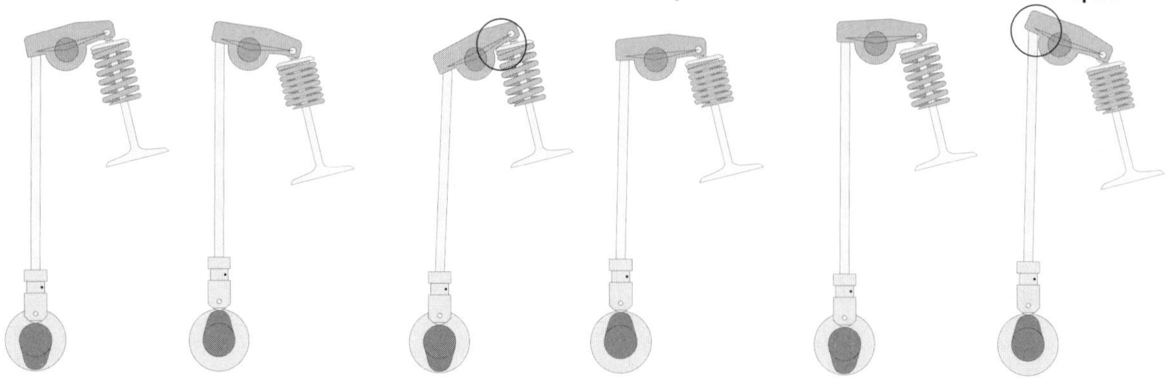

Minimal roller tip travel, no binding of rocker

Pushrod Too Short

Valve Closed Valve Open

Excessive roller tip travel, possible binding of rocker with nut or valve retainer

Pushrod Too Long

Valve Closed Valve Open

Excessive roller tip travel, possible binding of rocker with nut or pushrod

The components you select to build your engine and various machining operations affect the pushrod length you will need to obtain the correct geometry and avoid binding problems:

Shortens Required Pushrod Length

- Milling cylinder heads
- Milling block deck
- Raising camshaft location
- Larger cam base circle diameter

Increases Required Pushrod Length

- Smaller cam base circle diameter
- Taller cylinder heads
- Taller block deck height

Most low to medium performance engines have had the heads milled to increase the compression ratio. All have high performance camshafts with base circles that are smaller than stock.

Note in the previous table that milled cylinder heads and small base circles are offsetting pushrod length factors. You may wind up with something close to a stock pushrod length, but nearly every racing engine will have a unique requirement. Always follow the procedures recommended by the rocker arm manufacturer to be sure the rocker arm geometry is correct, then carefully measure the required pushrod length for your engine.

Rocker Arms:

Stock ball pivot type rocker arms have high levels of friction and usually do not hold up well in medium to high horsepower racing engines. They also may not have a long enough slot to allow the higher pivot angles created by high lift cams. We highly recommend quality high-strength aluminum roller tip rocker arms, available in either stud or shaft types as shown below.

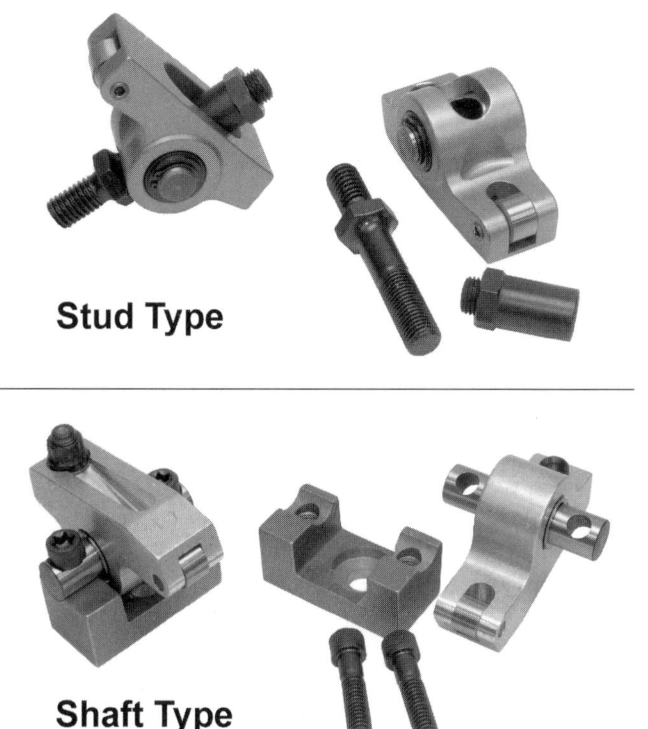

Racing roller tip rocker arms are stronger and hold up better under racing conditions than stock rocker arms. These are a must for medium to high horsepower racing engines.

Stud-type rocker arms require a pushrod guide plate to keep them from moving out of position. The guide plate is anchored by a pair of rocker studs. Some side wear may occur between the pushrods and the guide plate slots with this design.

This DART BBC 355 CNC racing head has pushrod guide plates to keep the pushrods and rocker arms aligned.

Shaft-type rockers attach with two bolts instead of one. This prevents the rocker arms from moving out of alignment and eliminates the need for pushrod guide plates. Heads that are designed for stud-type rocker arms can be adapted for shaft-type rockers by bolting machined stands to the head as shown in the photo below.

This Reher-Morrison 12º RAPTOR head with shaft rockers requires no stud girdle (valvetrain stabilizer).

Rocker Studs & Stabilizers:

The rocker studs (or bolts) really take a pounding in a racing engine at high rpm's, particularly with high ratio rocker arms. For this reason, you should avoid stock type cylinder heads with press-in rocker studs. Purchase race-only cylinder heads with screw-in rocker studs or stud bosses (if allowed by the rules).

These stock press-in rocker studs won't hold up in most racing applications. The stud can pull out or the wedging effect of the stud may crack the stud boss.

High-end heads may come pre-machined for shaft-type rockers.

This high-performance cylinder head is pre-machined for shaft-type rockers and stands. The register keeps the stand in the correct orientation.

The stud threads in aluminum heads should be drilled and tapped deeply enough to prevent thread pulling or Heli-Coiled® if the threads are damaged. Purchase only premium-quality high-strength steel rocker studs or bolts. Most intake rocker stud holes and many exhaust stud holes go all the way through to the ports. To prevent leaks, we apply Teflon® sealant to the threads before we install them into the heads.

Even high quality rocker studs are prone to flexing under racing conditions particularly when high ratio rocker arms pound on them. This flexing causes some loss of valve lift. It also leads to fatigue failure of the studs. If you have stud-type rockers, a great way to reinforce the studs is by using a *stud stabilizer* (girdle).

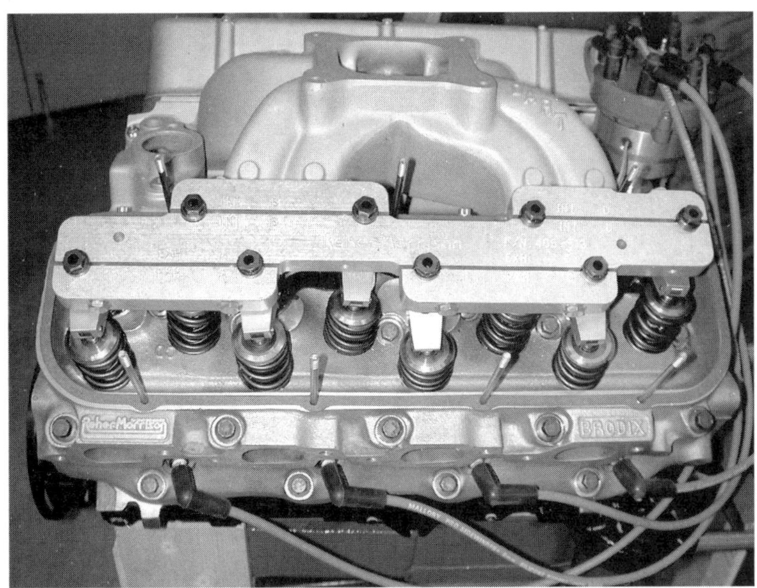

A stud stabilizer is a machined aluminum bar that adds support to the top of the rocker nuts.

The stud stabilizer clamps over all of the rocker nuts so that any flexing is shared by the other rocker studs on the head. Stud stabilizer kits are available that include the necessary long style rocker nuts.

Lash Adjusters:

If you have stud-type rocker arms, the valve lash (looseness) adjustment is made by turning the rocker arm nut. Stock rocker nuts are self-locking and have a tendency to loosen under the pounding of a racing engine. For this reason, we use an adjuster nut with an internal locking set screw on our street series engines that tightens against the top of the rocker arms stud.

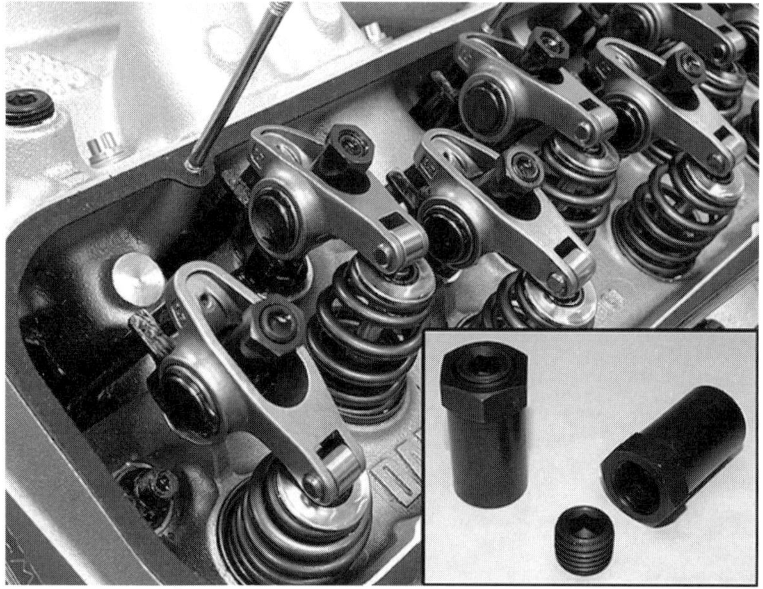

Stud-type rocker arms are adjusted by turning the adjusting nut. The adjustment is locked by tightening the inner set screw against the stud. This 540 CID street engine features the new Beehive valve springs.

Shaft-type rocker arms have an adjuster on the pushrod cup that allows you to set the valve lash. The jam nut ensures that the adjustment won't change during the race.

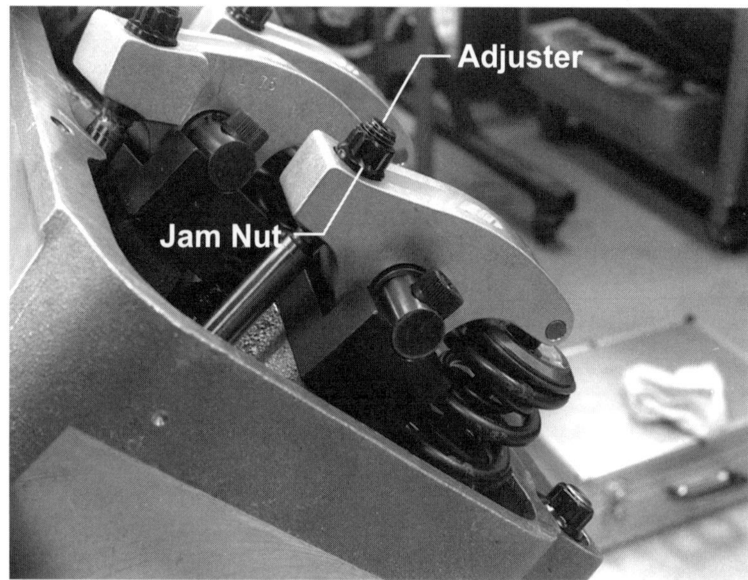

Valve lash is set by loosening the jam nut and turning the threaded pushrod cup adjuster.

Rocker Arm Ratio:

Valve lift is cam lobe lift multiplied by the rocker arm ratio. The rocker arm ratio affects valve opening and closing velocities.

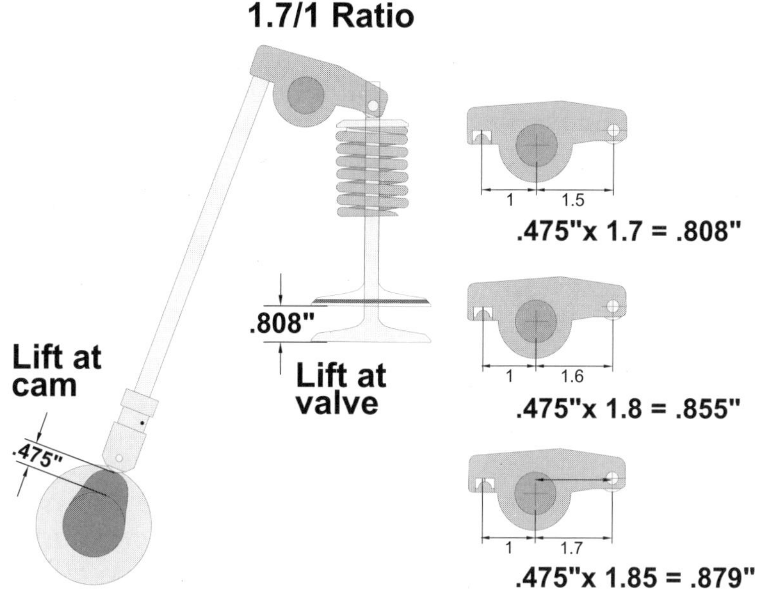

Valve lift at the cam is multiplied by the rocker arm ratio. With the same cam lift of .475", lift at the valve seat can be as high as .879" with 1.85 to 1 rocker arms.

Racing rocker arms are available in ratios as high as 2:1, but we usually don't use ratios higher than 1.85:1. High ratio rocker arms have the pushrod cup located closer to the pivot. This increases the shock loadings on the camshaft, lifters, pushrods, rocker arms, and the pivots.

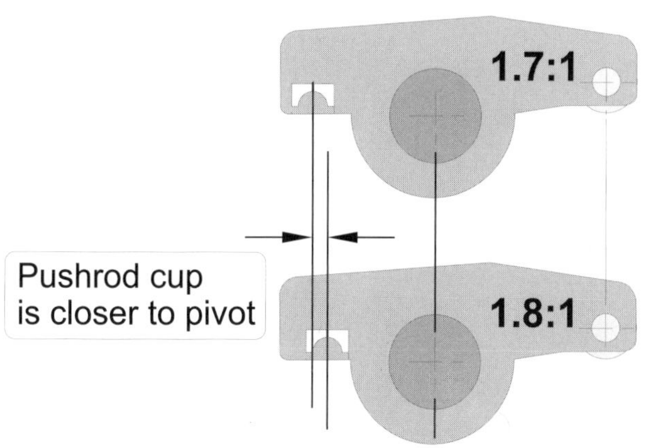

The pushrod cup is closer to the rocker pivot point to increase the ratio. Rocker arms with a very high ratio can flex or break valve train parts.

Although you can alter engine performance by a rocker arm ratio change, it is generally best to stick with the ratio recommended by the camshaft manufacturer. Always check piston-to-valve clearance after any modification to your valve train.

Intake Manifolds

The intake manifold can have nearly as much impact on engine performance as the cylinder heads and camshaft. It is very important that you select the right manifold for your engine and perform the necessary machine work to make it fit and work properly.

Types of Intake Manifolds:

There are a wide variety of intake manifolds available for high performance applications including the dual plane, single plane, and tunnel ram designs.

<u>Dual Plane Manifolds</u> - The *dual plane intake manifold* is primarily intended for use on passenger and street performance engines. It has the intake ports joined in two separate groups so that the engine draws on the carburetor in a left/right sequence. The runners are also very long. The results are high levels of torque with balanced fuel distribution to all of the cylinders.

Dual-Plane Manifold

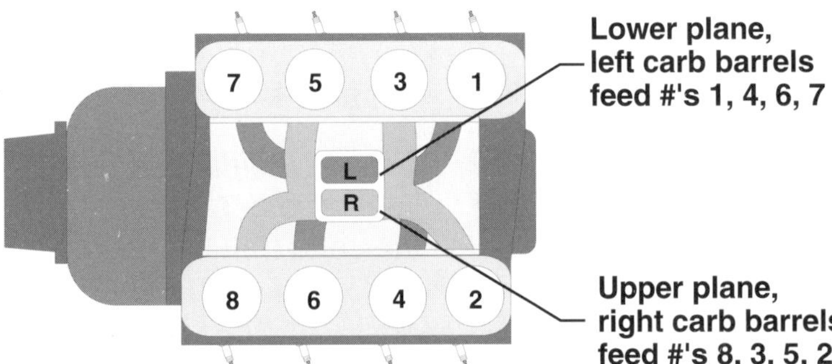

A dual plane manifold is designed to feed the cylinders in a pattern that alternates from the left carburetor barrel to the right. Note how each plane feeds every other cylinder in the firing order.

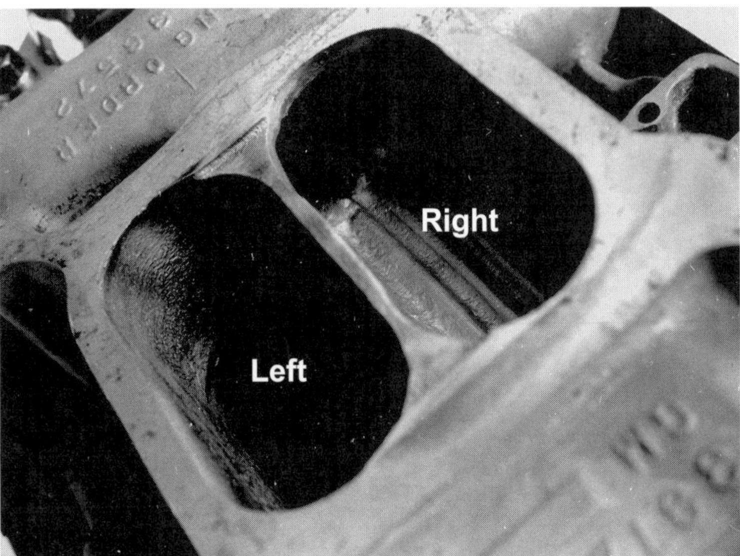

The divided upper and lower planes can be seen in the photo on the left.

A dual plane manifold is full of T-junctions and other sharp turns. The lower plane has a particularly tortuous path that the intake gases must take to get to the cylinder head ports. This causes the air/fuel mixture to become very turbulent at high engine speeds (above 6000 rpm's).

Another problem with a dual plane manifold is the very long and uneven runner lengths. Recall that long runners create low end torque, but short runners work better at high engine rpm's. Both problems cause dual plane manifolds to "shut off" at high engine speeds. We recommend dual plane manifolds only for low rpm, high torque engines.

Single Plane Manifolds - A *single plane manifold* feeds all the cylinders from a central *plenum* area. The plenum is an important buffer zone between the intake ports and carburetor barrels. It absorbs a lot of the pulsations and reversion waves that are present in the intake ports. This helps maintain a smooth, consistent flow through the carburetors and a well-mixed supply of air and fuel for the cylinders.

Single-Plane Manifold

GM V8 Engine
Firing Order 1-8-4-3-6-5-7-2

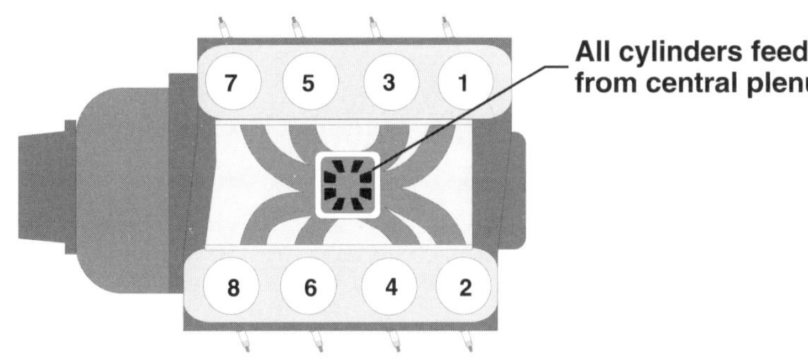

All the runners converge at a central plenum area on a single plane intake manifold. Note how much more direct the path is to the cylinders with this design.

The relatively short, straight runners of a single plane manifold converge in an open plenum area under the carburetor.

A single plane intake manifold design features a relatively short and direct path from the plenum to the cylinder head ports. These manifolds may make a little less low end torque than the dual plane designs, but they work much better at engine speeds above 6000 rpm's.

Single plane racing manifolds almost always outperform dual plane manifolds for medium to high horsepower applications. However, the single plane design is not entirely free of design problems. Runner lengths are inconsistent—they vary by the distance of the cylinder from the central carburetor location. The firing pattern of the engine also causes some runners to "scavenge" from one another.

Tunnel Ram Manifolds - Developed in the 1960's, the *tunnel ram manifold* offers the highest potential for horsepower development of all designs. It features a large, high plenum and very straight runners. The tunnel ram manifold creates the least flow restriction of any design because of the very direct path from the carburetor barrels to the cylinder ports.

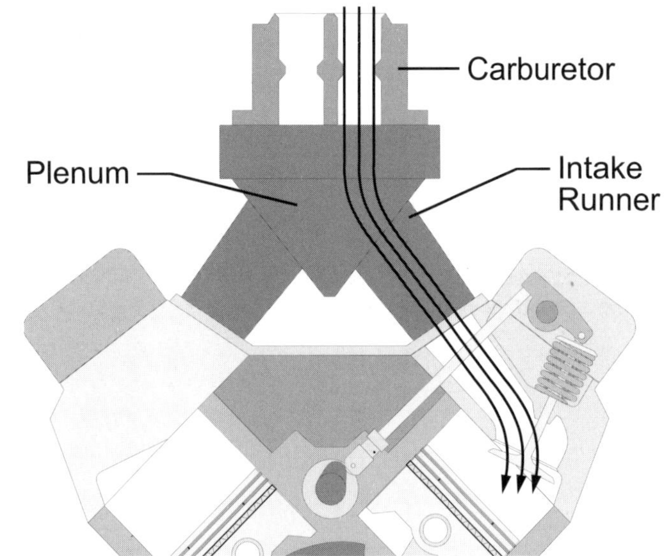

The tunnel ram creates a very direct path into the cylinders.

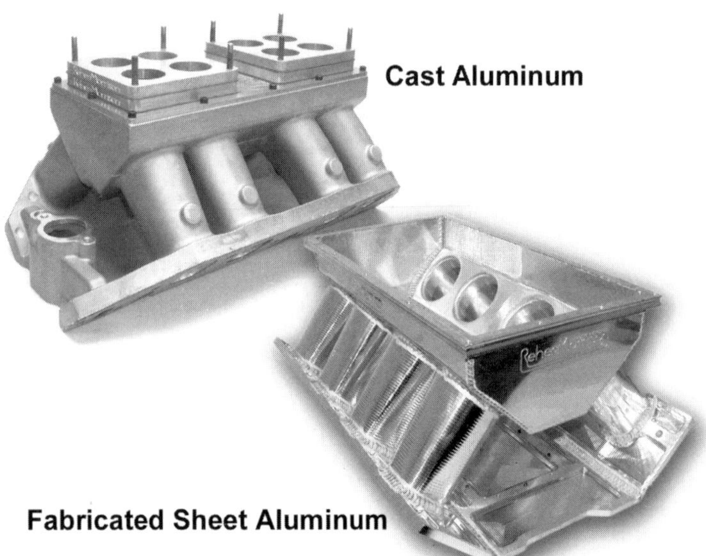

The tunnel ram is the breathing king of intake manifolds. It is the way to go for high-horsepower drag racing engines.

When two 4-barrel carburetors are used on a tunnel ram manifold, the runner lengths can be very consistent. The free-flowing nature of this design and the relatively large plenum make the tunnel ram the king of horsepower in high-rpm racing engines. These manifolds really start to "come alive" at engine speeds above 7000 rpm's.

Tunnel ram manifolds are either cast from aluminum or fabricated from sheet aluminum. The sheet metal manifolds can be custom made for a particular cylinder head/block configuration.

Our custom made sheet aluminum tunnel ram manifolds are the result of many hours of design and dyno testing. It takes a highly-skilled TIG welder many hours to create a piece like this.

There are drawbacks to the tunnel ram design. They tend to have very poor low to medium rpm range torque and require the use of very tall hood scoops. Minimum clearances must be maintained to avoid flow restrictions.

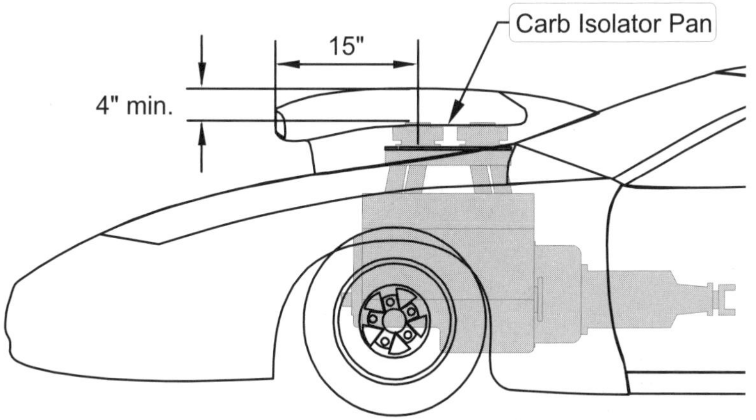

The scoop configuration is important when using a tunnel ram manifold. There must be at least a 4" clearance between the top of the carburetors and the underside of the hood scoop.

NOTE: Be sure to check with your race sanctioning organization about rules concerning the use of tunnel ram manifolds and tall hood scoops.

The plenum and runner volumes are critical to the performance of a tunnel ram manifold. Recall our rule about selecting induction system components:

The smaller you can make induction system components without reducing the horsepower output, the better your race car will perform.

The larger the engine displacement and the higher the operating range, the larger the plenum and runners should be. However, if you increase plenum volume beyond the minimum that the engine really needs, any small power gains that show up on the dyno are more than offset by the loss of low speed torque and throttle response. In testing, we reduce the size of the plenum and ports until we begin to see losses. This approach always results in the best on-track performance.

With the carburetors sitting high atop the engine, a tunnel ram can be a visually impressive piece, but remember that they generally lose power until the engine gets above 7000 rpm's. An engine must be engineered from the ground up for this kind of speed and flow demand. Sportsman type racing engines and street/strip engines usually perform a lot better with a single plane manifold.

This BBC engine will make plenty of power with this singe plane intake manifold. The ½" reversion (shear) plate and matching 1" funnel spacer will add 10-15 Hp and improve the throttle response in most applications.

The biggest challenge when selecting any type of manifold/carburetor combination is to balance low end torque and drivability with top end performance. Tricks like carburetor spacers nearly always show better power on the dyno, but can adversely affect low end torque and throttle response. We recommend that you talk to racing manifold manufacturers or an experienced engine builder to select the right manifold for your engine.

Carburetors

The carburetor mixes air and fuel in the right proportions and controls how much of this mixture enters the engine. Before you select a carburetor, it is helpful to have a good understanding of how it operates.

Basic Carburetor Operation:

A carburetor utilizes airflow through the throat (barrel) to draw fuel from the bowl. Carburetors work on two principles, the *Bernoulli effect* and the *venturi effect*. Recall that the Bernoulli effect describes how vacuum (low pressure) increases as velocity increases. The carburetor has a *fuel nozzle* (see the figure below) that is placed in a region of high velocity and low pressure. This draws the fuel into the air stream and *atomizes* it (blasts it into a mist of tiny droplets).

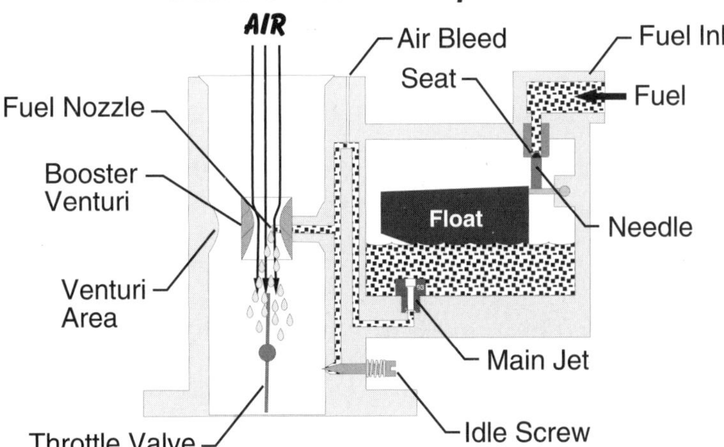

Air flowing through the venturi area of the carburetor creates low atmospheric pressure and draws fuel into the air stream and atomizes the fuel.

A *venturi* is a narrow passageway in a tube that increases flow velocity. The *venturi effect* describes this relationship between passageway size and velocity. A carburetor has a *venturi area* near the middle of the throat that increases the velocity of the air stream. A *booster venturi* is placed in this main venturi area to further increase the air velocity and create a region of very low pressure. The *fuel nozzle* is located inside the booster venturi where the pressure is lowest. This allows fuel to be drawn into the air stream and atomized. The *throttle valve* position determines how much of this air/fuel mixture can enter the engine.

The *needle & seat* assembly acts as a shutoff valve to maintain the same level of fuel in the carburetor bowl at all times. As fuel is consumed, a *float* drops and relieves pressure from the needle valve. This allows more fuel to enter, until the float again presses the needle against the seat and shuts off the supply.

There is one *main jet* for each barrel (throat) of the carburetor. A jet is a replaceable restrictor that controls the amount of fuel that the carburetor can deliver. *Air bleeds* at the top of the carburetor help aerate the fuel and prevent it from being siphoned from the bowl when the engine is shut off. The *idle screw* adjusts the fuel mixture when the throttle valve is nearly closed at engine idle.

This is how the parts look in a Holley 1150 cfm racing carburetor:

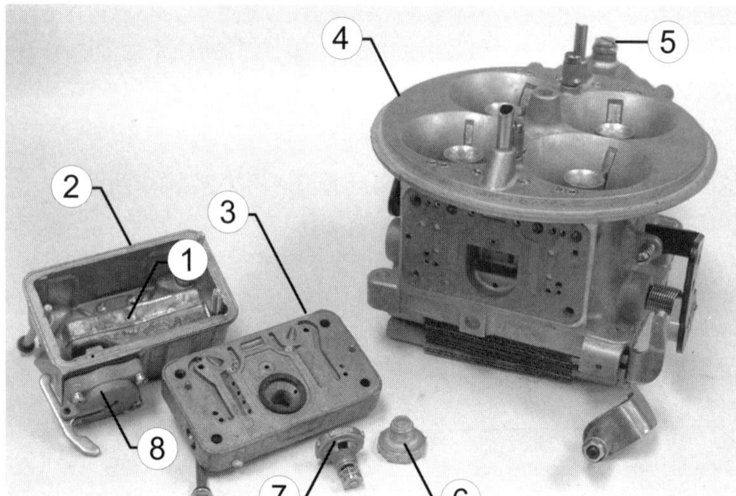

1. *Float*
2. *Bowl*
3. *Metering Block*
4. *Body*
5. *Needle & Seat Adjustment*
6. *Power Valve Plug*
7. *Power Valve*
8. *Accelerator Pump*

Choosing a Carburetor:

For the best performance, the carburetor should have a flow capacity that matches the demands of the engine. Engine displacement has a lot to do with how much air can be drawn into the cylinders, but carburetor flow requirements also depend on the rpm operating range and volumetric efficiency of the engine.

Carburetor flow capacity is expressed by the manufacturer in *cfm* (cubic feet per minute). This cfm rating reflects the amount of air that can flow through the carburetor at *WOT* (wide open throttle) when a standard vacuum of 1.5 in. hg. (inches mercury) is applied.

While under load at WOT, a racing engine must have at least 1 in. hg. pressure differential between the air outside the carburetor and that in the intake manifold. This causes air to continue to flow through the carburetor with adequate velocity.

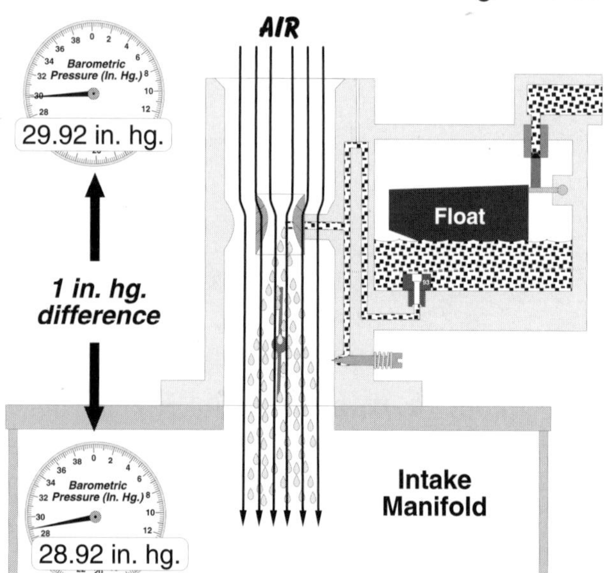

The pressure in the intake manifold should be about 1 in. hg. lower than atmospheric pressure to keep the air flowing through the carburetor at a high enough rate.

Over-Carburetion - *Over-carburetion* means that the carburetor is too large (has too much cfm capacity) for the engine. An over-carbureted racing engine performs very poorly. Installing carburetors that are too large for the engine is probably the single most common mistake made by inexperienced racers. Our rule for choosing induction system components is applicable again:

The smaller you can make induction system components without reducing the horsepower output, the better your race car will perform.

Over-carburetion destroys performance because it creates a lean condition in the engine. Recall that it is high air velocity that pulls fuel from the nozzles. The larger the barrels of the carburetor are, the lower the velocity through the carburetor will be. In an over-carbureted engine, the air velocity falls below a critical level at low to moderate engine speeds. The vacuum through the carburetor venturi is too low to pull enough fuel into the air stream. The engine leans out and "falls flat on its face".

If you try to compensate the lean low-speed air/fuel mixture by installing larger main jets, a new problem arises. The engine will run too rich at high rpm's when velocities finally rise above the critical level. Because it is not possible to balance the mixture across the operating range, an over-carbureted engine can never achieve its performance potential.

The two Holley 750 cfm carburetors on this 305 SBC Competition Eliminator engine result in a whopping 817 horsepower. However, this engine has very high volumetric efficiency and operates at extremely high rpm's. This same setup on a low to medium performance engine would be seriously over-carbureted.

Under Carburetion - *Under-carburetion* occurs if you choose a carburetor that is too small (cfm capacity too low) for the engine. Air velocities in an under-carbureted engine will be high across the rpm operating range. Although there may be a slight flow restriction and loss of power at high rpm's, the engine will have excellent low end power and throttle response.

There are various published formulas that can be used to estimate the required carburetor cfm capacity for most racing engine applications. However, it is not wise to rely too much on mathematical calculations when choosing a carburetor for your engine.

Most carburetor size formulas are based on Volumetric Efficiency (VE) calculations, but the actual volumetric efficiency of your engine can only be measured on a dyno. Even if you know the VE for your engine, most carburetor size formulas tend to recommend a cfm capacity that is too small for the real needs of your engine. The chart below shows some of the applications and carburetors that we have found work well together.

Application	***Carburetor(s)***	****Total CFM Capacity***
327-366 CID, sportsman	(1) 650-800 cfm	650-800 cfm
400-460 CID, sportsman	(1) 780-850 cfm	780-850 cfm
500+CID, sportsman	(1) 1050-1150 cfm	1050-1150 cfm
350-366 CID, pro	(2) 850-1050 cfm	1700-2100 cfm
500 CID, pro	(2) 1150-1300cfm	2300-2600 cfm

*Approximate

<u>Primary and Secondary Carburetor Barrels</u> - Most 4-barrel carburetors are divided into *primary barrels* ("primaries") at the front and *secondary barrels* ("secondaries") at the rear. The secondary throttle plates can be opened by a vacuum diaphragm (*vacuum secondaries*) or by mechanical linkage (*mechanical secondaries*).

A *spread-bore carburetor* has small primaries and large secondaries. The small primaries improve part throttle response and fuel economy on street-driven vehicles. In a *square-bore carburetor*, all throttle plates are the same size. This provides a more uniform flow rate to all cylinders for pure racing applications.

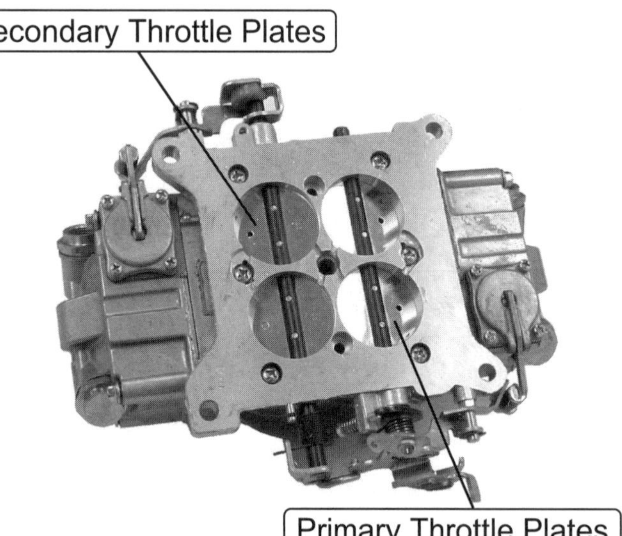

The primary and secondary barrels and throttle plates are the same size on this square bore carburetor. Use square bore carburetors on racing engines unless otherwise specified in the rules.

A vacuum secondary system works off flow demand created by the engine as the vehicle accelerates. At low speeds, the secondary throttle plates are kept closed by spring pressure. A port in the venturi area of the carburetor sends a vacuum signal to the vacuum diaphragm that increases with engine rpm's. At some point, the vacuum diaphragm overcomes the pressure of the throttle valve spring and the secondaries open.

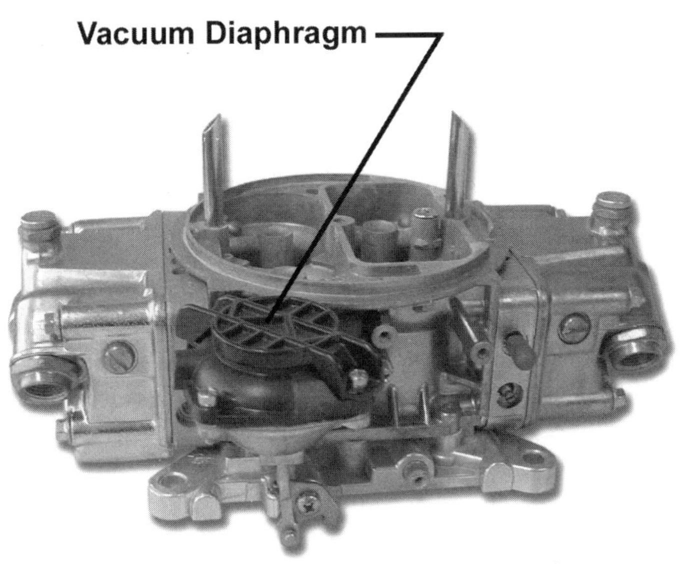

The vacuum secondary diaphragm opens the secondaries when needed on this Holley 780 cfm carburetor.

If the secondaries open too soon, the velocity loss in the carburetor will cause a lean condition and the engine will bog. If they open too late, air/fuel flow is restricted and the performance potential of the engine will not be fully realized.

The opening time of vacuum secondaries is controlled by the rate of the spring on the throttle plates. You can change to a weaker spring to make the secondaries open sooner, or to a stiffer spring to make them open later. High performance carburetor manufacturers can supply springs or spring adjustment procedures that will allow the secondaries to open at the best possible time.

Carburetors with vacuum secondaries have this "on-demand" characteristic that makes them a great choice for street driven vehicles. However, the vacuum diaphragm may not be able to react quickly enough for maximum performance at the race track. Most pure race cars perform better with a carburetor that has a *progressive linkage*.

A progressive linkage opens the primary barrels first for low speed operation, then the secondaries open beyond a certain point for full power with no time lag. Eliminating any time lag in opening the secondaries is important in most racing applications, but it becomes extremely important to match the size of the carburetor with the engine. If a progressive linkage carburetor is too large for the application, it will stumble on acceleration.

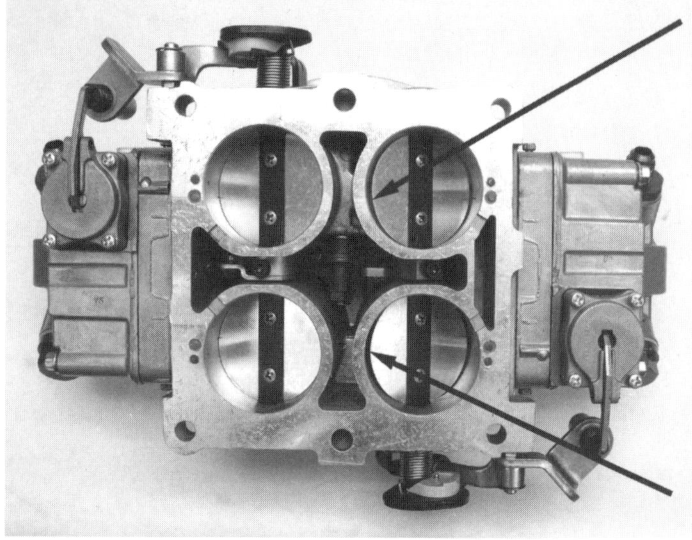

The primary barrels on a progressive linkage carburetor open the primaries first, then the secondaries beyond a certain point. Unlike a vacuum secondary carburetor, this happens instantly with throttle operation.

A street performance engine cannot usually handle a lot of carburetor flow, so multi-carb (2x4 and 3x2) street engines have one carburetor that is a primary carb with the other barrels opened by a progressive linkage. On racing engines with two four barrels (2x4), the carburetors work simultaneously. The primary barrels of both carburetors open first at part throttle, then progressive linkage opens the secondaries.

We recommend square-bore carburetors with progressive mechanical secondaries for the majority of single four barrel racing applications unless they are specifically prohibited by the rules.

A tunnel ram must feed each cylinder evenly. Mechanical secondaries are a good idea when using this kind of manifold.

Accelerator Pumps - When you open the throttle plates quickly, there is a momentary drop in carburetor throat air velocity. This happens because it takes more time for the engine to accelerate and start pulling more air into the engine than it does to open the throttle plates. The air in the carburetor throat will slow down so much that there is no vacuum to pull fuel from the nozzles. The result is the characteristic lean hesitation or "flat spot" that is a problem for all carburetors.

To overcome the hesitation, a carburetor must have an *accelerator pump* (or pumps). They are operated by the throttle linkage and squirt additional fuel into the throat of the carburetor every time you open the throttle. This compensates for the temporary loss of fuel from the nozzles and eliminates the hesitation.

Every carburetor has at least one accelerator pump. These are the external parts of a Holley accelerator pump system:

1. *Throttle Linkage*
2. *Pump Actuating Arm & Spring*
3. *Pump Lever*
4. *Diaphragm Housing*

Four barrel carburetors with vacuum secondaries require only a single accelerator pump for the two primary barrels. The secondaries open only on demand and at a rate that is slow enough to prevent a hesitation. Most high performance carburetors with mechanical secondaries have two accelerator pumps and are sometimes called "double-pumpers". One accelerator pump feeds the primaries and the other feeds the secondaries.

The manufacturer selects an accelerator pump and actuating cam that provides an adequate stream of fuel for most applications. If your engine still hesitates with the stock accelerator pumps, the problem can usually be cured by installing larger (usually 50 cc) pumps, or by changing the actuating cam. Contact your carburetor manufacturer for technical support if you encounter persistent hesitation problems.

Power Enrichment Systems - Engines require a much richer mixture under load than they do in cruise conditions. The stoichiometric for gasoline when the engine is at cruise is about 14.7/1 (or leaner), but under load it is around 13/1 (rich mixture). In a carburetor, there are two common ways to achieve power enrichment—a *power valve* or *metering rod* system.

A power valve is a device with a rubber diaphragm that acts like a third main jet that opens under load. It is actuated by the drop in intake manifold pressure that occurs when the throttle plates are opened in the carburetor.

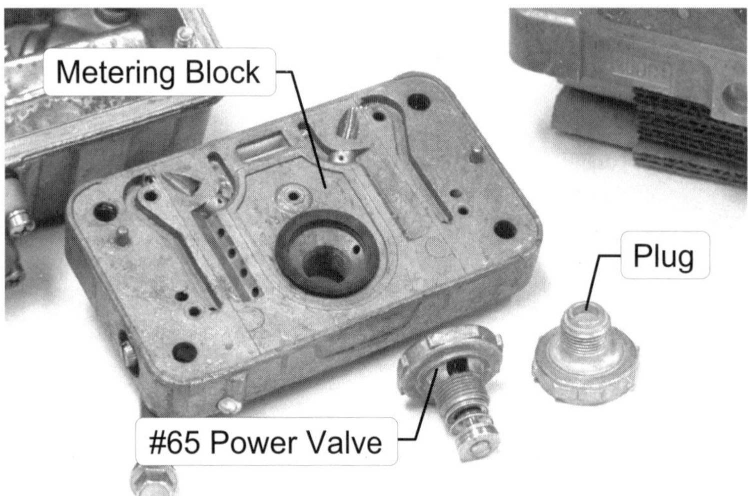

Many Holley carburetors are shipped with a #65 power valve installed in the metering block. This valve is designed to open when manifold vacuum falls to 6.5 in. hg. under load. You can adjust the amount of power enrichment by changing to a different power valve or eliminating it altogether with a plug.

Power valves have a rubber diaphragm that can rupture and leak fuel into the engine. If you are building a drag racing engine or any other application that requires only wide open throttle operation, it makes sense to eliminate the power valve with a plug. This modification will require the installation of larger main jets to compensate for the fuel that will no longer be metered by the power valve.

Plugging the power valve is especially important on engines with tunnel rams. This helps prevent uneven fuel distribution problems to the cylinders. We recommend that you talk to a carburetor specialist or your engine builder about blocking the power valves for your application.

Many stock-type carburetors use metering rods for power enrichment. Metering rods are tapered rods that are inserted into the main jet orifices. When the rods are fully inserted, the jets are restricted to create a leaner air/fuel mixture. As you open the throttle, the loss of vacuum in the intake manifold causes a spring to raise the rods part way out of the main jets. This allows more fuel to flow through for a richer air/fuel mixture under load.

Lean Part Throttle Mode

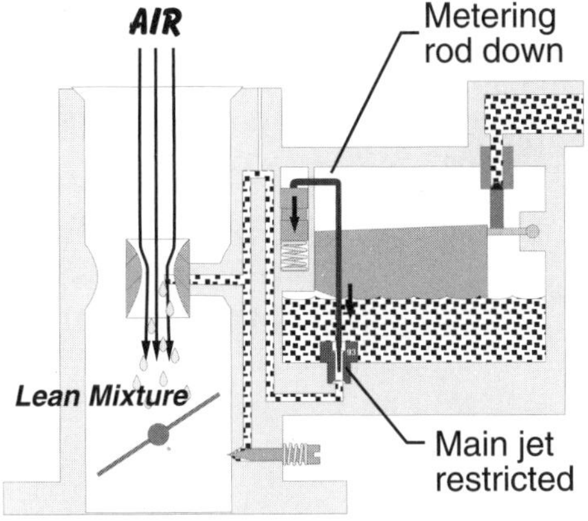

At part throttle, vacuum keeps the metering rod in the down position, restricting flow.

Power Enrichment Mode

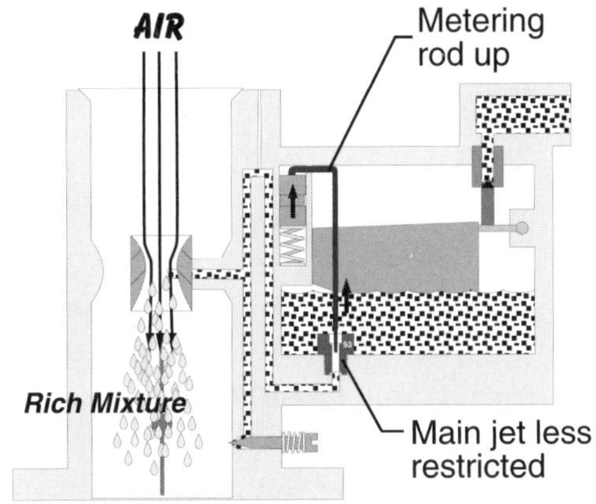

Under load, manifold vacuum drops and the metering rod is raised. This creates the rich mixture needed for power.

Stock carburetors with metering rod systems are very difficult to tune for racing purposes. If you must run a stock-type carburetor because of rulebook restrictions, you will have to obtain different main jet and metering rod sizes in order to tailor the fuel curve of your engine.

Be sure to read your rulebook for carburetor restrictions before making your carburetor purchase. We recommend that you talk to an experienced racing engine builder. They can give you a more detailed analysis of your engine application and estimated carburetion requirements. Also, see what types of carburetors competitive cars in your class are using. These are the best ways to find the right carburetor choice for your racing engine.

Exhaust Headers

For many racers, exhaust headers are a kind of afterthought when planning an engine. However the size and type of exhaust headers that you choose affect the horsepower output and power curve of a racing engine.

The headers must fit the engine and chassis, but they should also be designed for maximum power output throughout the operating rpm range.

Exhaust Header Features:

These are the basic parts that make up the exhaust headers:

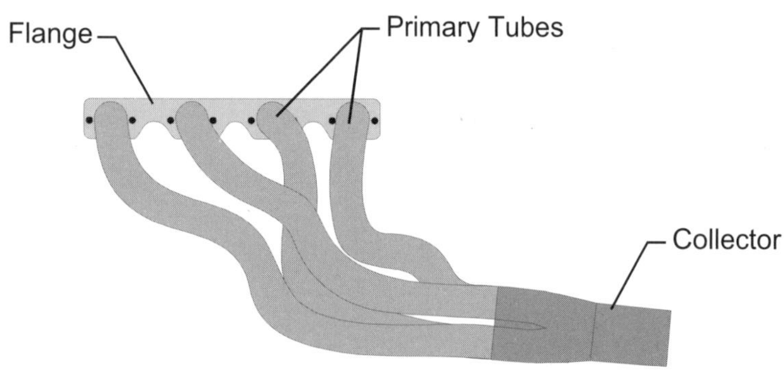

The flange seals the primary tubes to the cylinder head. The collector joins the exhaust gases into a single outlet tube.

Types of Exhaust Headers:

There are several different types of headers for racing engines including:

- Conventional 4 into 1
- 4-2-1 (Tri-Y)
- 180 Degree
- Stepped

Conventional 4 into 1 Headers - These headers collect the exhaust for one side of the engine into a single collector. Despite their simplicity, we have found no advantage in using any other more complex header design for most race cars.

Conventional 4 into 1 Header

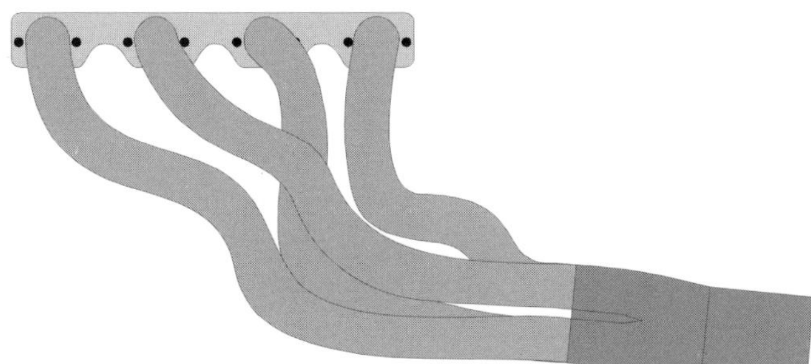

It's hard to beat the simple, yet effective conventional header design. You'll find this style header on the vast majority of race cars.

4-2-1 & Tri-Y Headers - These headers collect the exhaust by pairs of cylinders that are as far apart as possible in the firing order. The idea is that the gases racing past the silent tube will scavenge a vacuum in it, reducing exhaust reversion. We have found no advantage in this design for the majority of racing applications.

4-2-1 Header

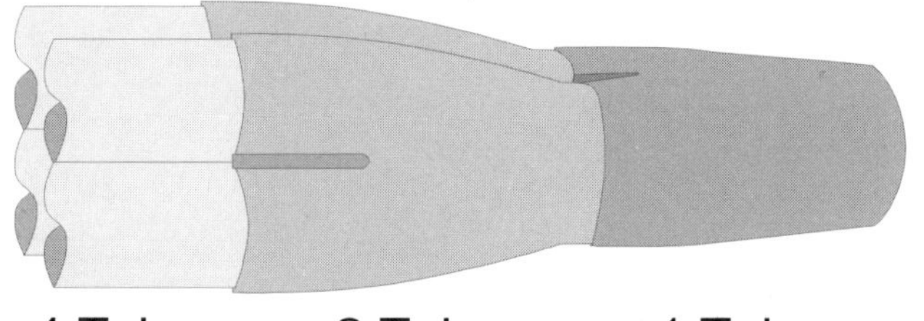

The 4-2-1 or Try-Y design has not consistently proved to be a superior design for most racing applications.

180° Headers - The idea behind these headers is to fill the collectors alternately from each of the cylinders in the firing order. To do this, two tubes have to cross between the sides of the engine. Unfortunately, the extremely long primary and collector tubes wipe out any gains from this improved distribution of the exhaust pulses.

180° Headers

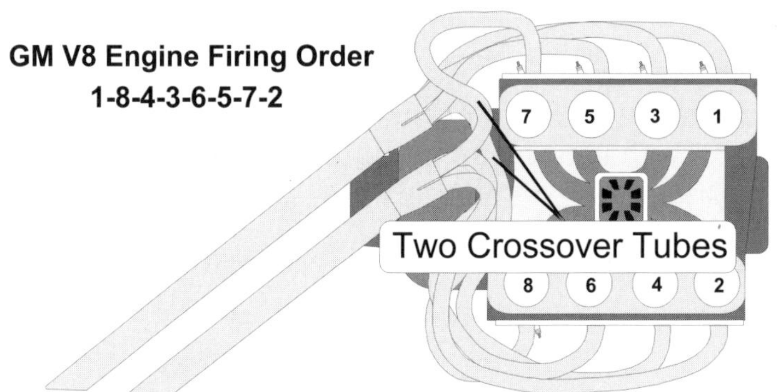

180° headers are a real plumber's nightmare. These have far too many problems with tube and collector lengths to be seriously considered for most racing applications.

Stepped Headers – Stepped headers have increasingly larger tubes connected together in the primary tubes. The theory is that the steps create a sort of funnel that reduces downstream exhaust velocity and broadens the rpm range of the engine.

3-Step Header

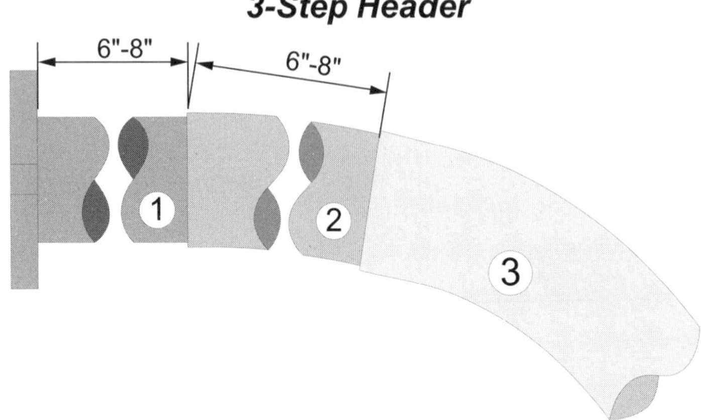

Stepped headers usually have two or three different tubing sizes that become increasingly larger as the gases flow through the tubes. In testing, we haven't seen a measurable performance gain when running this design.

Choosing Exhaust Headers:

The most important design considerations when choosing headers are:

- Tube Diameter
- Tube Length
- Collector Diameter
- Collector Length

Tube Diameter - There is a direct relationship between the primary header tube diameter and exhaust velocity. The key when selecting a tube diameter is to find a happy medium between the free-flowing characteristics of large tubes and the superior scavenging of small, high-velocity tubes. Header tube diameters normally range from 1 3/4" to 1 7/8" for smaller, low performance engines up to big 2 3/8" tubes for large displacement, high-horsepower applications.

Tube Length - The ballistic velocities of exhaust gases create some interesting "tuning" effects in the exhaust system. A beginner may think that an engine would make the most power if you didn't even install headers—simply let the exhaust dump from the exhaust ports in the heads directly into the atmosphere.

This would actually reduce engine power because it would destroy the scavenging effects of the headers. Long header tubes create a column of high velocity gases. This has a sort of "freight train" effect, with inertia that tends to drag (scavenge) most of the remaining gases out of the combustion chamber.

The ideal header tube length depends on the rpm's of the engine. At lower engine rpm's, long tubes help maintain good exhaust scavenging and increase torque output. As engine speed increases, exhaust gas velocities increase and a shorter tube length tends to work better.

The best you can do is to find a header tube length that offers the best compromise between low and high end power. This is also why header length can be an effective aid in "tuning" the rpm range of a racing engine. Most racing engines will work best with tubes between 28 and 30 inches long.

It is also very important that all header tubes are as close as possible to the same length. The tubes from the rear cylinders are closer to the collectors and need a few extra twists and bends to be as long as those at the front of the engine.

Poor Header Design
(unequal tube lengths)

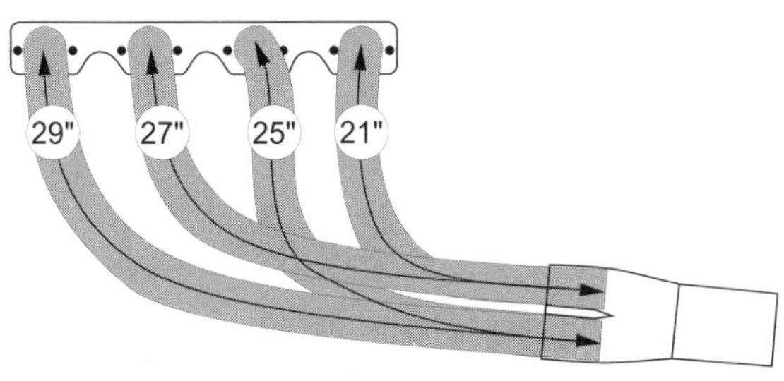

This header may be pleasing to the eye, but the unequal tube lengths create a different "tune" for each cylinder.

Good Header Design
(equal tube lengths)

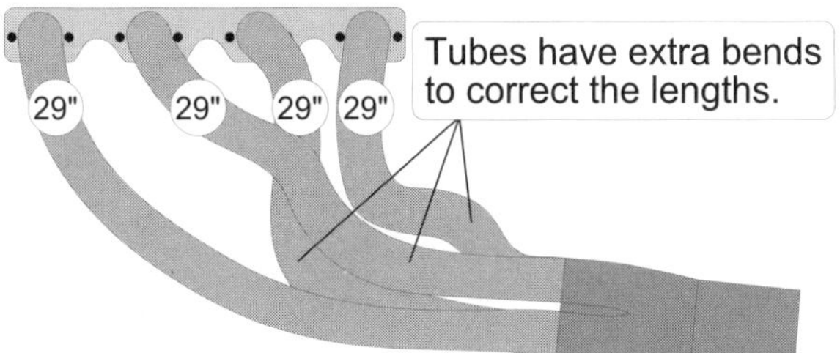

This header has additional bends in the rear tubes to make them all the same length. Extra bends do not add any significant flow restrictions if they are not too tight.

Well-constructed headers should have very little distortion of the tubing around bends. The tubes must also create a straight, smooth transition with the exhaust ports.

Poor Transition
(tube at angle to port)

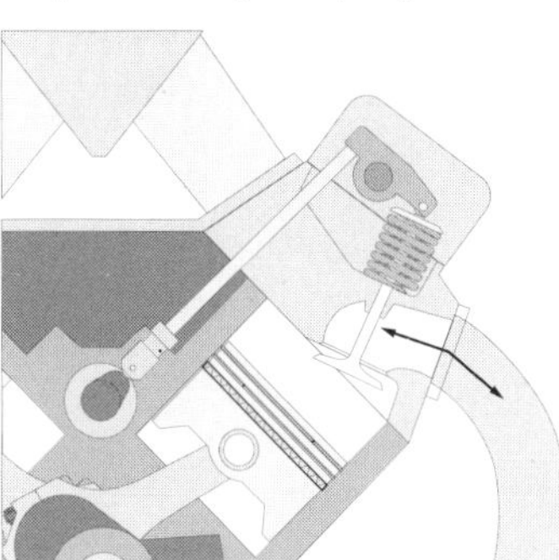

Good Transition
(tube in line with port)

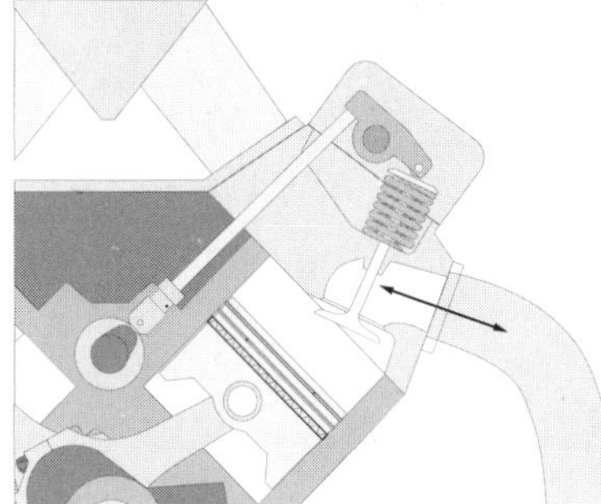

The headers should not force the exhaust gases to change directions abruptly as they enter the tubes.

Collector Diameter & Length - Like tube diameter, the diameter of the collector affects the exhaust restriction and velocity. Many small block racing engines perform better with collector diameters between 3" and 3 1/2". Large displacement, high-horsepower engines require 4"-5" collectors. The length for most drag racing applications varies between 8" and 14". Most stock car and road race sanctioning organizations require that the exhaust exit the side or rear of the car. This requires you to use much longer collector tubes that can affect top end power somewhat.

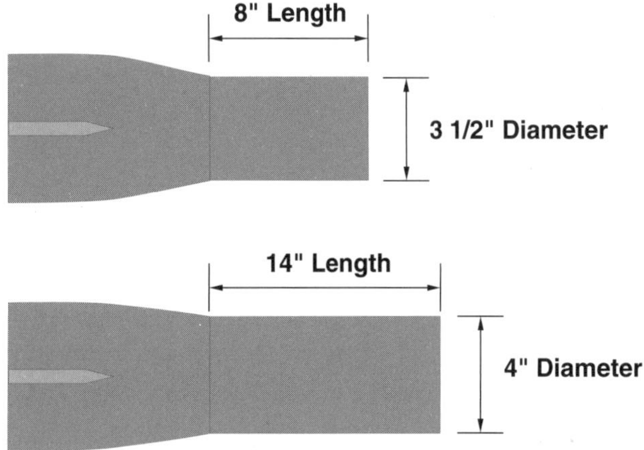

Header collectors are available in several diameters. They can be easily cut with a hacksaw to the desired length.

The only way to really know what headers will work best on your engine is through dyno and on-track testing, but in the end, header choice is usually the result of a series of compromises. Often, the tubes must bend in less than desirable ways to create clearance with chassis members or steering linkage.

If you are unable to test different header sizes & types, we recommend that you take a look at what the competitive cars in your class are using and talk with your racing engine builder. You may want to buy adjustable headers that can be assembled with different primary tube and collector lengths, then try a few combinations to find out what works best on your car. For pro applications, we build our own headers from pre-bent lengths of tubing. Adjustable headers and pre-bent tubes are available from most exhaust header manufacturers.

We test many different header sizes and types to find those that work best and fit the car.

Ignition Systems

Racing engines place severe demands on the ignition system. The same components and system that works just fine under the hood of your street-driven vehicle are entirely inadequate for a true race car. The ignition system can be divided into two sections by voltage:

- Primary Ignition Circuit (low voltage)
- Secondary Ignition Circuit (high voltage)

Primary Ignition System Components:

These are the main parts the primary ignition circuit:

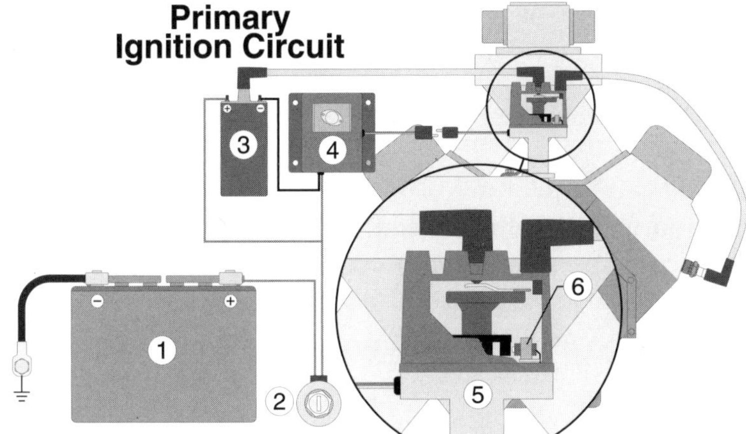

1. *Battery*
2. *Ignition Switch*
3. *Ignition Coil*
4. *Module*
5. *Distributor*
6. *Pickup*

Battery (1) - The battery supplies the electrical current needed to charge the ignition coil. If the car does not have an alternator, it is a good idea to use a higher voltage (16V) racing battery to avoid problems with low ignition coil output.

Ignition Switch (2) - This switch turns on power to the ignition coil (+ side) and the module.

Ignition Coil (3) - The ignition coil is actually two coils—a primary (low voltage) and secondary (high voltage).

Module (4) - The module is an electronic switching device with a series of transistors that interrupt the voltage to the negative (-) primary side of the coil to charge and discharge it.

Distributor (5) - The distributor contains both primary and secondary components. It may be driven by the camshaft or from a belt at the front of the engine.

Pickup (6) - The pickup is usually a coil that senses the position of the engine to time the charging and discharging of the coil.

Secondary Ignition System Components:

These are the main parts the secondary ignition circuit:

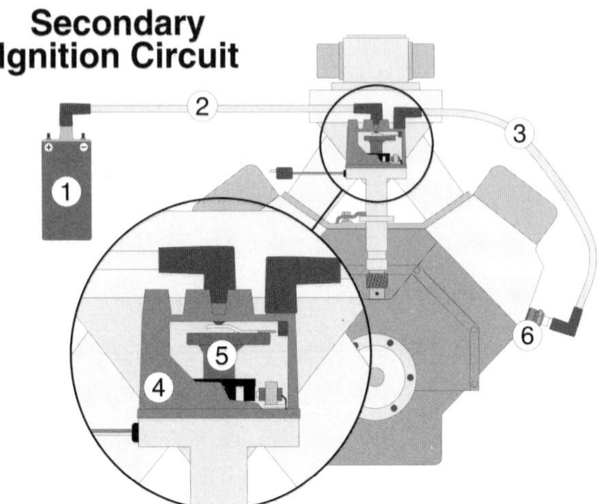

1. *Ignition Coil*
2. *Coil Wire*
3. *Plug Wires*
4. *Distributor Cap*
5. *Rotor*
6. *Spark Plugs*

Ignition Coil (1) - The ignition secondary side of the ignition coil creates the very high voltage required to fire the spark plugs. The peak output voltage of a racing ignition coil ranges from 35,000 to 90,000 volts.

Coil Wire (2) - This carries the high voltage from the ignition coil to the center of the distributor cap.

Spark Plug Wires (3) - These carry the high voltage from the distributor cap to the spark plugs.

Distributor Cap (4) - The cap has a center contact and terminals to send the coil voltage through the rotor to each spark plug wire.

Rotor (5) - The rotor spins on the distributor shaft and delivers the high voltage to the terminals inside the cap. The electricity must jump a small air gap between the tip of the rotor and the terminals.

Spark Plugs (6) - These present the air gaps in the cylinders across which an electric arc can jump.

Racing Electronic Ignition Systems:

A number of great high performance electronic ignition systems are available from aftermarket manufacturers. The main advantage of these systems is that they can produce a precise and intense spark throughout the rpm range.

One choice that you'll need to make with electronic ignition is the type of triggering system you will use. The *trigger* is a sensor that tells the module when a piston is in the right location to fire the spark plug. The module then unloads the coil and the spark is sent to the right cylinder through the rotor, cap, and plug wires.

Racing electronic ignition systems may be triggered by an optical device, magnetic pickup, or a Hall effect transistor (similar to magnetic pickup). The optical systems use an LED (light emitting diode) and chopper wheel in the distributor. A magnetic pickup system works like this:

Electronic Ignition Triggering

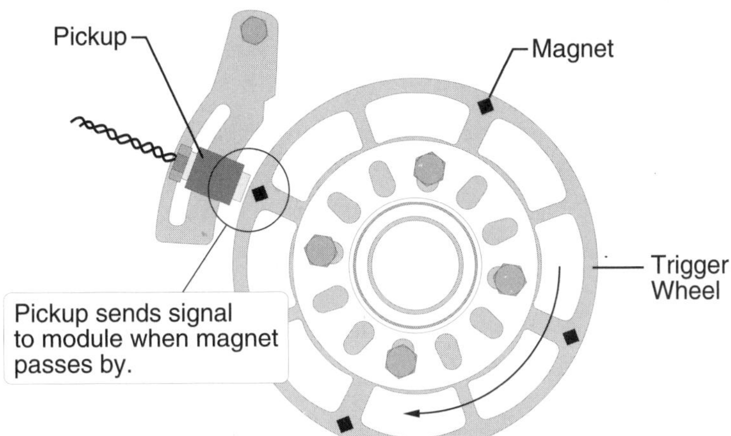

Magnets imbedded in the trigger wheel create a small electrical current each time they pass by the pickup coil. This triggers the module to discharge and recharge the ignition coil.

The pickup can be located inside the distributor housing or may be mounted externally on the front of the engine for a crank-triggered system. A crank-triggered system is the most accurate because it eliminates the timing fluctuations caused by camshaft twist and drive speed variations.

This crank-trigger ignition system provides the most precise spark timing. It costs more, but is worth the money on a high-end racing engine.

Timing Retard Systems - A couple of decades ago, it was discovered that some naturally aspirated racing engines run better with a couple of degrees *less* spark advance under high-load/high-rpm conditions. This is because there is less time between power strokes to get rid of all the combustion chamber heat. Cylinder temperatures and pressures rise, speeding up the rate of combustion.

Delaying the spark a couple of degrees at high rpm's under load can compensate for the faster burn time and improve performance. Supercharged and nitrous-injected drag racing engines also have different pressures in the cylinders at various points in the run and may also benefit from a timing retard system.

Some drag racers like to set up their ignition system so that it retards the timing one or two times during a race. This can be done by the use of a *two-step* or *three-step* device. The changes (steps) can be made by pushing a button or triggered by a switch or switches on the transmission shift linkage.

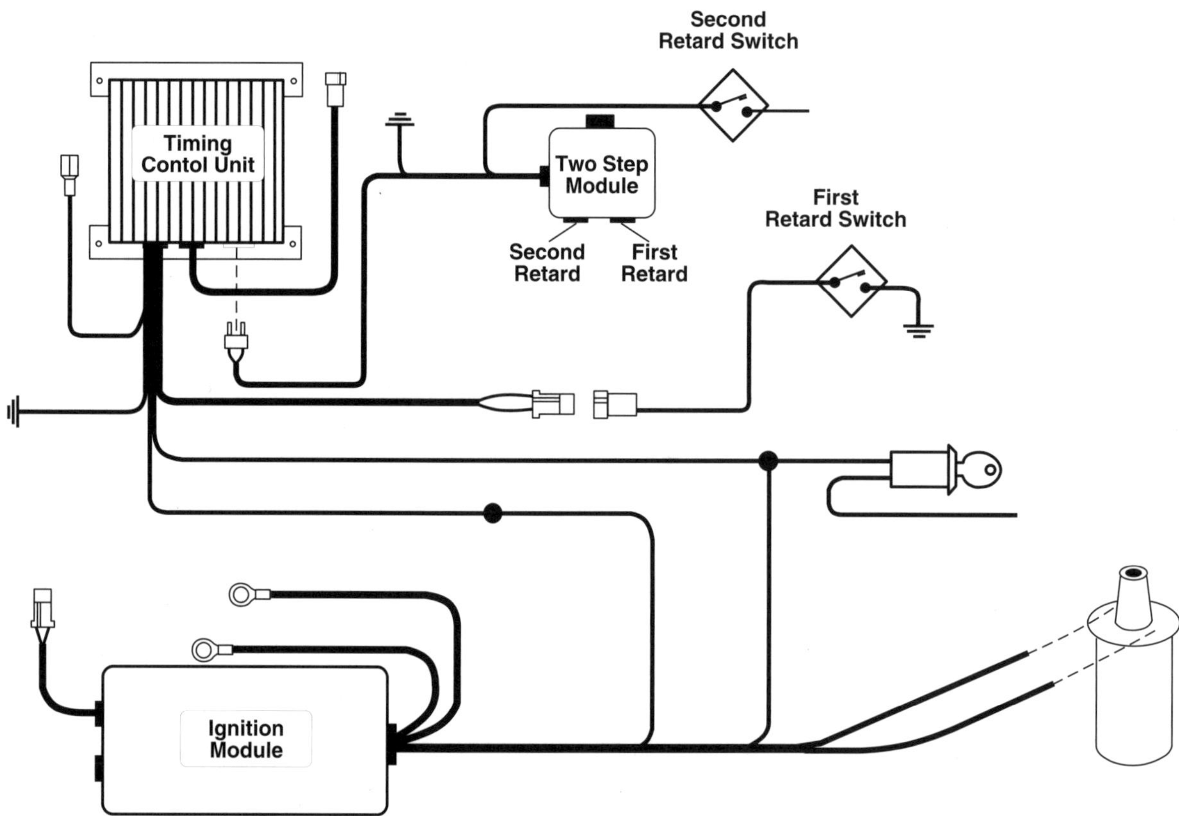

This ignition system uses a two-step switch that retards the timing twice during a run. The amount of retard is determined by the "modules" that are plugged into the two-step device.

Camshaft vs. Belt Drive Distributors - The majority of racing engines use a camshaft-driven distributor. On GM V8 racing engines, the stock distributor location is in the intake manifold at the rear of the engine. Often, tunnel ram manifolds and the car body create clearance problems with rear-mounted distributors.

For this reason, some racers prefer a front mounted distributor. This system requires the use of a belt drive on the camshaft. The distributor mounts horizontally and is driven by a small cogged belt as shown below.

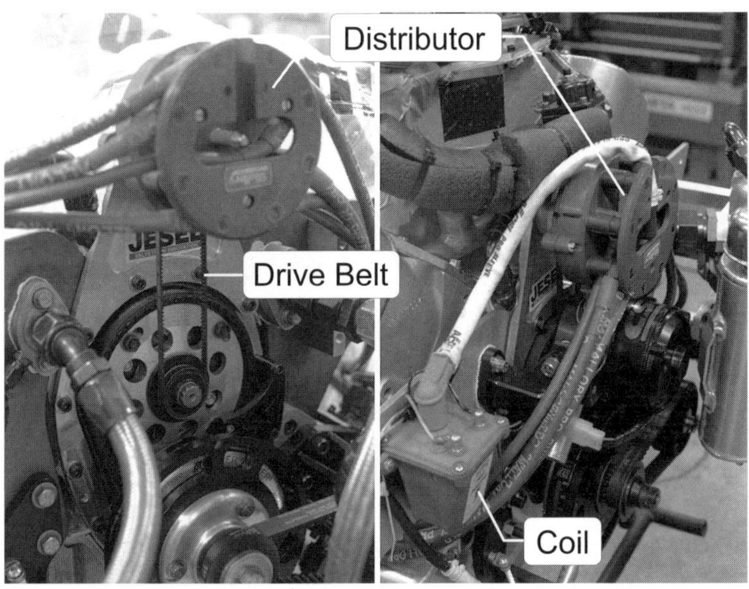

A front-drive distributor eliminates a lot of clearance problems. Note the horizontal mounting and small 1/4" wide cogged belt drive. The ignition coil must also be relocated to the front of the engine.

Distributor Cap & Rotor - If you have room, it is better to use a distributor with a large diameter cap. This separates the terminals inside the cap better to discourage cross-firing. The rotor must be the design that works with the distributor and cap that you have selected. Both the cap and rotor should be molded out of a plastic with good insulating properties. Most of these materials are of some color other than black.

Photos courtesy of Mallory, Inc.

If you the have room, a distributor with a large diameter cap has better separation between the terminals. Quality racing caps & rotors are molded from plastics with excellent insulating properties.

Coil Wire & Spark Plug Wires - The coil and spark plug wires must be able to handle the very high voltage of the secondary ignition circuit. Stock carbon resistance core wires and those under 8 mm in diameter will not hold up under the high-heat/high-voltage environment in a race car. Wire leakage is the root cause of many ignition and electrical system problems.

We recommend that you use special silicone racing wires with a spiral copper conductor. The spiral core design cuts the "dipole" (antenna) effect of the wire and induces far less RF (radio frequency interference) into the car's electrical system.

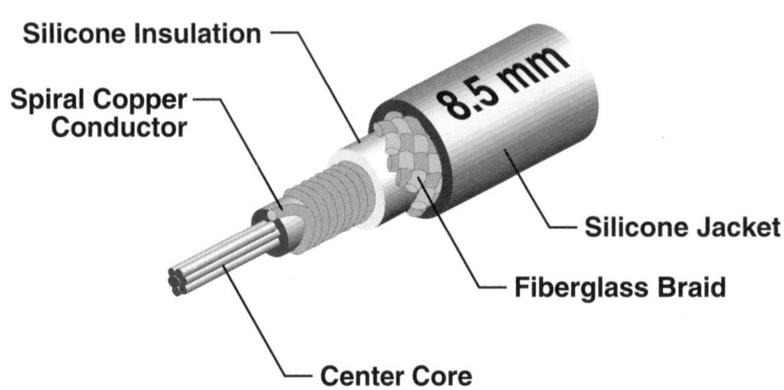

A quality racing spark plug wire has a spiral copper conductor wrapped around a center core of high-strength fibers and ferrous material. Silicone provides a high degree of insulation and resistance to heat. The fiberglass braid adds additional strength to the wire.

You can buy pre-made racing spark plug wire kits, but it is not likely that the lengths will be right for your engine. A better approach is to buy a spark plug wire kit and crimping tool. Follow the instructions supplied with the kit and tool to make your own wires.

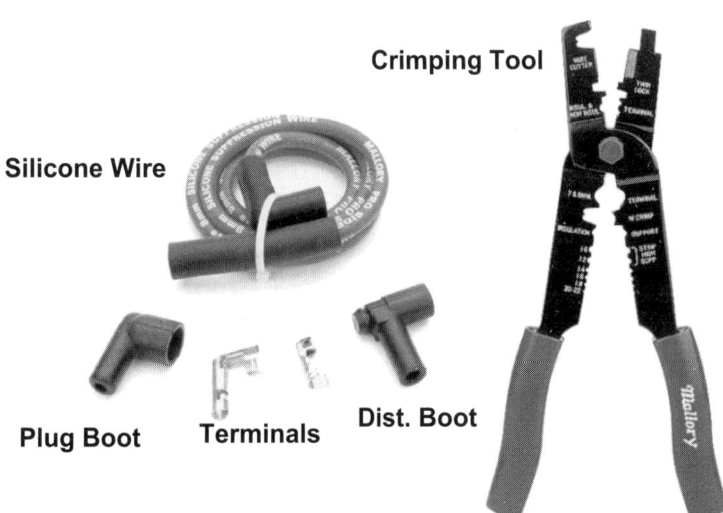

Photos courtesy of Mallory, Inc.

Most racers prefer to make their own coil and spark plug wires from 8 mm or larger spiral core silicone wire. This allows you to get the length exactly right for each cylinder.

Give a lot of thought to the spark plug wire routing. They should be arranged neatly through looms that keep them away from hot exhaust headers tubes. All spark plug wires leak some energy. Never tie them into tight bundles—this can induce unwanted voltages into other wires and cause *cross-firing*. Cross-firing is a damaging condition in which two plugs fire at the same time.

Route the plug wires as far away as possible from all other electrical wiring harnesses and sensors. This prevents possible interference that can upset delicate computer system sensors.

Neatness counts when routing your coil and spark plug wires. Make sure they are away from hot engine components and other electrical wires.

Spark Plugs - When choosing spark plugs for a racing engine, you should consider the thread, reach, seat type, and heat range. All spark plugs have metric threads (usually 14 mm), but the hex is made to fit into a standard 5/8" or 13/16" spark plug socket. The seat may be either a gasket or tapered style.

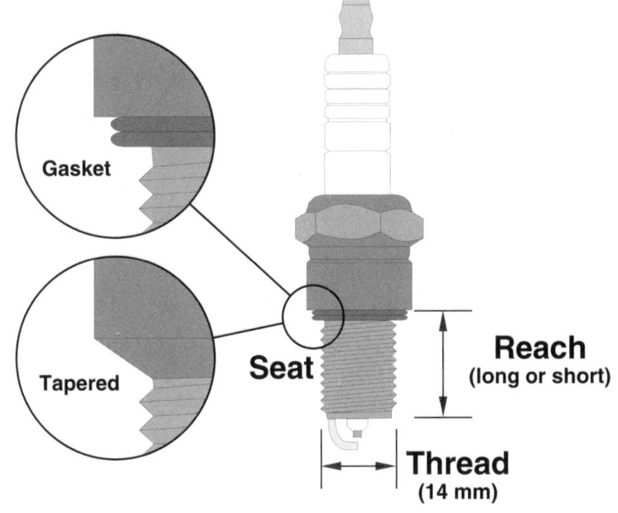

The thread, reach, and seat style must match that of the cylinder heads. Short reach plugs measure about 1/2" length. Long reach plugs measure 3/4".

When plugs with the correct *reach* are installed, the threads will be close to flush with the combustion chamber. If you install short reach plugs into a long reach cylinder head, the tip of the plugs will be somewhat shrouded in the spark plug hole and some compression will be lost. More serious damage can result if you install long reach plugs into a short reach cylinder head. The threads and tip of the plugs will protrude into the combustion chambers and will collide with the pistons.

Spark Plug Reach

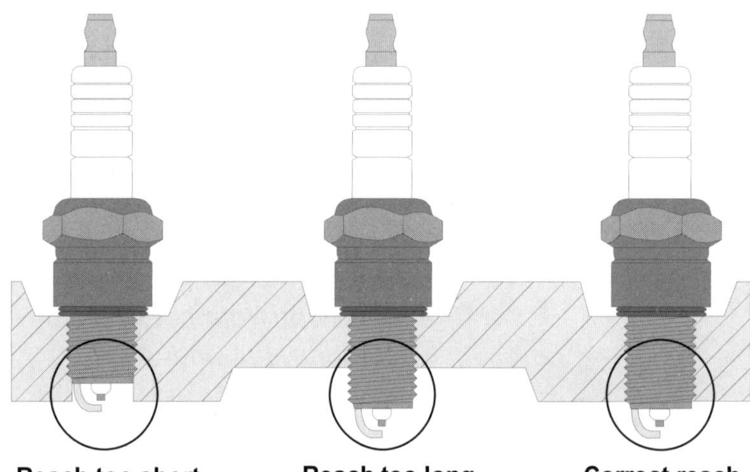

When you install plugs with the correct reach, the threads will be close to flush with the interior surface of the combustion chamber. It's a good idea to check the reach of your plugs before you install the heads on the engine.

The spark plugs must be the right *heat range* for a racing engine. Heat range refers to tip temperature of the plug. A hot spark plug has a deep insulator and does not conduct heat away efficiently. The tip remains at a high temperature when the engine is running. A cold plug has a shallow insulator and conducts the heat away better. This makes the tip run cooler.

Hot Spark Plug ***Cold Spark Plug***

N-14

N-8

HEAT HEAT

Coolant

HEAT HEAT

Deep insulator does not conduct heat away quickly.

Shallow insulator depth conducts heat away better.

A cold spark plug gets rid of combustion chamber heat more efficiently than a hot plug. This makes the tip run cooler. The number on the plug indicates the temperature range of the spark plug. A colder plug may have a higher or lower number, depending on the particular manufacturer.

Like a self-cleaning oven, the tip of the spark plug must run hot enough to burn away fouling deposits. Deposit buildup was much more of a problem years ago than it is today. Modern racing engines tend to have much better oil control from the rings and the racing gasoline's you can buy burn much cleaner. Here is a general rule to follow when choosing the spark plug heat range:

You should run the coldest spark plugs that you can in a racing engine that do not allow fouling.

If you select a spark plug that is too hot, the tip may glow and cause pre-ignition. You should choose high-quality racing spark plugs that are as cold as possible, yet stay clean during the race. Try plugs that are several steps colder than stock or talk to a racing engine builder for a heat range starting point for your application.

The plug gap specification for a stock passenger car is usually around .045". Racing engines operate with far higher pressures and cylinder temperatures. This raises the voltage that is required to establish an arc. We recommend a .030"-.035" plug gap for most racing applications. This helps ensure a good spark at high rpm's when temperatures and pressures are high and the coil has very little time to charge.

Electricity can jump off sharp edges much more easily, so the center electrode should be flat and sharp. The ground electrode on a racing spark plug should be a *clipped-gap* style—trimmed so that the ground electrode only overlaps half of the center electrode. The electricity can jump more easily to the sharp edge at the end of the ground electrode and the arc is well exposed to the air/fuel mixture.

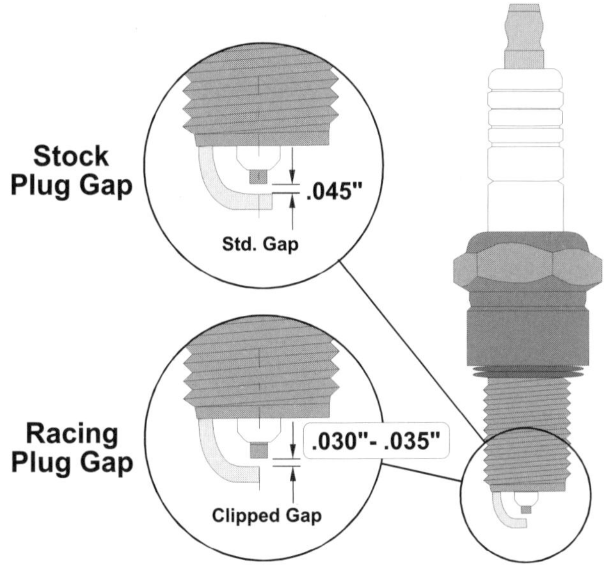

Racing spark plugs usually have a 'clipped gap" or split ground electrode. The ground electrode is also bent for a smaller (.035") racing end gap.

Contact aftermarket ignition companies for available setups and parts recommendations for your application. Also, talk to your engine builder and some successful racers in your class to see what type of ignition system and advance/retard system they are running.

Review Questions

1. Why is cylinder head selection so important when planning your racing engine?

2. Describe the advantages and disadvantages of cast iron cylinder heads.

3. Describe the advantages and disadvantages of aluminum cylinder heads. What type of welding process can be used to repair aluminum cylinder heads?

4. Identify the valve layouts in the figures below:

Layout "A" **Layout "B"**

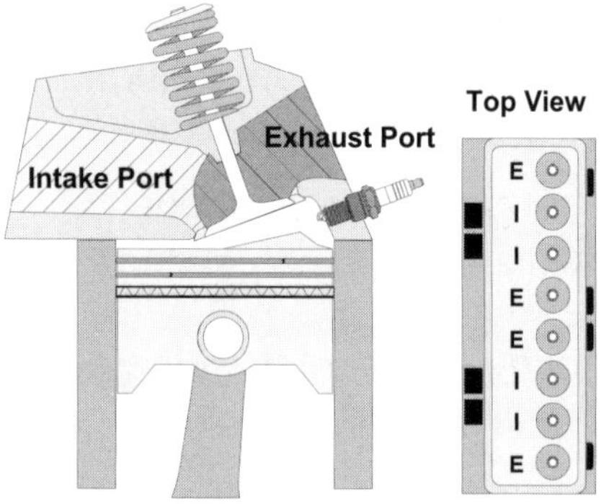

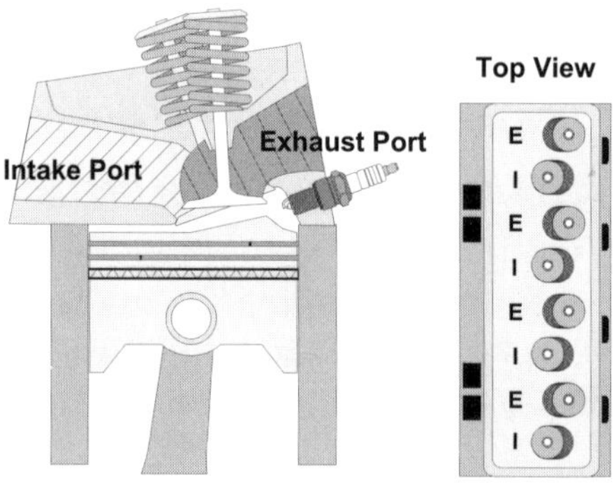

5. Name and describe two combustion chamber styles that are used on big block GM racing engines.

6. How does combustion chamber volume affect engine performance? How is combustion chamber volume related to the required piston dome volume?

7. What types of engines usually have custom-made combustion chambers? How does the use of custom-made combustion chambers influence your piston selection?

8. What is valve angle? Why do some racers angle mill their cylinder heads?

9. What is valve tilt? What is the reason that some racing cylinder heads have tilted valves?

10. How does the radius of a port affect its ability to flow? What is a good rule to follow when choosing heads with different port radii? What are "high port" heads?

11. Explain how the port shape and size can affect flow. What is a good general rule to follow with regard to the size of almost all induction system components? Where are port velocities highest? Where are they lowest?

12. What is an exhaust port intermediate plate? What does it do? What is "mapping ports", and why is it done?

13. Why is it a bad idea to polish intake ports to a high gloss? What type of finish is best for an intake port? Why?

14. Why is it important to obtain a rulebook before selecting cylinder heads?

15. What is a flow bench? How is it used to test cylinder heads? What is a water manometer? What does it indicate on a flow bench?

16. What is a heat riser system? Why is the heat riser port required for most street applications?

17. Identify the parts of the valve in the figure below:

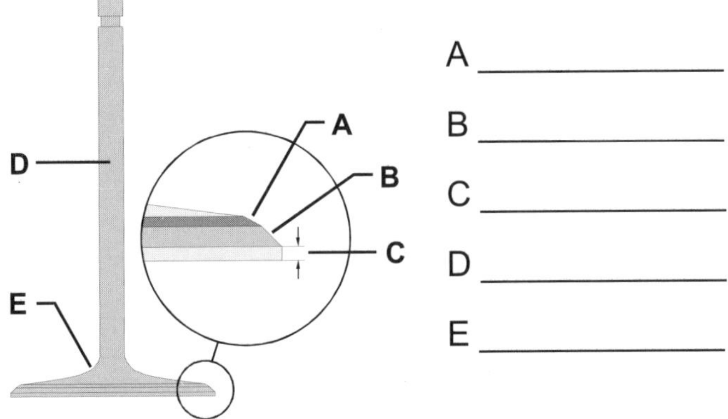

18. Which of the two valves, intake or exhaust, is larger? Why?

19. Why are titanium valves a great choice for use a high rpm racing engine?

20. Why is it so important to have adequate valve spring pressure? Which is harder on a roller tappet valve train—too much or too little valve spring rate? Why?

21. How does the valve spring design affect harmonics? What is a spring dampener?

22. Identify the valve hardware in the figure below:

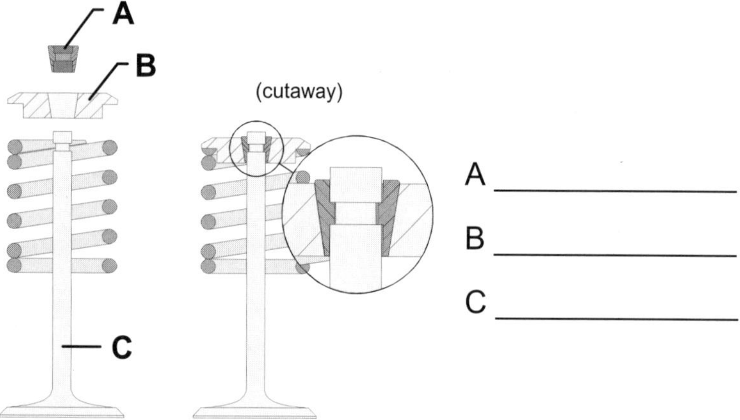

23. Why do titanium valves require special hardened caps on the tops of the valve stems?

24. Name and describe two main types of lifters.

25. Describe how hydraulic lifters work. What is the main problem with using hydraulic lifters in a racing engine?

26. Describe how a flat tappet operates on the camshaft.

27. What are some advantages of using roller tappets in a racing engine? How do they operate on the camshaft?

28. Explain how rpm operating range, budget constraints, engine breathing characteristics, and mechanical limitations affect camshaft selection. How is it possible for two camshafts with the same lift, duration, and lobe centers to perform differently in the same racing engine?

29. Name problems with using racing camshafts in street-driven vehicles.

30. How fast does the camshaft turn relative to the crankshaft? What is the ratio between cam sprocket teeth and crank sprocket teeth?

31. Identify the camshaft drive assemblies in the photos below and describe the advantages and disadvantages of each:

A _______________

B _______________

C _______________

32. Describe important features of racing pushrods. How does pushrod length affect the geometry and action of the rocker arms? Describe how the roller tip should roll across the top of the valve stem as it operates.

33. Identify the two types of racing rocker arms in the photo below:

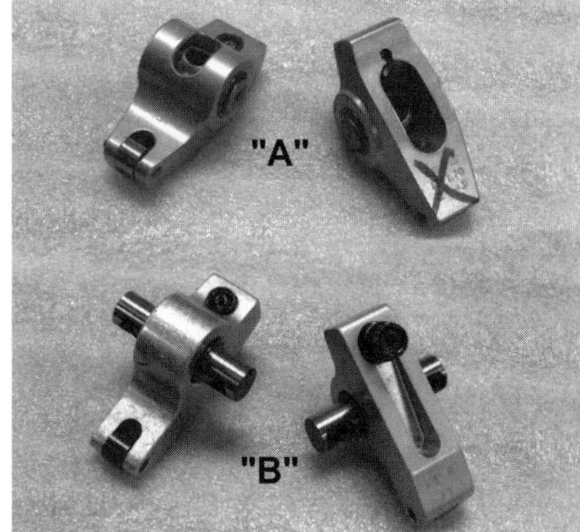

A _______________

B _______________

34. Why are screw-in rocker studs better than press in studs? What is the device in the photo below called and what is it for?

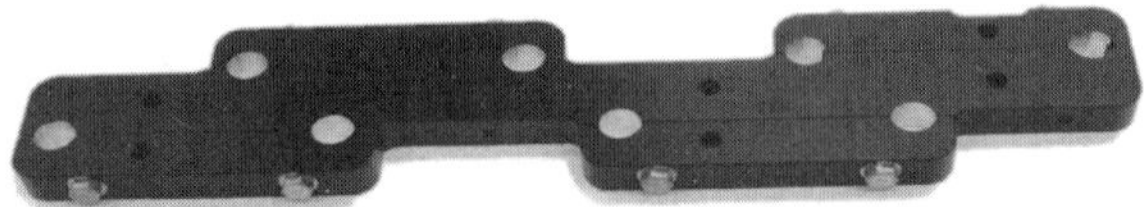

35. Describe two types of rocker arm adjustments.

36. What is rocker arm ratio? What effect does rocker arm ratio have on valve operation? Why do high ratio rocker arms add stress to the pushrods and studs?

37. What is a dual plane intake manifold and how does it work? What is an appropriate application for a dual plane intake manifold?

38. What is a single plane intake manifold and how does it work? What are some appropriate applications for a single plane intake manifold?

39. What is a tunnel ram intake manifold and how does it work? What is an appropriate application for a tunnel ram intake manifold? What is the minimum scoop-to-carb clearance for a drag race car?

40. Identify the carburetor components in the figure below and explain basic carburetor operation:

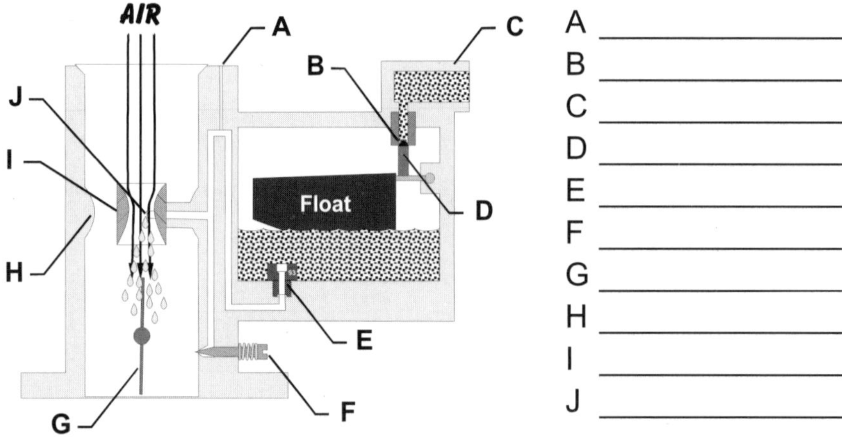

A ____________________
B ____________________
C ____________________
D ____________________
E ____________________
F ____________________
G ____________________
H ____________________
I ____________________
J ____________________

41. What is over-carburetion? What is under-carburetion? What effects do over-carburetion and under-carburetion have on engine performance? How do you choose a carburetor size and type for a racing application?

42. What are mechanical secondaries, and when do they open? What are vacuum secondaries, and when do they open? What are mechanical secondaries?

43. What is the purpose of the accelerator pump? Name two types of power enrichment systems, and describe how they work. When should a power valve be plugged?

44. Identify the types of headers in the figure below.

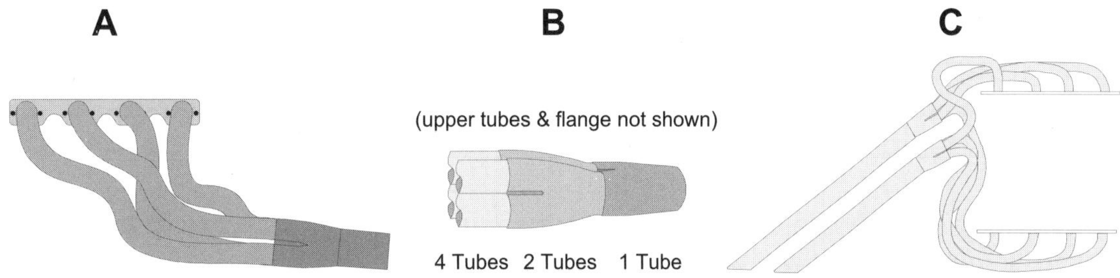

45. How do tube diameter, tube length, collector diameter, and collector length affect engine performance? Why is it important that the primary tubes are close to the same length?

46. Identify the parts of the primary ignition system in the figure below:

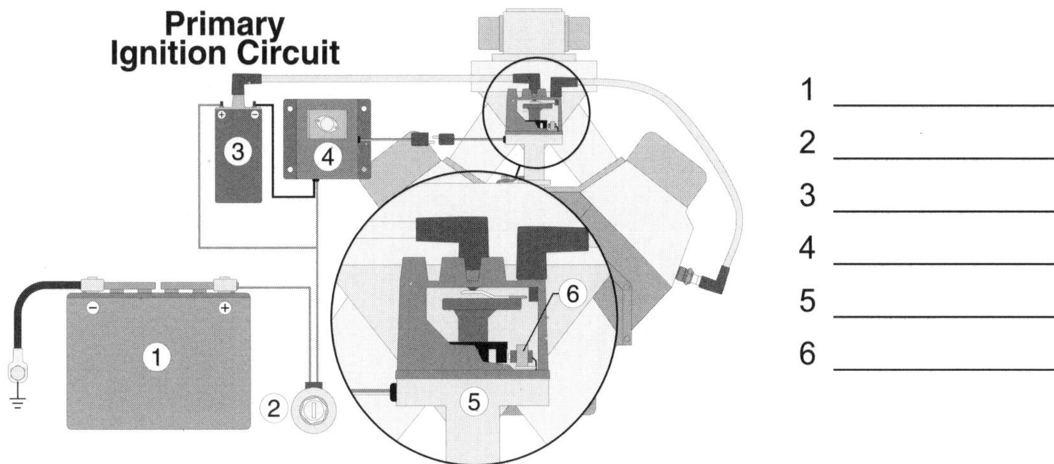

1 ______________
2 ______________
3 ______________
4 ______________
5 ______________
6 ______________

47. Identify the parts of the secondary ignition system in the figure below:

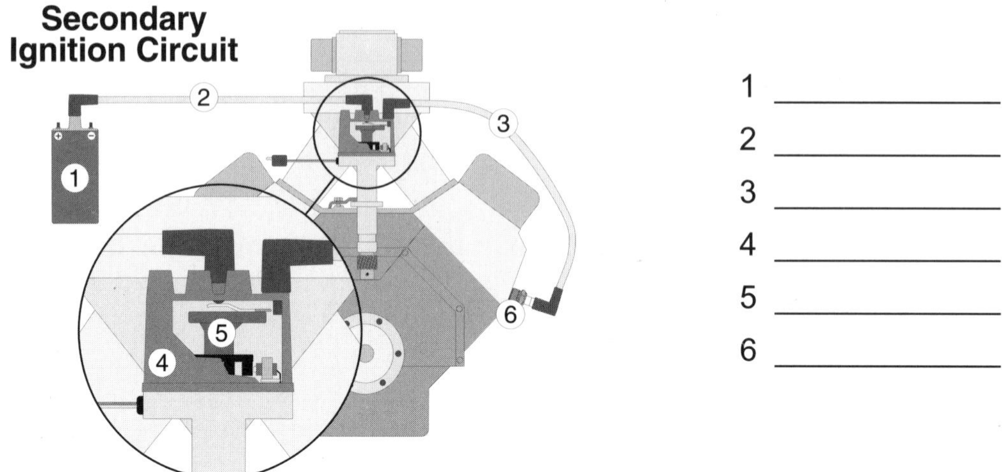

1 ______________
2 ______________
3 ______________
4 ______________
5 ______________
6 ______________

48. What are some important features of a racing electronic ignition system? Describe a crank-triggered system.

49. Why do some racing engines benefit from timing retard at high rpm's? How can the timing retard be adjusted and triggered?

50. What is a belt drive distributor? Why are they used in some racing applications?

51. What are some characteristics of a good racing distributor cap and rotor?

52. Describe the construction of a good racing coil wire/spark plug wire. Why do they usually have a spiral conductor? Explain why spark plug wires should be neatly loomed and kept away from other wires. Why is it a bad idea to tape spark plug wires together in a bundle?

53. Name two types of spark plug seats. What is spark plug reach? How can you tell if your spark plugs have the correct reach? What is spark plug heat range? What is the difference between a hot spark plug and a cold one? What heat range plug should be used in a racing engine?

54. Describe the gap on a racing spark plug. Why are racing spark plugs gapped smaller than those used in street driven vehicles?

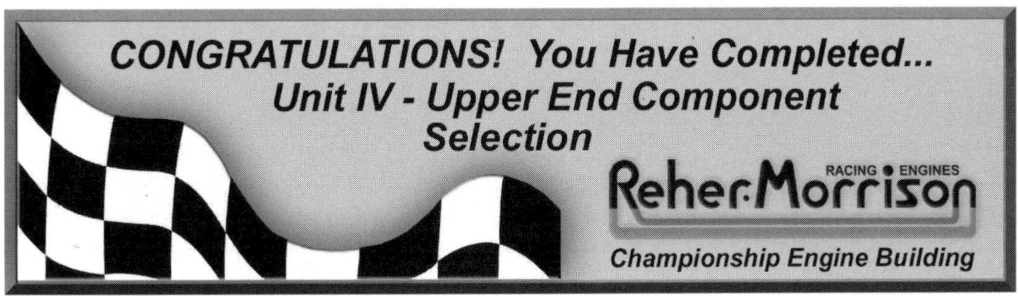

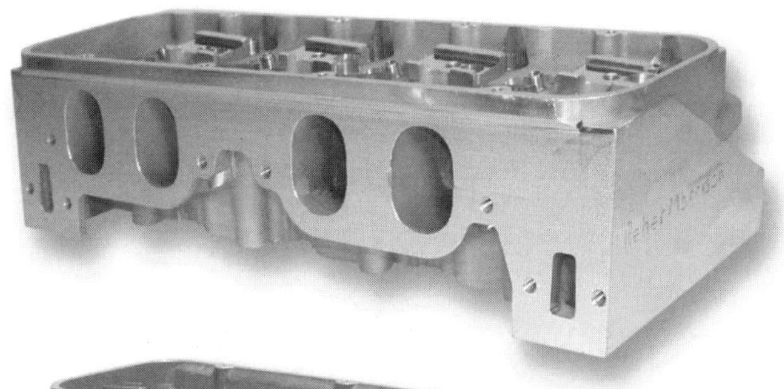

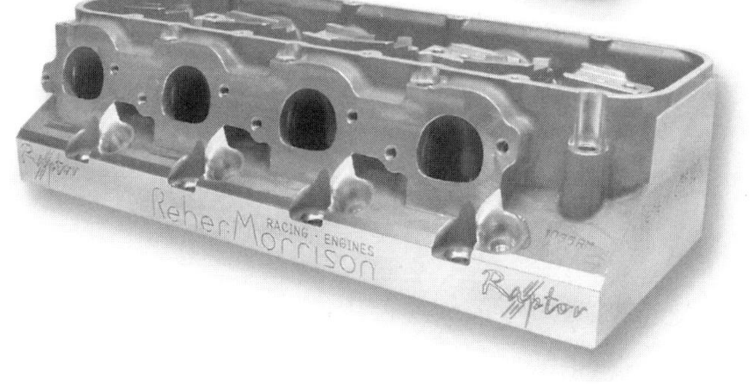

Championship Engine Assembly

Unit V – Upper End Measurements & Preparation

Although some upper engine assembly parts are ready to bolt on right out of the box, many require a little measurement and preparation first. This ensures that the parts will fit properly and perform reliably. With some simple steps and attention to detail you can also pick up a few horsepower here and there.

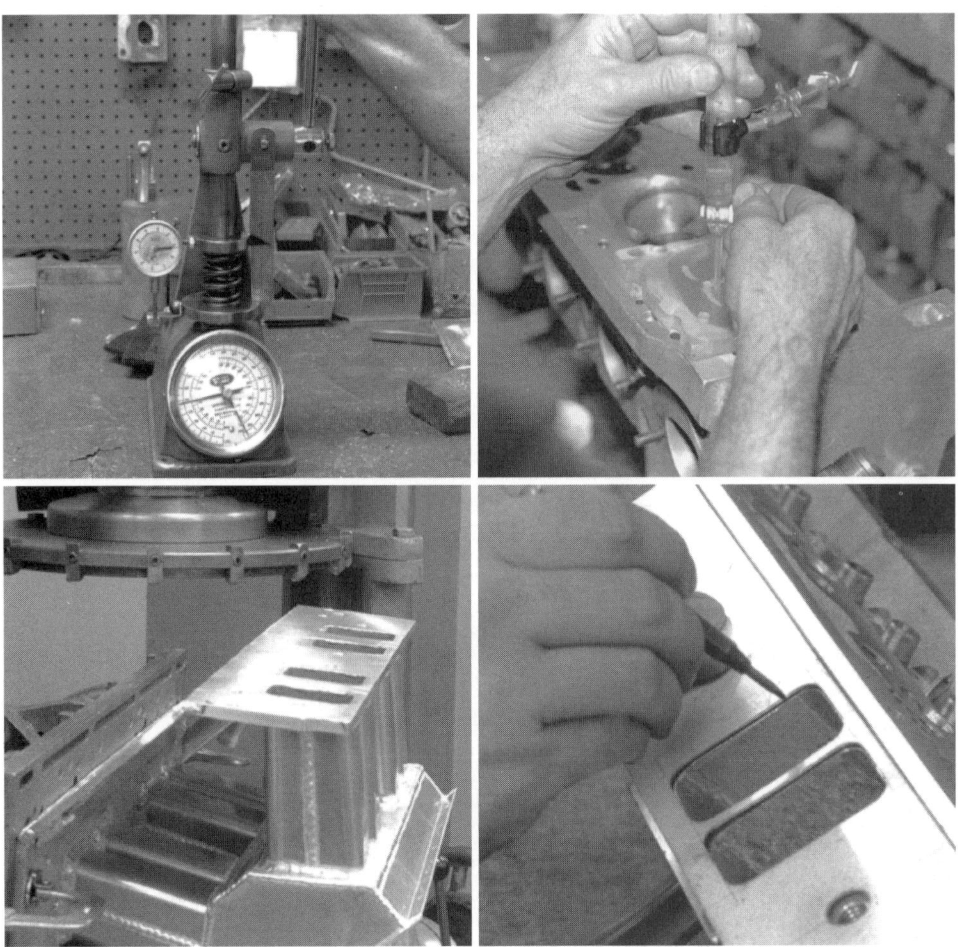

Measurement and preparation often make the difference between average engines and championship winners.

Cylinder Heads, Valves, & Springs

Cylinder Head Inspection:

Before you perform any machine work or modifications to cylinder heads, you should check the castings for the following conditions:

- Cracks or Broken Parts
- Previous Modifications
- Guide & Seat Wear
- Damaged Threads

Cracks or Broken Parts - If you find any cracks or broken parts on cast iron heads, steer clear of them. Damage can be satisfactorily repaired on aluminum heads, but the head should be re-heat treated and will need a fresh valve job.

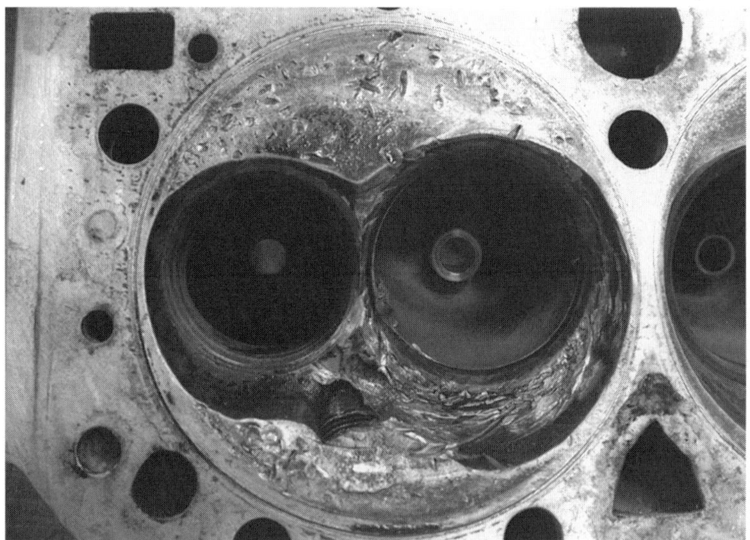

This aluminum head was severely damaged when the piston and valves met in a violent collision. Although it looks hopelessly ruined, an experienced cylinder head specialist can restore this head to like-new condition.

Always have used or repaired heads tested for leaks. The machinist first seals the water passages on the head mating surfaces, then connects the water jacket to a regulated air supply. The head is submerged in a tank or coated with a soapy water spray. Bubbles indicate leaks that will allow coolant to seep from the water jacket.

This technician is spraying soapy water over the head to check it for leaks. Note the air hose connection to one of the water ports.

Previous Modifications - The closer the cylinder heads are to the way they were shipped by the manufacturer, the better are the chances that you can make them into quality pieces that fit right. If the mating surfaces have been re-machined, you may have problems installing your intake manifold.

There should be enough material left on the block deck surface so that you can clean up the surface for a good head gasket seal and to obtain the right static compression ratio. If the ports or mating surfaces of the heads have been modified, find out who performed the work and if they have any flow bench data on them.

These heads still have plenty of material left between the valve seats and deck surface for milling operations. Recall that a lot of damage can be done to the flow characteristics if the ports have been modified. If you see signs of this work, have them flow tested by a qualified shop to find out if they've been ruined.

Guide and Seat Wear - The valve guide condition and clearances are extremely important to the performance of a racing engine. Perform a visual inspection of the seats and valve guides for cracks or other damage. Check the guides for wear with a dial indicator as shown below. For a racing engine, the guides should have no more than .0025" clearance with the valve stems. Titanium valves require bronze guides and tighter valve guide clearances than do steel valves in steel guides. Check with your engine builder for the best clearances for your application.

Measure the valve guide wear. Pay special attention to the exhaust guides—they usually wear much faster because of higher operating temperatures.

If the guides are worn, they must be repaired. The valve guides in iron heads are machined into the castings. Never have the guides knurled to restore valve guide clearance. We recommend the installation of *silicone bronze-wall guides.* These soft, slick guides provide better bearing surfaces for the valve stems and are a must if you are using titanium valves. A good machine shop can perform any needed valve guide repair on your heads.

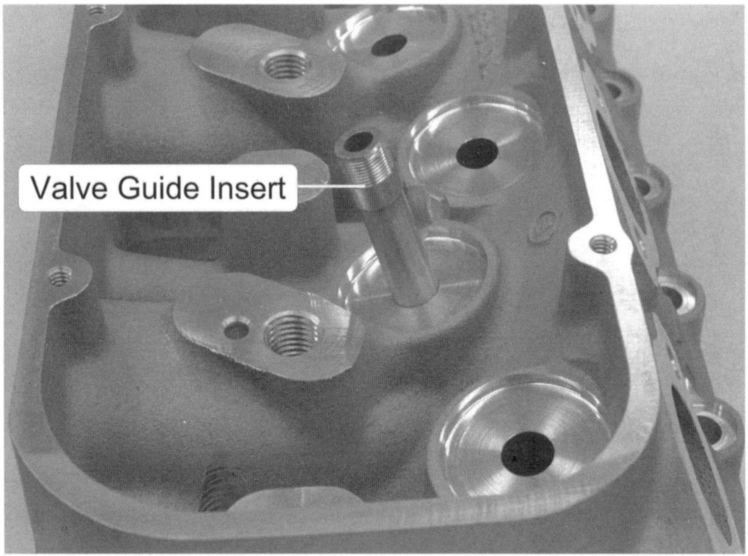

This valve guide will be pressed into place on this new aluminum cylinder head casting.

Inspect the valve seats for cracks and wear. The seats and guides in iron heads are usually machined into the base metal casting and can be reground if they have not already been sunk too deep. Aluminum heads have hard seat inserts that can be installed by a racing engine builder or specialty machine shop.

An experienced racing engine builder or cylinder head specialist should have the special equipment required to install new valve seats.

Damaged Threads - Any pulled or damaged threads must be repaired. It is especially important that the spark plug and rocker stud threads are in good condition. Aluminum is soft and tends to corrode around bolt threads. For these reasons, aluminum heads should have Heli-Coils installed in all high-stress threaded holes before they are installed on the engine. This procedure should be performed by a reliable machine shop.

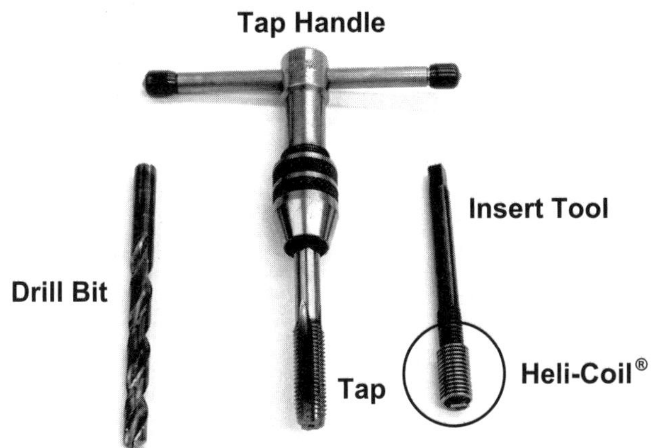

Always Heli-Coil all the high-stress threaded holes on aluminum cylinder heads. You can buy a kit that contains the necessary bits, taps, inserts, and insert tools needed for the job.

Cylinder Head Preparation:

Careful preparation of the cylinder heads is important to the performance and longevity of the engine. These are the steps to get the cylinder heads ready for installation:

- Blend the Bowls and Match the Ports
- Perform a Racing Valve Job
- Measure the Combustion Chamber Volumes
- Mill the Deck Surfaces
- Installation of Valve Seals & Final Cylinder Head Assembly

Blending the Bowls and Matching the Ports - Most cylinder head specialists will tell you that, in the hands of an inexperienced operator, a grinder will usually do more harm than good to a cylinder head. This is particularly true of the area around the valve seats. As much as 35% of the total port flow can be attributed to modifications in this area. We strongly advise you not to perform seat-of-the pants porting of your heads and leave this work to qualified professionals.

There are two basic procedures that can help the flow characteristics of some non-CNC machined cylinder heads. These are *blending the bowls* and *matching the ports*.

The *bowl* is the machined area of the port above the valve seat. The bowls in most cylinder heads are bored with a vertical mill. This usually leaves a sharp transition to the rest of the port that can cause turbulence and restrict flow. We strongly suggest that if you are not experienced and skillful with a grinder that you leave the blending to a qualified pro.

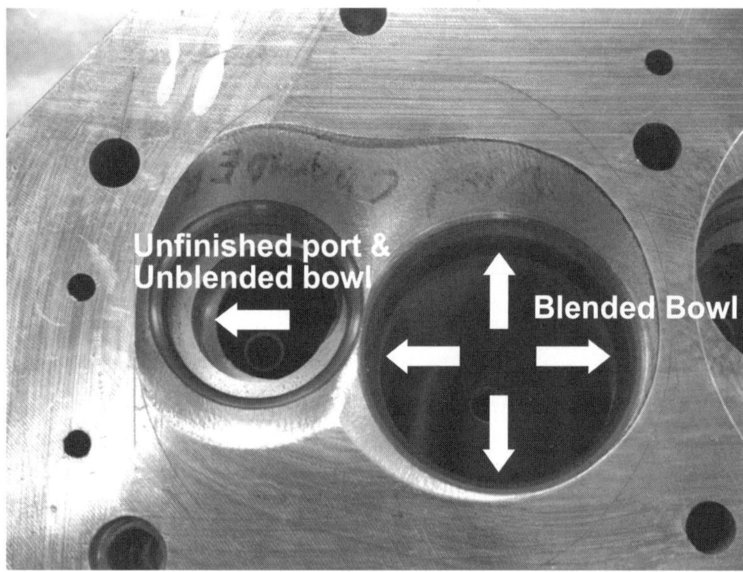

The exhaust port on this head has not been fully machined and there is a sharp edge between the bowl and seat. The intake port shows a finished port with a well-blended bowl.

IMPORTANT! Always wear approved eye and ear protection when grinding metal.

For cast iron heads, a qualified cylinder head porter uses a high-speed grinder with sand rolls to blend the bowls with the seats. Aluminum is soft and can best be removed with a burr type bit. Sand rolls and burrs are available in a variety of shapes and coarseness grades. It takes a lot of experience to know which bits work best for the job and to gain complete control of the grinder. As he performs this work, the porter will be very careful not to increase the venturi diameter or flatten the short side radius.

The goal when blending the bowls is to remove as little material as necessary and to avoid altering the venturi areas.

If you are a more experienced head porter, you can narrow and streamline the valve guides to further improve port flow. This must be done very carefully with rounded burr bits to create the teardrop shape shown in the photo below.

You can do some work to the guides to improve airflow. Keep a teardrop shape in mind as you grind and be careful not to shorten or weaken the guide.

Matching the ports helps create a good transition between the intake manifold and cylinder head ports. If the port in the head is smaller than that in the manifold, it leaves a ledge in the direction of flow. The ledge causes turbulence that can restrict flow. Get the correct intake manifold gasket and use it as a template, or make your own gasket that fits the intake manifold ports. Use a scratch awl to inscribe the port shapes onto the mating surfaces of the heads. Blend the ports to the line, but do not go deeper than one inch into the port.

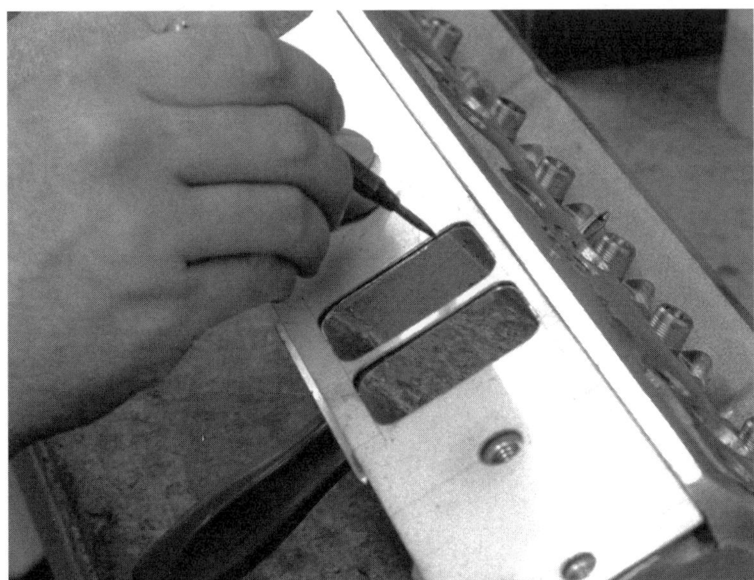

Matching the ports can help reduce turbulence. Use the intake manifold gasket as a template and scribe lines around the intake ports. Use a high speed grinder to create a smooth transition from the inscribed line to about an inch inside the port.

IMPORTANT! Always wear approved eye and ear protection when grinding metal.

Perform a Racing Valve Job - A quality professional racing valve job is easily one of the best values in high performance engine building. It provides a good seal for the valves, improves flow, and ensures reliable valve spring operation.

The best angles and treatment for a racing valve job vary by the particular application. Be sure to have this important work performed by an experienced racing engine builder. The steps for performing a racing valve job include:

1. *Grind the valves with multi-angles*
2. *Cut the valve seats*
3. *Check valve spring installed height & pressure*

Step #1, Grind the Valves with Multi-Angles:

If the heads are used, the machinist first disassembles, cleans, and inspects them. Valve stem diameters are measured and guides are checked for wear. A valve grinder is used to make the 45°-55° seat angle, depending on the particular application.

Recall that gases can make a smooth transition from one valve seat angle to another so long as the angular change is no more than 15°. For this reason, a relief angle of 30° is added above the 45° seat cut, or 40° with valves that have a 55° seat.

This special valve grinder rotates the valve in a direction opposite that of the stone. An experienced machinist keeps a watchful eye on the process and removes only enough material to clean up the valve face. A constant flow of fluid keeps the valve head cool.

The margin width is particularly important on the exhaust valves. If the exhaust valve margin is too narrow, hot spots can develop that result in burned valves and pre-ignition problems. If an intake margin of at least .050" and exhaust margin of .080" cannot be maintained after grinding the 45° angles, the valves should be replaced.

NOTE: Valve preparation requires a lot of experience and well-maintained equipment. We strongly recommend that you leave this work to the qualified pro.

Step #2, Cut the Valve Seats:

We use a carbide-tipped valve seat cutter to make the necessary angle cuts. This leaves a much better sealing surface than those ground with abrasive stones.

This valve seat cutter is an expensive piece of machinery, but can create the precise angles in hardened seats that are a must for any high performance engine.

The diagram below shows the angles that are cut into the seats. Depending on the application, the 45°-55° seat cut is made first. Relief cuts are made to narrow and move the seat in or out. We remove only the minimum amount of material necessary to clean up the seat to avoid sinking the valves into the combustion chamber.

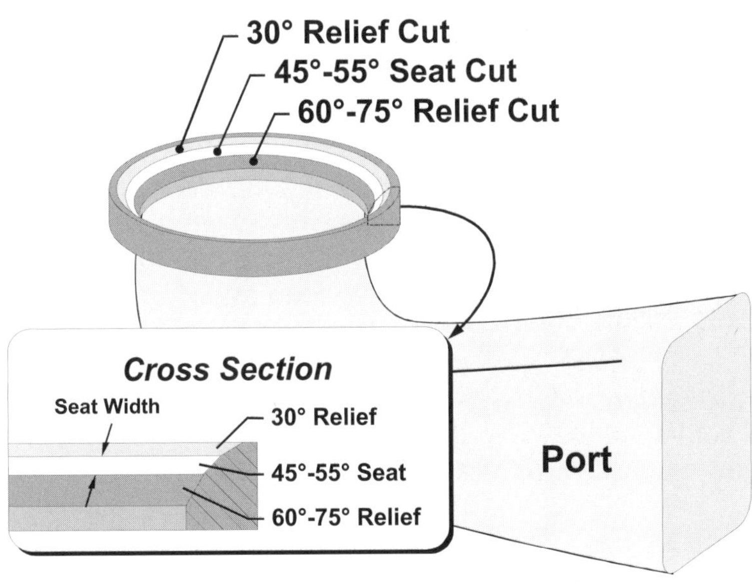

This is how the cuts are made on a typical multi-angle valve job. The seat angle (45°-55°) must match that of the valve.

We spray machinist's dye onto the valve and seat, and then lap the valves by hand. After applying an abrasive compound to the seat, a suction cup tool is used to grip and rotate the valves. The area of contact between the valve face and seat is revealed by this procedure. Relief cuts are made as required to center the seat on the valve face and narrow it to the desired width.

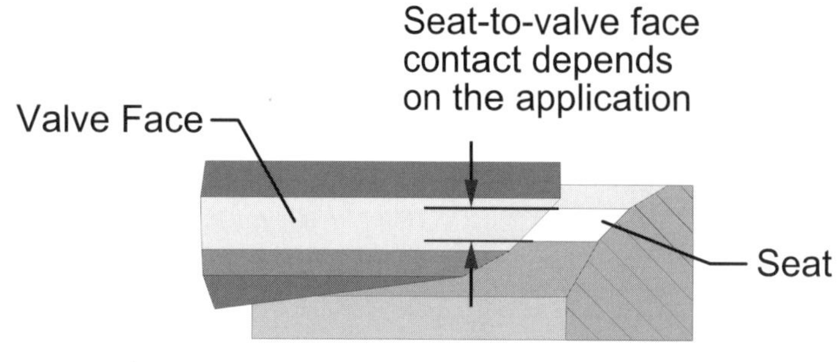

Intake Seat Width = .060"
Exhaust Seat Width = .075"-.080"

If the seat contact is too wide and close to the valve edge (margin), the 30° cut is deepened. If the seat contact is too wide and high on the valve face, the 60° cut is deepened.

NOTE: The seat angles and widths are dependent on the particular application. An experienced racing engine builder can choose the appropriate seat angles and widths for your racing engine.

For some high-end racing applications, we create a radiused seat on the exhaust side. This means that the break lines on the seat angles are carefully blended away with a high-speed grinder or radius cutter to create the smoothest possible transition.

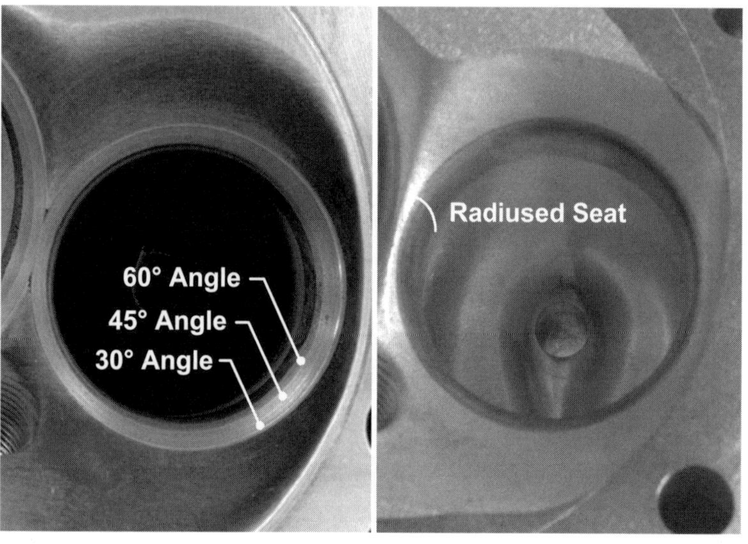

The photo on the left shows a typical multi-angle valve seat. The sharp breaks between the seat angles are carefully blended away for the radiused seat shown on the right. We recommend this tricky procedure only for unlimited drag racing engines.

Step #3, Check the Valve Spring Installed Height & Pressure:

Grinding the valves and seats sinks the valves deeper into the cylinder head. This changes the *installed height* of the spring. Installed height is the distance from the valve spring pocket to the outer spring ledge on the retainer. Measure the installed height for each spring as shown below and compare it to the spring manufacturer's specifications.

Measure the installed height with a height micrometer as shown.

Add shims to reduce the height. If the installed height must be increased, it is safer to change to valves with longer stems on most cylinder heads. Cutting the spring pockets cut deeper often cuts into the water jacket or port.

NOTE: Aluminum heads always require at least one hardened shim to prevent the spring from damaging the soft aluminum spring pocket.

Over time, valve springs can lose pressure. Each spring must be checked for minimum pressure at both the installed and compressed spring heights.

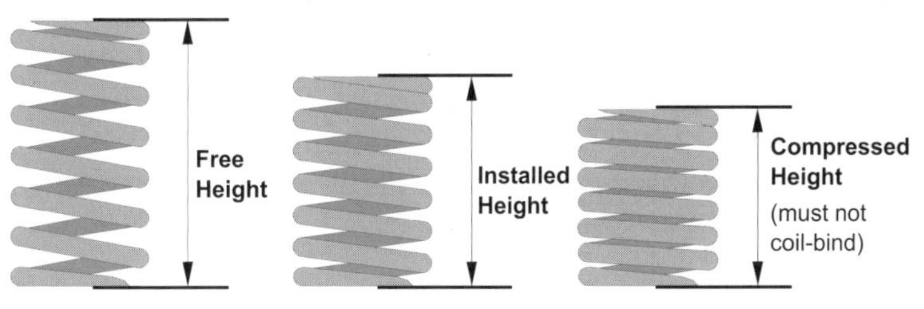

The spring pressure in lbs. must be correct at both the installed height and the compressed height. At the fully compressed height, the spring must not be coil-bound.

Check double and triple-wound springs for pressure as an assembly with the retainer on top. The correct specifications for valve spring rates at different heights can be obtained from the spring manufacturer. This special machine is used to measure valve spring pressure:

The machinist pulls a lever on a special valve spring checking machine to compress the spring assembly to both the installed and compressed heights.

If a valve spring is weak at either the installed or compressed height, it must be replaced. New steel high rate valve springs usually lose about 10% of their pressure within a few runs. After that, they usually retain their remaining rates for a long time.

If the springs coil-bind before they can be compressed to the shortest specified height, compress each spring individually to determine which one in is causing the issue. You may need to use a different style retainer to solve coil-binding problems.

Measure the Combustion Chamber Volumes - The volumes of the combustion chambers must be right in order to obtain the correct static compression ratio for the engine. A chemist's buret and water are used to measure the volume of each chamber in cubic centimeters (cc's).

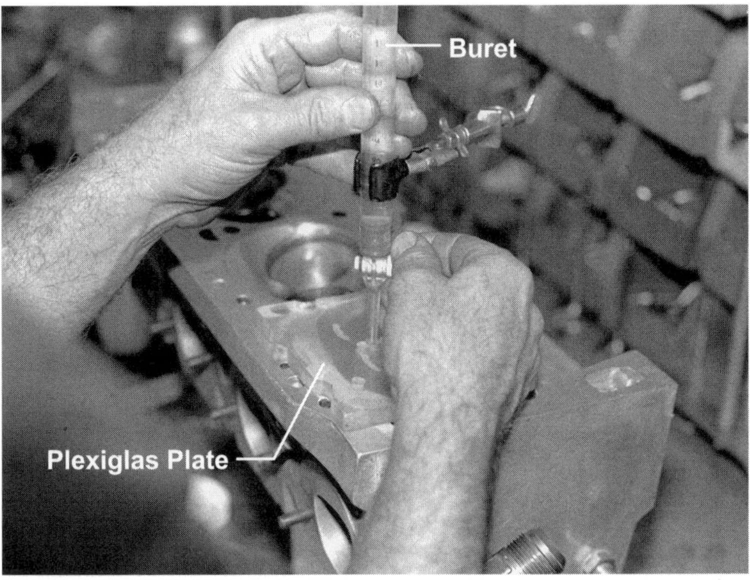

To measure the combustion chamber volumes, seal a Plexiglas plate with grease to the deck surface. Measure the amount of water required to fill the combustion chamber completely with the buret.

It's very important to have quality valve seat machining performed by an experienced racing engine builder. The valve margins and seat heights must be uniform to ensure that the combustion chamber volumes are consistent.

Measure the volume of each combustion chamber in the cylinder head to be sure that they are close to the same size. If all of the chambers are too small, you may have to install a thicker head gasket or have the piston domes cut to reduce the static compression ratio.

To reduce the size of a chamber, the valve or seat may need to be replaced. If all the chambers are too large, the head may be milled to reduce the size. This is often the case when you are using new cylinder heads.

Milling the Deck Surfaces - Whether or not you need to correct combustion chamber volumes, it is always a good idea to mill the heads. This ensures that the surface is flat and has the right texture for a good head gasket seal. The type of finish that is best depends on the type of head gasket that you intend to use.

An experienced racing engine builder or cylinder head specialty shop can mill your heads to correct combustion chamber cc's and prepare the mating surface.

Installation of Valve Seals & Final Cylinder Head Assembly - Any oil that burns in the cylinders reduces engine power and may foul the spark plugs. *Valve seals* are an effective way to prevent oil from being drawn into the cylinders past the valve guides. This can happen any time that intake vacuum is high, such as part throttle operation or sudden deceleration.

Have valve seals installed on engines that encounter a lot of part-throttle and off-throttle operation to limit guide-related oil consumption. Quality racing valve seals usually have a spring ring that holds them in place on the top of the valve guide and a Teflon® or other low-friction material on the inside valve stem surfaces.

Valve seals should be installed on the intake and exhaust valve guides of street/strip, endurance, and most stock car engines. Some types require special machining operations to the valve guides. Any racing engine builder or cylinder head specialty shop can perform this work.

We prefer not to install valve seals for high-end drag racing applications because the engines are operated almost exclusively at wide open throttle. Valve seals would only add another source of friction and could break apart and wind up in the oiling system.

WARNING! Cylinder heads should only be assembled by experienced technicians. Valve springs are under many hundreds of pounds of pressure when compressed. Improper adjustment or use of a valve spring compressor can cause the release of hardware at ballistic speeds. Always wear safety glasses and a full face shield when compressing valve springs.

Any grit that may be present in the valve guides can be particularly harmful to the engine. First, clean the heads thoroughly in a parts washer with clean solvent. Use a blow-gun to dry the heads, and then assemble them immediately. Lubricate the valve stems with assembly oil or Moly lube if they are going to be stored for a period of time. Slip the valves into the guides, and then install the shims, springs, and retainers.

NOTE: Use of the correct assembly lubricant is especially important when installing titanium valves because of the tighter guide clearances. See your engine builder for assembly lube recommendations.

Compress the valve springs only enough to install the keepers and retainers. Make sure the keepers are correctly positioned as you slowly release the compressor.

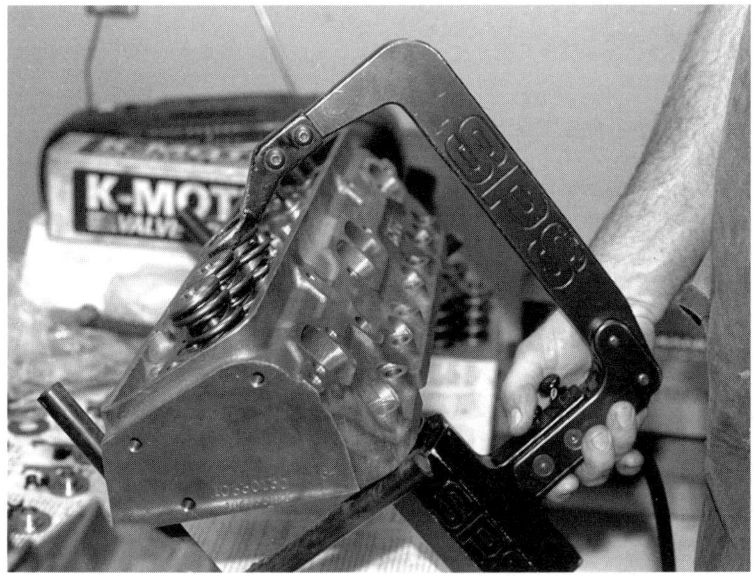

This technician is using a pneumatic valve spring compressor to assemble the valves, springs, and hardware. This dangerous procedure should only be performed by experienced technicians. Always wear the proper eye protection when compressing valve springs.

Pushrods & Rocker Arms

To determine the required pushrod length for your engine, install one cylinder head with a head gasket. Install an intake and exhaust rocker arm. The adjustment procedure varies by the type of rocker (stud or shaft) and by the manufacturer. Shaft-type rockers must first be checked for the correct stand height. If the stand height is wrong, you will have poor rocker arm geometry. Shims are used to change the height of the rocker stands. We recommend that you obtain the procedures for setting rocker arm height from the manufacturer.

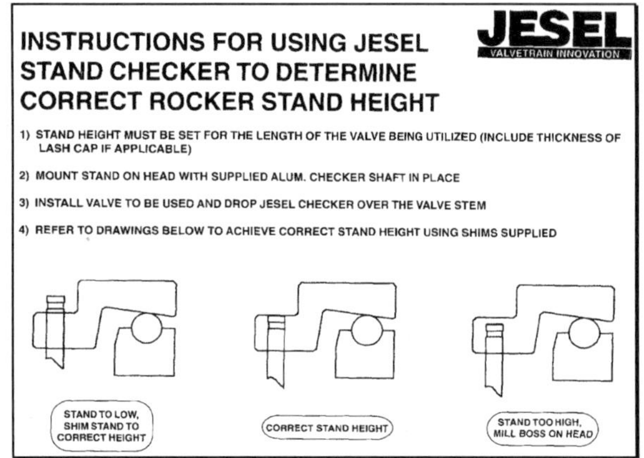

INSTRUCTIONS FOR USING JESEL STAND CHECKER TO DETERMINE CORRECT ROCKER STAND HEIGHT

JESEL
VALVETRAIN INNOVATION

1) STAND HEIGHT MUST BE SET FOR THE LENGTH OF THE VALVE BEING UTILIZED (INCLUDE THICKNESS OF LASH CAP IF APPLICABLE)

2) MOUNT STAND ON HEAD WITH SUPPLIED ALUM. CHECKER SHAFT IN PLACE

3) INSTALL VALVE TO BE USED AND DROP JESEL CHECKER OVER THE VALVE STEM

4) REFER TO DRAWINGS BELOW TO ACHIEVE CORRECT STAND HEIGHT USING SHIMS SUPPLIED

STAND TO LOW, SHIM STAND TO CORRECT HEIGHT

CORRECT STAND HEIGHT

STAND TOO HIGH, MILL BOSS ON HEAD

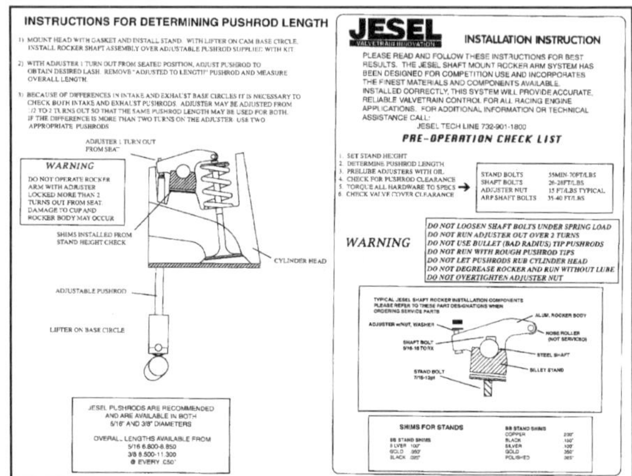

INSTRUCTIONS FOR DETERMINING PUSHROD LENGTH

1) MOUNT HEAD WITH GASKET AND INSTALL STAND. WITH LIFTER ON CAM BASE CIRCLE, INSTALL ROCKER SHAFT ASSEMBLY OVER ADJUSTABLE PUSHROD SUPPLIED WITH KIT

2) WITH ADJUSTER 1 TURN OUT FROM SEATED POSITION, ADJUST PUSHROD TO OBTAIN DESIRED LASH. REMOVE "ADJUSTED TO LENGTH" PUSHROD AND MEASURE OVERALL LENGTH.

3) BECAUSE OF DIFFERENCES IN INTAKE AND EXHAUST BASE CIRCLES IT IS NECESSARY TO CHECK BOTH INTAKE AND EXHAUST PUSHRODS. ADJUSTER MAY BE ADJUSTED FROM 1/2 TO 2 TURNS OUT SO THAT THE SAME PUSHROD LENGTH MAY BE USED FOR BOTH. IF THE DIFFERENCE IS MORE THAN TWO TURNS ON THE ADJUSTER USE TWO APPROPRIATE PUSHRODS

WARNING
DO NOT OPERATE ROCKER ARM WITH ADJUSTER LOCKED MORE THAN 2 TURNS OUT FROM SEAT. DAMAGE TO CUP AND ROCKER BODY MAY OCCUR

JESEL PUSHRODS ARE RECOMMENDED AND ARE AVAILABLE IN BOTH 5/16" AND 3/8" DIAMETERS

OVERALL LENGTHS AVAILABLE FROM 5/16 6.800-8.850 3/8 6.500-11.300 @ EVERY .050"

JESEL
VALVETRAIN INNOVATION
INSTALLATION INSTRUCTION

PLEASE READ AND FOLLOW THESE INSTRUCTIONS FOR BEST RESULTS. THE JESEL SHAFT MOUNT ROCKER ARM SYSTEM HAS BEEN DESIGNED FOR COMPETITION USE AND INCORPORATES THE FINEST MATERIALS AND COMPONENTS AVAILABLE. INSTALLED CORRECTLY, THIS SYSTEM WILL PROVIDE ACCURATE, RELIABLE VALVETRAIN CONTROL FOR ALL RACING ENGINE APPLICATIONS. FOR ADDITIONAL INFORMATION OR TECHNICAL ASSISTANCE CALL:
JESEL TECH LINE 732-901-1800

PRE-OPERATION CHECK LIST

1. SET STAND HEIGHT
2. DETERMINE PUSHROD LENGTH
3. PRELUBE ADJUSTERS WITH OIL
4. CHECK FOR PUSHROD CLEARANCE
5. TORQUE ALL HARDWARE TO SPECS →
6. CHECK VALVE COVER CLEARANCE

STAND BOLTS	55MIN-70FT/LBS
SHAFT BOLTS	26-28FT/LBS
ADJUSTER NUT	15 FT/LBS TYPICAL
ARP SHAFT BOLTS	35-40 FT/LBS

WARNING
DO NOT LOOSEN SHAFT BOLTS UNDER SPRING LOAD
DO NOT RUN ADJUSTER OUT OVER 2 TURNS
DO NOT USE BULLET (BAD RADIUS) TIP PUSHRODS
DO NOT RUN WITH ROUGH PUSHROD TIPS
DO NOT LET PUSHRODS RUB CYLINDER HEAD
DO NOT DEGREASE ROCKER AND RUN WITHOUT LUBE
DO NOT OVERTIGHTEN ADJUSTER NUT

TYPICAL JESEL SHAFT ROCKER INSTALLATION COMPONENTS
PLEASE REFER TO THESE PART DESIGNATIONS WHEN ORDERING SERVICE PARTS

SHIMS FOR STANDS

Courtesy of Jesel, Inc.

After you have the rocker arms and stands at the correct installed height, insert a feeler gauge with the correct lash thickness between the stem and rocker arm tip. Install an adjustable pushrod between the rocker arm and lifter, then set it to the length that eliminates all lash. Remove the rocker arm and measure the pushrod length with a dial caliper as shown below.

Use a large dial caliper to measure the length of the adjustable pushrod.

Repeat the procedure for both valves. If you cannot find off-the-shelf pushrods of the required lengths, have them custom cut by a racing engine builder.

Intake Manifold

Fitting the Intake Manifold:

New manifolds normally fit well on a stock engine, but racing engines usually have had machine work performed that changes the intake manifold fit.

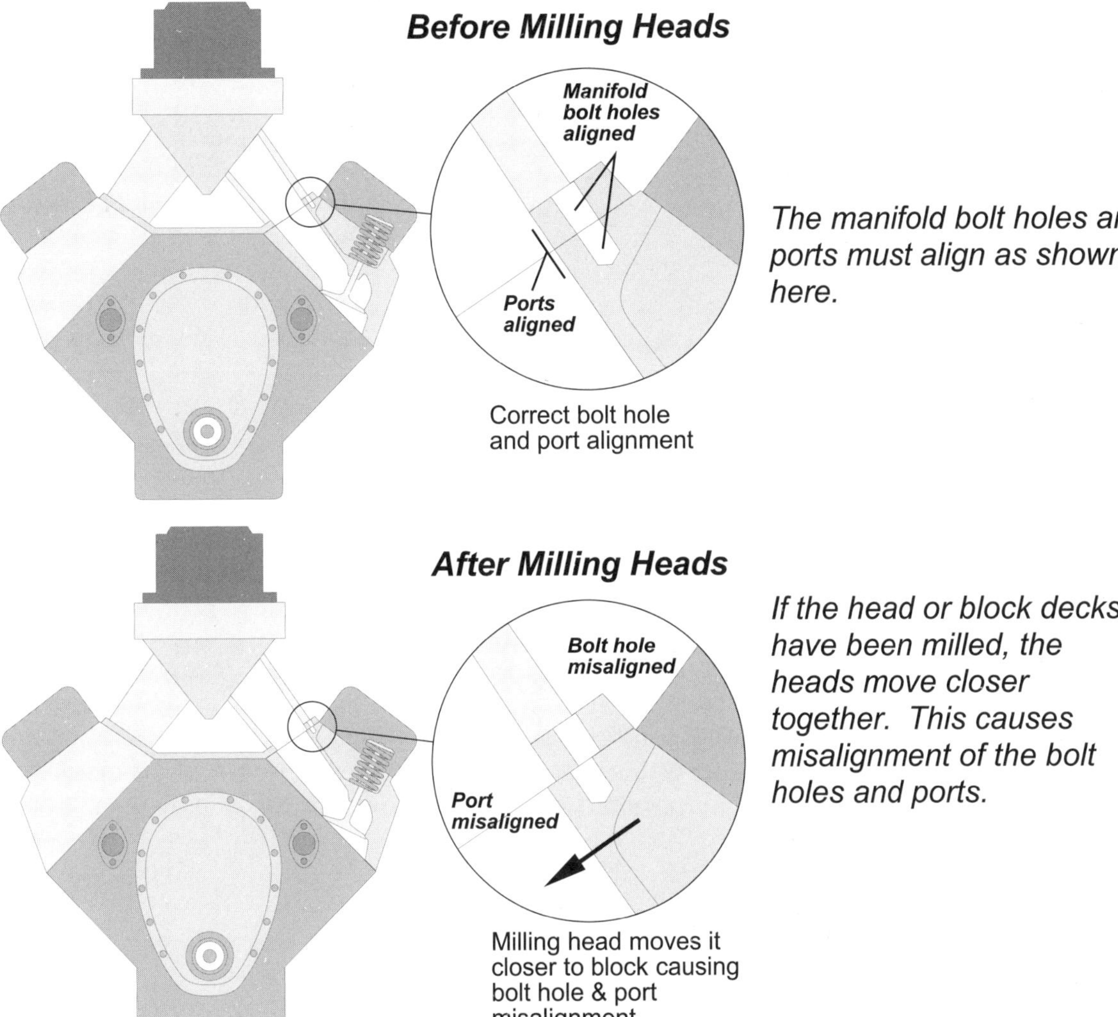

Correct bolt hole and port alignment

The manifold bolt holes and ports must align as shown here.

Milling head moves it closer to block causing bolt hole & port misalignment

If the head or block decks have been milled, the heads move closer together. This causes misalignment of the bolt holes and ports.

When they discover that the manifold bolts won't fit, many racers make the mistake of elongating the holes with a round file. This makes it possible to bolt the manifold onto the engine, but leaves the runners and ports badly misaligned. The result is an overhanging ledge that creates turbulence and lost power.

To make the manifold fit, it is often necessary to cut the mating flange surfaces of the intake manifold. If the heads have been "rolled over" in an angle milling procedure, the intake surface angle on the head must also be corrected.

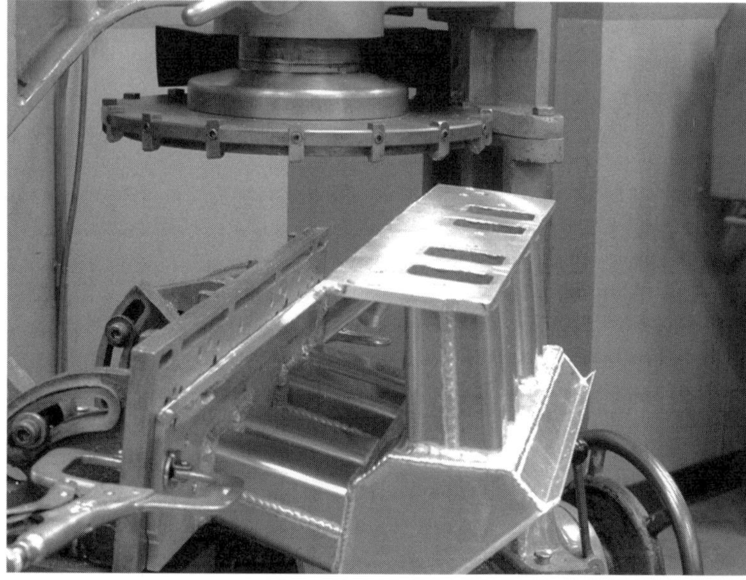

This tunnel ram manifold is about to be milled to create a good fit with the cylinder heads.

Milling the intake manifold head flanges lowers the manifold vertically on the engine block. This causes two other manifold mounting problems. The first problem is with the manifold end gaskets. Both big and small block GM V8 engines use rubber gaskets to seal the front and rear of the intake manifold to the lifter valley.

After the head mating flanges have been milled, there will be little or no space between the block and manifold for these gaskets. Most racers use a bead of RTV silicone sealer at both ends of the manifold instead of the rubber end gaskets.

You can replace the stock rubber end gaskets with RTV silicone to seal the ends of the intake manifold with the valley area.

On most GM V8 racing engines, the distributor fits into a hole at the rear of the intake manifold. Milling the cylinder heads and intake manifold lowers the location of the manifold on the engine. This can result in serious problems. The distributor gear may bottom inside the block or it may bear on the oil pump shaft. This forces the gear inside the pump against the cover and can lead to oil pump failure. The distributor body has an annular groove that creates a passage for oil flow to one of the lifter galleries. If the body is too high or low, the passage may be restricted.

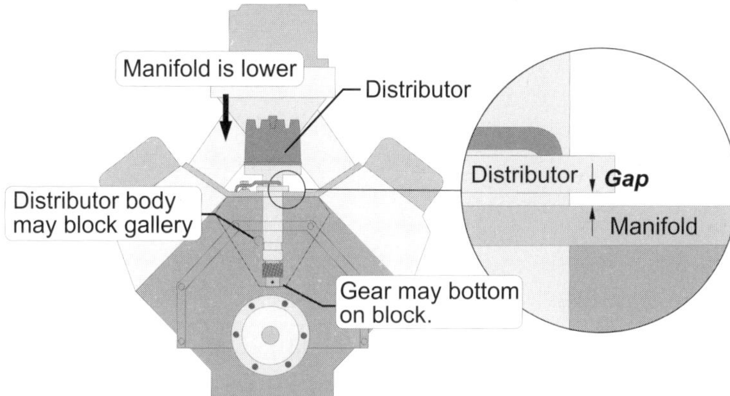

Machining of the intake manifold flanges lowers the manifold on the engine. The distributor may bottom inside the block, place the oil pump in a bind, or cause an oil gallery restriction.

Check the fit of the distributor by slipping it in place with no gasket. If the housing can rest against the manifold, there is adequate clearance. If the flange will not rest on the manifold, an adjustment is required. Some racing distributors feature an adjustable flange that can be repositioned as needed to correct this problem. Don't assume it's adjusted correctly out of the box—follow the manufacturer's procedures for setting the distributor height. We always remove the rear oil gallery plug and make a visual inspection to be sure the distributor body is not cutting off oil flow.

Stock non-adjustable distributors often require the use of a shim at the base of the distributor to correct the fit. Measure the gap with a feeler gauge and buy a shim that is about .020" thicker to prevent binding of the distributor shaft. Don't raise the distributor too high—there must be at least 1/4" engagement with the oil pump driveshaft (wet-sump systems) and .060" clearance between the bottom of the gear and the engine block. Always install a gasket with the shim to prevent oil leakage.

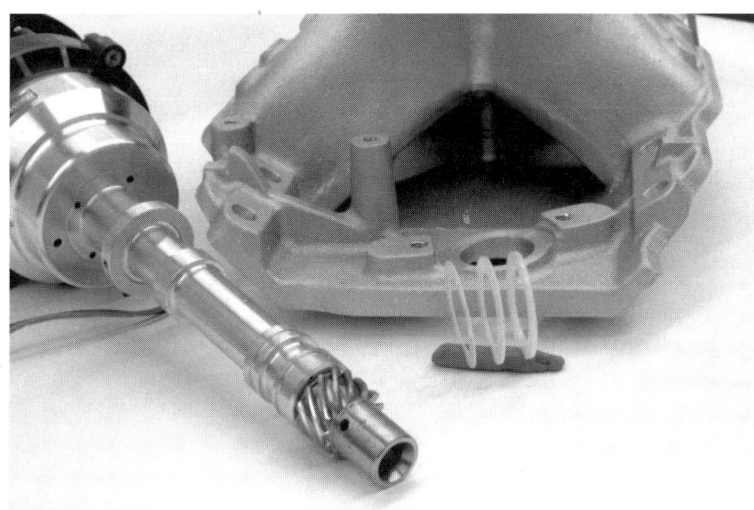

Distributor shims are available in several thicknesses to compensate for material that was milled off the intake manifold and heads.

Carburetors

IMPORTANT! The initial carburetor adjustment procedures covered in this section are for general informational purposes only. Always follow the manufacturer's specific adjustment recommendations for adjusting your carburetor.

Carburetors require a few adjustments before they are installed on the engine. New carburetors are normally pre-adjusted at the factory, but it is still a good idea to check them to be sure they are correct. Initial carburetor adjustments include:

- Power Valve Type (Holley)
- Float Level
- Idle Richness
- Accelerator Pumps

Power Valve Type (Holley):

Most Holley carburetors are shipped with a #65 power valve. This valve opens when manifold vacuum drops to 6.5 In. hg. and is usually about right for most street engines. If you are building a true racing engine, we usually recommend that you remove and plug the power valve. These plugs are available through Holley and many other aftermarket manufacturers.

Remove the four screws that hold the primary bowl in place, and then remove the bowl and metering block. Use a box-end wrench to unscrew the power valve and replace it with a plug and a new gasket.

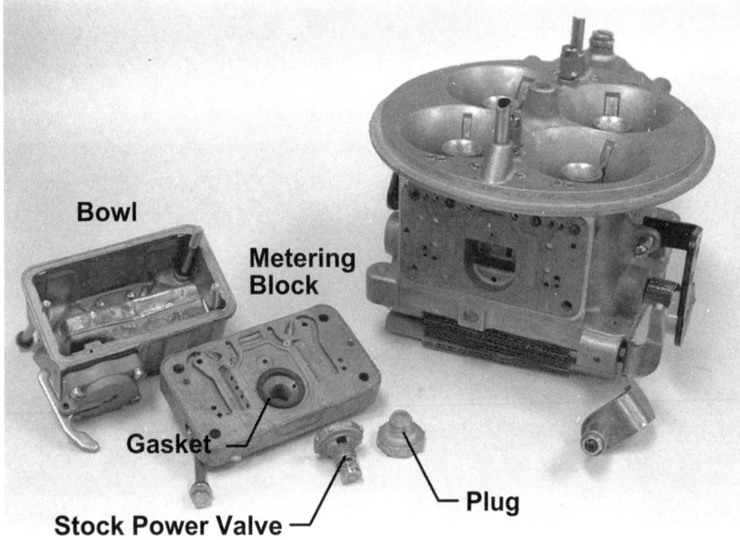

Street applications require a power valve. For most racing applications, you should remove the power valve and replace it with a special plug and new gasket.

When you replace the power valve with a plug, you must also replace the main jets with a larger size to provide the right mixture for full power. These are some common starting jet sizes for Holley carburetors:

Carb CFM	Starting Jet Size (blocked power valve)	Carb CFM	Starting Jet Size (blocked power valve)
600	73	800	84
650	74	850	86
700	76	1050	90
750	79	1150	93

The jet size number is stamped on the side of the main jets. When you replace main jets, be sure to use a screwdriver with the right size blade to avoid damage to the slot in the jet.

Be careful not to damage the slot when replacing main jets. Burrs in the slot can affect the fuel flow rates.

IMPORTANT! After the first run at the race track, you will need to shut off the engine while it is under full power. This allows you to check the coloration of the spark plugs and determine if the fuel mixture is correct.

Float Level:

With the bowl off the carburetor, you can adjust the initial float level. Follow the directions supplied with your carburetor. Usually, the procedure is to turn the bowl upside down and adjust the needle & seat until the float hangs at the right distance from the base of the carburetor bowl.

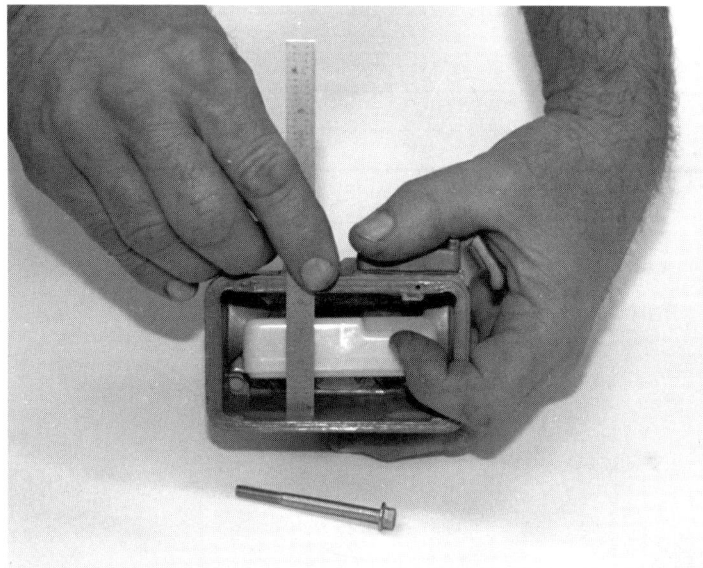

Follow the manufacturer's recommended procedure for initial float level settings. A running setting will be made later when you start the engine.

Idle Richness:

The beginning idle richness adjustment for most Holley carburetors is to gently tighten the mixture screws until they are fully seated, then back them out 1 1/2 turns.

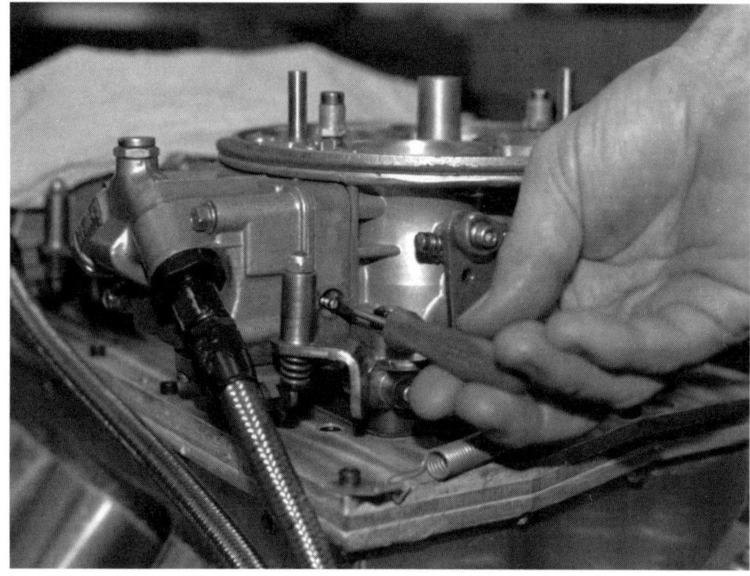

Refer to the manufacture's specifications for initial idle richness settings. This Holley carburetor requires 1 1/2 turns out from the fully seated position.

Accelerator Pumps:

The accelerator pump actuating lever is often adjustable. To adjust the lever on most high performance Holley carburetors, shorten the spring loaded actuating lever until there is some free play in the linkage. Lengthen the lever just enough until the lash is gone. This adjustment provides an instant squirt when the throttle is moved and ensures full stroke and discharge volume.

Use two end wrenches to adjust the length of the accelerator pump actuator. Tighten it to compress the spring until there is some lash, then slowly lengthen the spring just enough until all the lash is gone.

> ***NOTE:*** There may be several other initial carburetor adjustments recommended by the manufacturer before you start the engine. Be sure to read all of the installation information supplied with your carburetor.

One of the many advantages of dyno-testing is that the performance and tuning of the carburetor can be checked before you head to the race track. At that point, only minor changes should be necessary.

Review Questions

1. Name four pre-installation inspections that should be performed on racing cylinder heads. How can you check cylinder heads for leaks?

2. How do you check for valve guide and seat wear? What are some ways that worn guides can be repaired? How are damaged repaired? Why should Heli-Coils be installed in the threaded holes of aluminum heads?

3. How do you blend the bowls of racing cylinder heads? How much material should be removed from the venturi area? What shape should you create around valve guides?

4. How do you match the intake ports of racing cylinder heads? Why is this done?

5. What is the first step in a racing valve job? What is the normal range of seat angles? How does the machinist compensate for material removed from the valve faces?

6. What is the difference between a multi-angle seat and a radiused seat? Where is a radiused seat used?

7. How do you check valve springs for pressure and height? What is the tool used for in the photo below?

8. How do you measure the combustion chamber volumes? Why is this important? What should be done if the combustion chambers are too large? What should be done if the combustion chambers are too small?

9. Why are special valve seals installed on racing cylinder heads? How are they constructed?

10. Describe the final assembly of the cylinder heads. Why is it important for experienced technicians to assemble the heads? Why should a full face shield be worn when assembling cylinder heads?

11. How do you determine the correct pushrod length?

12. Why is it important to check the fit of the intake manifold? What is wrong with elongating manifold bolt holes to enable the bolt installation? Describe how to fit and seal an intake manifold.

13. How do milling the cylinder heads and intake manifold mating surfaces affect the fit of the distributor? How do you compensate for this to correct the fit of the distributor?

14. How do you remove the power valve in a Holley racing carburetor? When should the power valve be plugged? Why must the main jets be changed if you plug the power valve? Where is the main jet size stamped? Why is it important to avoid damage to the slot on main jets?

15. Describe the initial float level adjustment for a Holley carburetor.

16. Describe the initial idle richness adjustment for a Holley carburetor.

17. Describe the initial accelerator pump adjustment for a Holley carburetor.

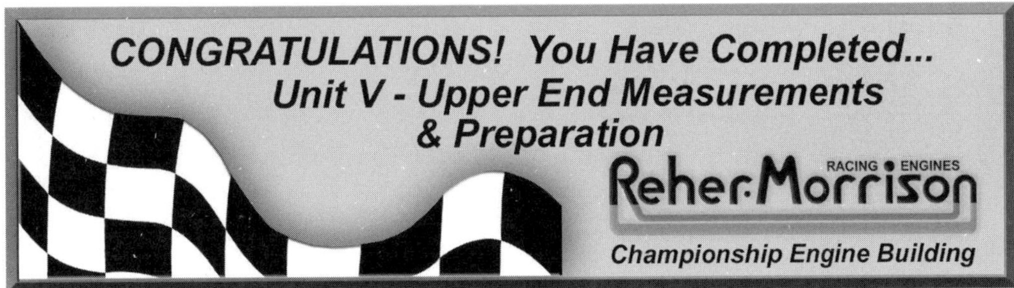

RehecMorrison
Raptor

Championship Engine Assembly

Unit VI - Short Block Pre-Assembly Measurements

A racing short block cannot be fully machined and assembled without performing some initial measurements. This ensures that the finished engine has the right displacement, compression ratio, cam phasing, and enough clearance to prevent valve clash. In this unit, you will learn how to perform the following measurements and calculations:

- Engine Displacement
- Static Compression Ratio
- Degreeing-In the Camshaft
- Piston-to-Valve Clearance

A few measurements, including combustion chamber volume should be made prior to the final short block assembly.

Measuring Engine Displacement

Engine displacement is the way we express the size of an engine. When the pistons move through the 4-stroke cycle, they move, or *displace*, a certain volume based on the size and number of cylinders. Although engine displacement may be expressed in metric liters or cubic centimeters, it is usually expressed in cubic inches in the United States. This is the formula for calculating the standard or "swept" volume of a cylinder:

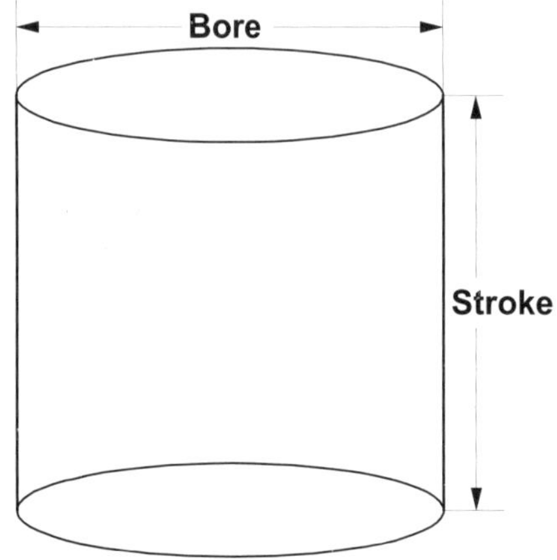

This is the formula for calculating the swept volume of a standard cylinder. The term "stroke" represents the height of the cylinder in the formula. The small number "2" above the line next to "bore" means "squared", or to multiply the number by itself.

Cylinder Volume = bore^2 x stroke x .7854

Most race sanctioning organizations have engine displacement limitations for each race car class. The penalties for violating these rules are usually quite severe, regardless of how small the infraction may be. It is very important that you measure your engine displacement accurately and make any needed corrections before you assemble and test your engine.

Stroke length is determined solely by the throw length of the crankshaft, <u>not</u> by the length of the rods, piston compression height, dome, or deck clearance.

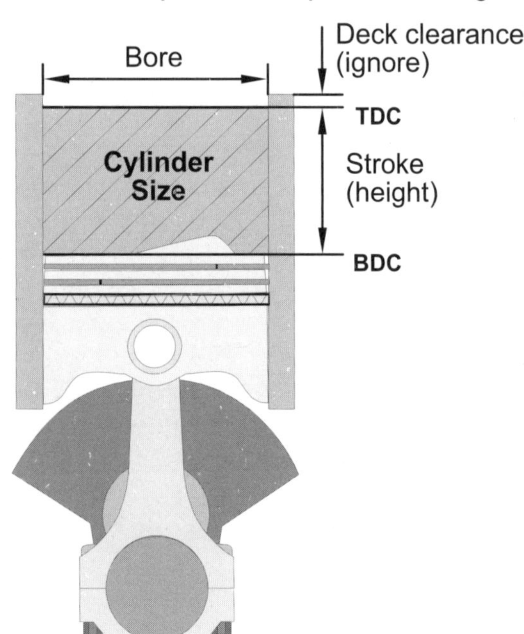

The bore and stroke of the engine determine the size of one cylinder. Ignore the deck height and piston dome when calculating engine displacement.

Engine Displacement Formula:

Multiply the displacement for one cylinder by the number of cylinders to determine the total engine displacement.

$$\textbf{Displacement} = \textbf{bore}^2 \times \textbf{stroke} \times .7854 \times \#\ \textbf{of cylinders}$$

Example Engine Displacement Problem:

You are building a V8 racing engine for a class with a 500 cubic inch limit. The bore and stroke measurements for this engine are listed below. Will this engine exceed the maximum allowable displacement?

- Bore = 4.45"
- Stroke = 4.000"

Apply the engine displacement formula:

$$\textbf{Displacement} = \textbf{bore}^2 \times \textbf{stroke} \times .7854 \times \#\ \textbf{of cylinders}$$

$$\textbf{Displacement} = 4.45 \times 4.45 \times 4.0 \times .7854 \times 8$$

$$\textbf{Displacement} = 497.69\ \textbf{Cubic Inches}$$

Answer to Example Engine Displacement Problem:

The answer (497.69 cu. in.) is well under the maximum displacement limit of 500 cubic inches.

If the bore is larger than the stroke, the engine is said to be *oversquare*. Oversquare engines typically make more horsepower per cubic inch than other engines of the same size. This is largely because there is room in the bore for proportionately bigger valves.

The short stroke of an oversquare engine also results in lower piston speeds. This reduces frictional losses and places less strain on parts at high rpm's. Our 500 cubic inch NHRA Pro Stock engines are good examples of oversquare engines. They usually have something close to a 4.725" bore and 3.560" stroke.

An undersquare engine has a bore that is smaller than the stroke. Undersquare engines may not make as much horsepower per cubic inch as oversquare engines, but the long stroke creates more torque at lower rpm's. The monster 800 cubic inch engines used in Pro Mod racing are undersquare, often having a 4.875" bore and 5.350" stroke.

Correcting Engine Displacement:

If the example engine had exceeded the 500 CID (cubic inch displacement) limit, the bore or stroke would have to be reduced enough to provide at least some margin for measurement error. With a ferrous block, the only good way to reduce the bore is to buy a new one with a smaller bore diameter (sleeves are not recommended). Racers with seasoned blocks may be understandably reluctant to go this way. If you do replace the block, you'll also have to pay for new machine work, pistons, and rings.

Normally, the best way to reduce displacement is to install a crankshaft with a slightly shorter stroke. You must also buy new pistons with higher CH (compression height) or use longer rods to maintain the required deck clearance.

The NHRA Pro Stock class is limited to a maximum of 500 cubic inches. To allow for errors in tech inspection measurement, we don't like to exceed 499 cubic inches. Pro Stock engines require frequent rebuilding (after 20-30 runs) to maintain top power output. Each time the block is re-honed, the bore size increases and the engine becomes slightly larger. For this reason, we keep a number of crankshafts in stock in .005" stroke increments so that we can always restore the engine to our target of 499 cubic inches.

This newly-freshened NHRA Pro Stock engine must not exceed the 500 CID displacement limit. We compensate for the increase in bore that results from re-machining the cylinder bores by decreasing the stroke.

Measuring Static Compression Ratio

The static compression ratio of a racing engine must be correct to avoid fuel detonation or loss of power. Static compression is the ratio between the cylinder volume when the piston is at BDC (bottom dead center) versus the remaining volume when the piston is at TDC (top dead center).

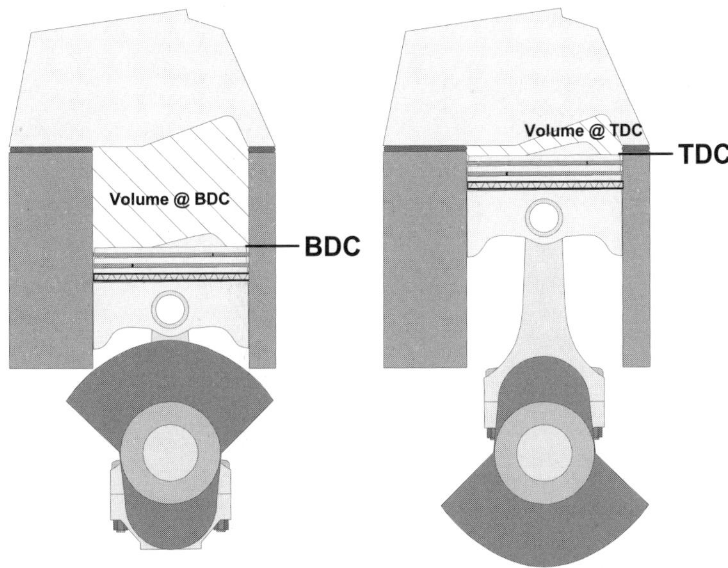

Divide the total cylinder volume when the piston is at BDC by the remaining volume with the piston at TDC to determine the static compression ratio.

$$\text{Static Compression Ratio} = \frac{\text{Volume @ BDC}}{\text{Volume @ TDC}}$$

The volume when the piston is at BDC is the sum of the combustion chamber volume (A), head gasket volume (B), deck clearance volume (C), and the swept cylinder volume (D), less the piston dome volume (E).

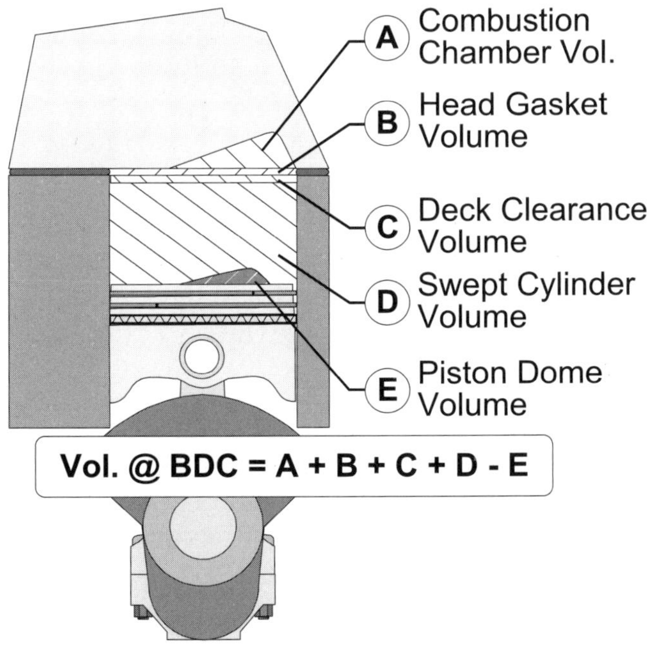

These are the individual volumes that determine the net cylinder volume when the piston is at BDC.

The volume when the piston is at TDC is the sum of the combustion chamber volume (A), head gasket volume (B), and the deck clearance volume (C), less the piston dome volume (E).

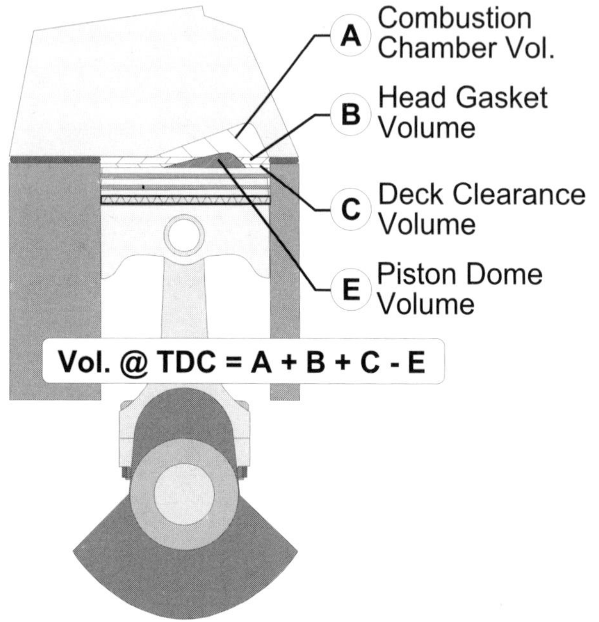

These are the individual volumes that determine the net cylinder volume when the piston is at TDC.

Static Compression Ratio Formula:

This is the formula for static compression ratio with the net cylinder volumes at BDC and TDC broken down (by letter) into the individual volumes:

$$\textbf{Static Compression Ratio} = \frac{\textbf{Vol. @ BDC} = A + B + C + D - E}{\textbf{Vol. @ TDC} = A + B + C - E}$$

A = Measured Combustion Chamber Volume

B = Head Gasket Volume

C = Calculated Deck Clearance Volume

D = Calculated Swept Cylinder Volume

E = Measured Piston Dome Volume

You can use this formula for calculating the static compression ratio for a racing engine. Measure and calculate all the volumes above, then divide the top number (total volume @ BDC) by the bottom number (total volume @ TDC). Your answer will be expressed as a ratio over 1.

NOTE: Some builders include the *crevice volume* in their static compression ratio calculations. A crevice volume is the small gap between the piston and cylinder wall above the top compression ring. This space is extremely small and has very little impact on your static compression ratio calculation. However, the crevice volume may be included in the static compression ratio formula as published by your race sanctioning organization. Always apply the formula as it appears in your rulebook to be sure you are in compliance with any limits on static compression ratio.

Determining a Target Static Compression Ratio:

You must build your engine with a static compression ratio that will provide close to the ideal dynamic compression for your engine. This depends on many factors including the engine volumetric efficiency, camshaft profile, quality of ring seal, and the density of the incoming air. The chart below gives some typical static compression ratio ranges by displacement and application.

Typical Static Compression Ratios

(Naturally Aspirated Gasoline Engines)

Engine Size/Application	*Typical Static Compression Ratio*
283-400 cubic inch small block drag racing engine, med. performance, sportsman class, naturally aspirated	12.5/1 to 14.0/1
283-400 cubic inch small block drag racing engine, high performance, pro class,	14.5/1 to 15.5/1
283-400 cubic inch small block stock car racing engine, med. performance, sportsman class	12.5/1 to 14.5/1
427-550 cubic inch big block drag racing engine, med. performance sportsman class	12.5/1 to 14.5/1
427-550 cubic inch big block drag racing engine, high performance pro class	15.0/1 to 16.5/1
550-800 cubic inch big block drag racing engine, high performance pro class	16.5/1 to 17.5/1

NOTE: This information is provided only for comparative purposes. Supercharged engines have far higher dynamic compression and usually require much lower static compression ratios. Similarly, engines equipped with nitrous oxide systems also require lower static compression ratios. The amount of compression required for your particular engine application may vary from that listed in the chart above.

To determine a target static compression ratio, we recommend that you talk to an experienced engine builder. They have built and tested a large number of racing engines and can provide you with a number that should work well for your engine.

Example Static Compression Ratio Problem:

You are building a 502 CID GM big block racing engine with aluminum rods and heads. Your target static compression ratio for this engine is 14.0:1. Calculate the static compression with these specifications.

Bore - 4.47"

Stroke - 4.000"

Deck Clearance - .014"

Head Gasket Compressed Thickness - .051"

NOTE: All sample problems included in this Measuring Static Compression Ratio section will refer to this 502 CID racing engine and specifications.

Using a Buret:

Before you can start plugging numbers into the static compression ratio equation, you must measure the volumes of the combustion chamber (A) and the piston dome (E). Both have very complex geometry that would make pure mathematical calculations nearly impossible.

Use a chemist's buret and liquid to make these measurements. The liquid can be water, alcohol solution, or a special measuring chemical. Food coloring or dye makes the water or alcohol solution easier to read.

A buret usually has metric markings in milliliters (ml). Milliliters are equivalent to cubic centimeters (cc's). In race engine building, piston dome and combustion chamber volumes are always expressed in cc's.

You will also need a Plexiglas plate like the one shown in the photo below. Buy a cc plate or cut your own from material that is at least ¼" thick. Drill a hole that fits the spout at the base of the buret. You can also drill an air bleed hole if you wish to help avoid air pockets.

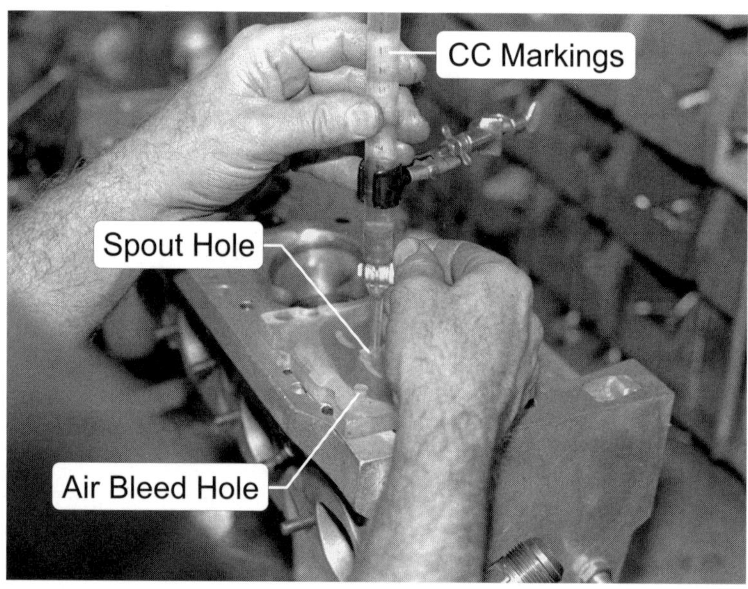

A buret is usually marked in milliliters, but these units can be read as cubic centimeters (cc's). The air bleed hole prevents air entrapment when filling the chamber.

IMPORTANT! Alcohol has less surface tension than water, making it a lot easier to eliminate bubbles and obtain accurate volume measurements. However, alcohol presents a fire hazard. Always keep flammable liquids away from heat or sparks and avoid inhaling fumes.

When you first fill the glass buret, the spout at the base will be empty. As you open the valve, the spout fills and the liquid level drops. With the buret vertical, crack the valve open slightly. Close it when the liquid level drops exactly to the "0" starting point. Be sure there are no air bubbles present in the liquid. Capillary action will keep the spout full as you insert the spout into the Plexiglas plate so long as you keep the buret vertical.

Preparing the Buret

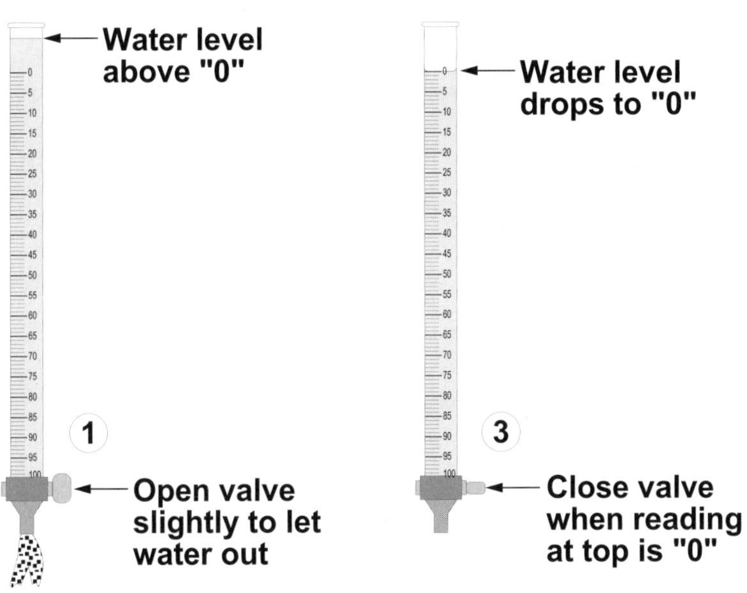

Fill the buret above the "0" mark, then crack the valve open. Close it when the level drops exactly to "0". Capillary action will keep the spout full so long as you keep the buret vertical.

Surface tension causes a film of water called the *meniscus* to creep up the sides of the glass. For accuracy, always read the level at the bottom of the meniscus, both at the "0" starting point and at the final reading.

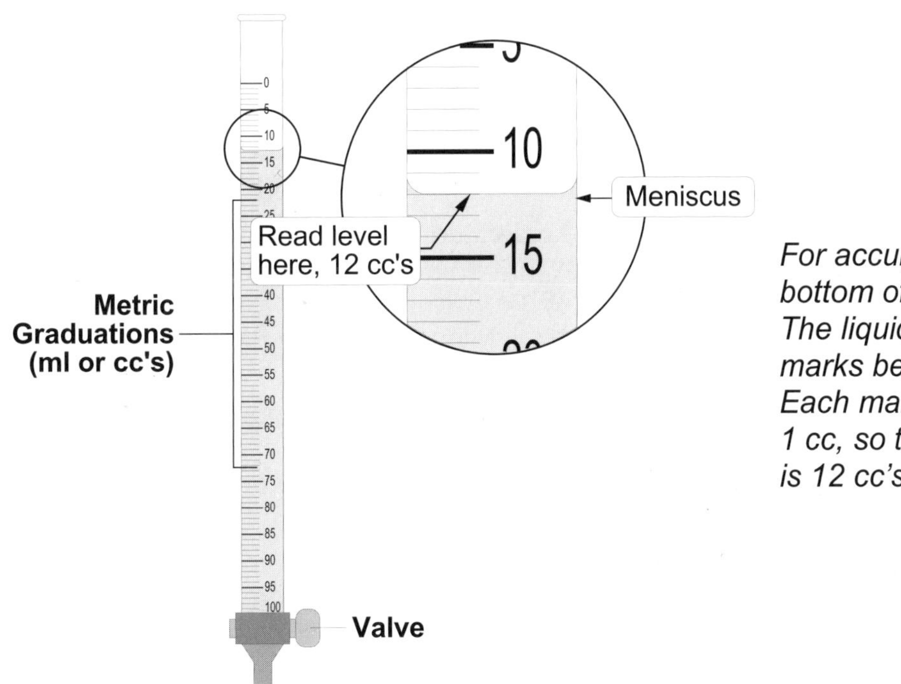

For accuracy, read the bottom of the meniscus. The liquid level is two marks below the 10 cc line. Each mark on this buret is 1 cc, so the correct reading is 12 cc's

Measuring Combustion Chamber Volume (A):

The valve job on your cylinder heads must be fresh so that the valves will not leak water during this measurement. If you are going to make the measurement without installing the valve springs, apply a layer of grease to the seats to create a good seal. Slip the valves into the heads, push them down to form a seal, and then install a spark plug of the same type that will be run in the chamber.

Place the cylinder head on a slight tilt and apply a thin layer of grease to the deck surface around the combustion chamber. Seal the Plexiglas plate over the combustion chamber with the fill hole at the highest point. Purge the spout and carefully fill the combustion chamber until there are no air pockets left. Write down your reading.

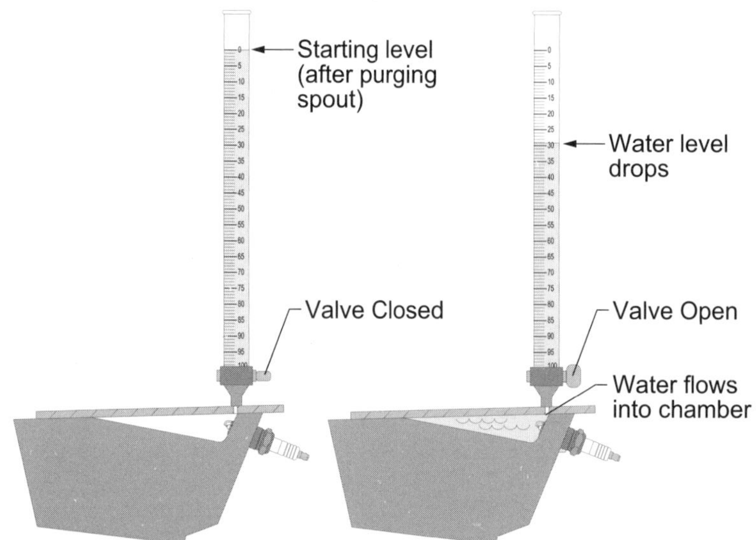

Start with the water level exactly on "0", then open the valve. Allow just enough water in to completely fill the combustion chamber.

If the chamber is larger than the buret capacity (100 cc's in the example above), do not allow the level to go below the lowest marked line (100 cc's). Refill and purge the buret again, then add more water until the level reaches the bottom of the fill hole in the plate. If you overfill the hole or allow any water to escape, you'll have to remove the plate, drain the water, and begin your measurement again.

If you have to fill the buret several times, you risk accumulating error from each reading. This is why we keep burets on hand that hold up to 800 cc's for making large volume measurements.

Example:

This is the result of your combustion chamber volume measurement:

Measured Combustion Chamber Volume = 118.0 cc's

Plug the measured combustion chamber volume (A) into the formula:

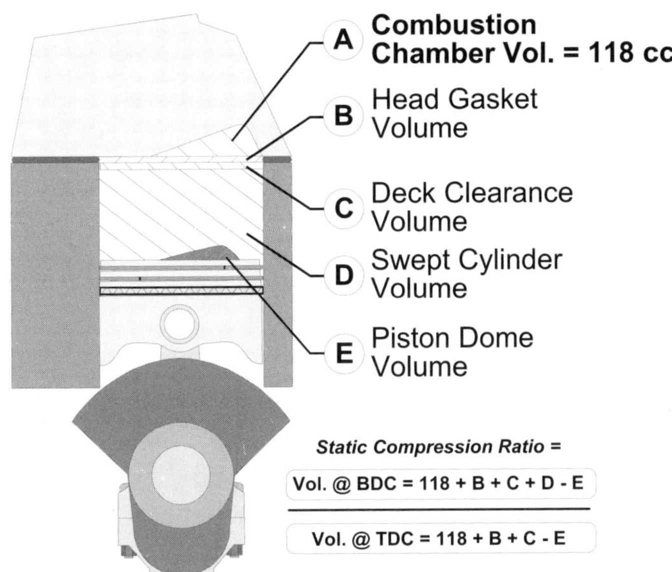

The combustion chamber volume (A) of 118 cc's has been added to the static compression ratio formula.

Measuring Piston Dome Volume (E):

If all pistons were perfectly flat on top, this calculation would not be necessary. However, domes and valve reliefs make the dome geometry very complex. The dome compresses the air/fuel mixture into a tighter space, but valve reliefs cut into the piston deck reduce the net dome volume and lower the compression.

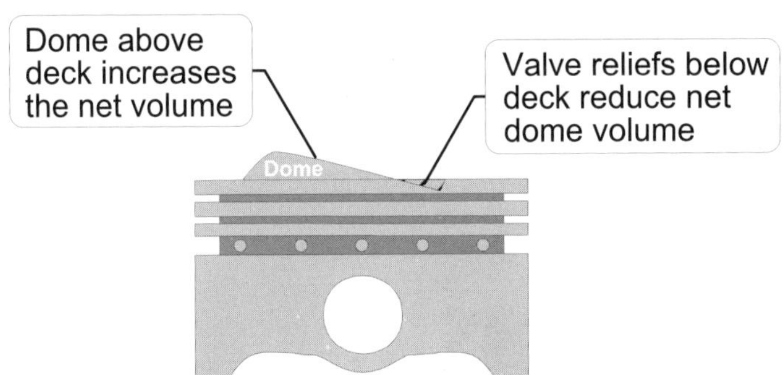

Piston dome volume (E) is the net volume of the piston geometry.

One way to determine the net piston dome volume is to seal a piston into the cylinder and then measure the amount of water required to fill the cylinder to the top. The dome volume (E) is the difference between the volume of water required to fill the cylinder to the top and the calculated volume for a perfectly flat cylinder of the same bore and height.

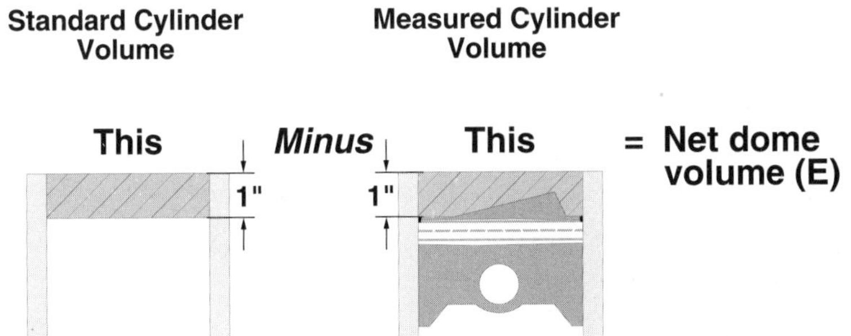

The net dome volume (E) is the difference between the volume of a perfect cylinder with a 1" height and the actual water measurement with the piston in the bore at 1" below the block deck surface.

Seal a piston with no rings into the bore so that the dome is below the block deck surface. If you put the piston at exactly 1" as in our example, the math is simplified.

Wipe the cylinder with a clean cloth to remove any dirt. Apply even layers of masking tape to keep the piston from rocking in the bore or sliding out of position. Test fit the piston in the bore as you add each layer of tape until the piston is stable (square) in the bore and will not slide when you fill the cylinder with water.

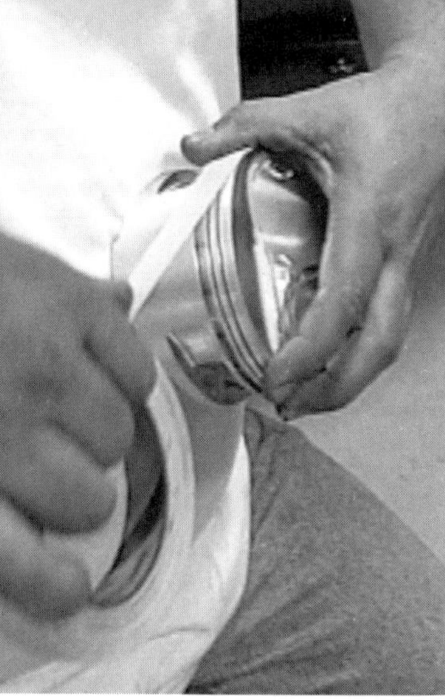

Wipe the cylinder clean, and then apply masking tape to the tapered ring groove portion of the piston above the oil ring.

To ensure an accurate water volume measurement, do not allow the tape to extend above the piston deck. Mount the block on an engine stand and rotate it until the deck is slightly tilted. Push the piston into the bore.

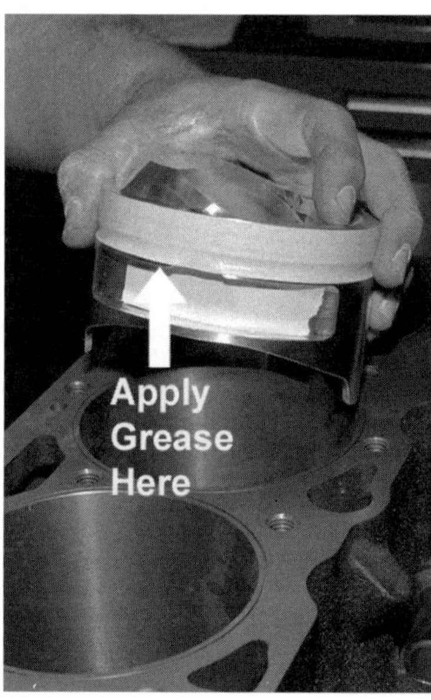

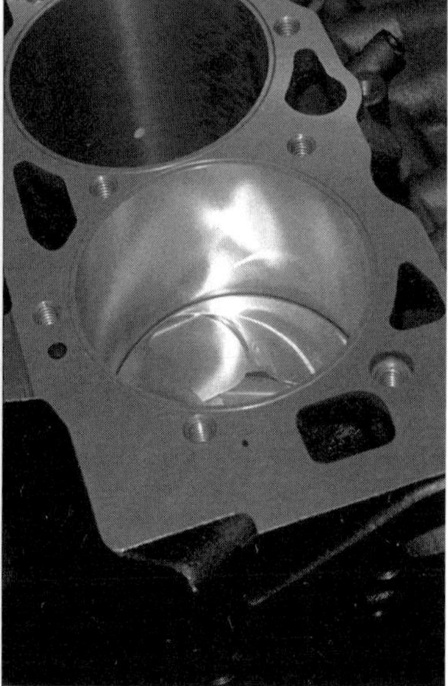

Apply grease all the way around the piston at the base of the tape to help it seal to the cylinder wall.

Push the taped piston into the bore. Check to be sure that the tape is not above the top of the piston.

Slide the piston up in the bore so that the piston deck is a little less than 1" below the block deck. Set and lock a dial caliper to exactly 1 inch. Use the depth bar to check the distance from the block deck to the piston. Tap gently on the piston until it measures 1" from the top at three points around the piston. This ensures that the piston is square in the bore and at a known (1") depth.

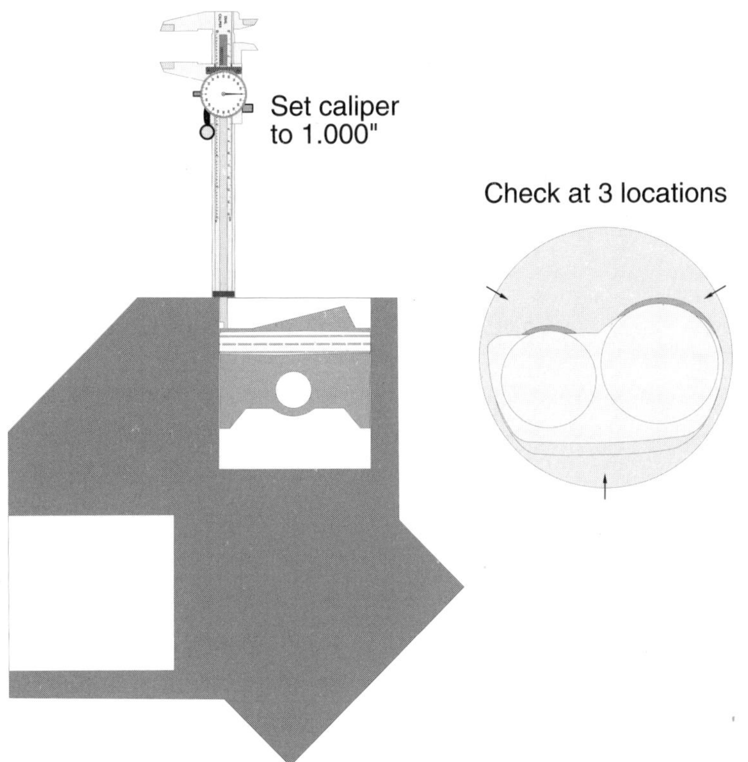

Use a dial caliper and slide the piston until it is exactly 1" below the deck surface. Check it in at least three locations to be sure the piston is not tilted in the bore.

Seal the piston around the perimeter to the cylinder wall with grease. Fill the gap so that the grease is flush with the top of the piston.

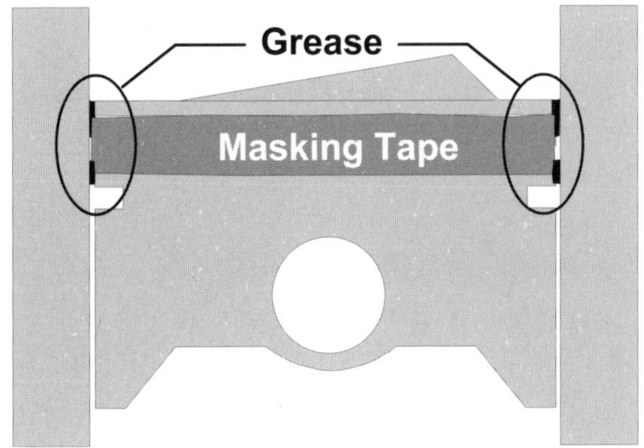

Create a water-tight seal between the piston and cylinder wall with grease. Recheck the position of the piston with the dial caliper to make sure it has not moved.

Coat the cylinder deck surface with grease, being very careful not to get any down into the cylinder. Seal the Plexiglas plate to the grease over the cylinder bore with the fill hole at the highest point. Fill and adjust the level in the buret to "0". Open the valve slowly and allow the engine cylinder to fill with water, then close the valve when the cylinder is full. Write down the buret reading.

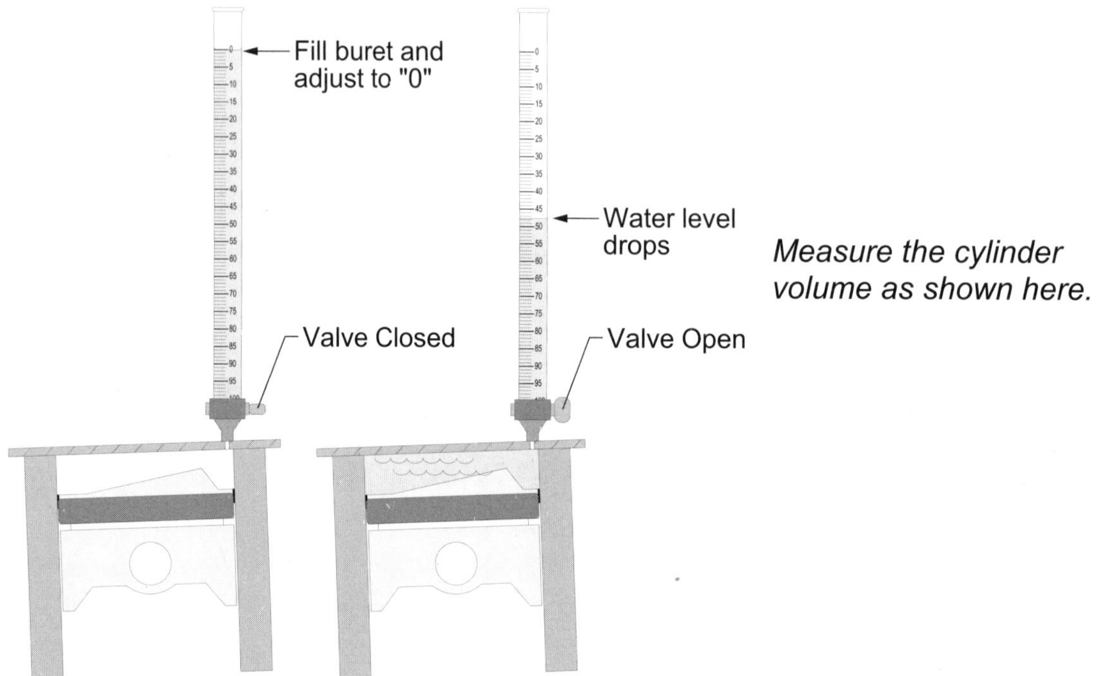

Measure the cylinder volume as shown here.

Example:

This is the result of your piston dome volume measurement:

$$\textbf{Measured Cylinder Volume} = \textbf{201.5 cc's}$$

Compare this measured volume to the calculated volume of a standard cylinder with the same bore diameter (4.47") and a height of 1". The difference between the two will be your net dome volume. Use our formula for the volume of a cylinder:

$$\textbf{Cylinder Volume} = \textbf{bore}^2 \times \textbf{stroke} \times \textbf{.7854}$$

$$\textbf{Cylinder Volume} = \textbf{4.47} \times \textbf{4.47} \times \textbf{1} \times \textbf{.7854}$$

$$\textbf{Cylinder Volume} = \textbf{15.69 Cubic Inches}$$

The calculated standard cylinder volume with the piston 1" below the deck is in English cubic inches, but the water volume measurement is in Metric cubic centimeters (cc's). Here is an important rule to remember whenever you work with a mathematical formula:

When applying math formulas, all numbers must be in the same system (either English or Metric).

This is the standard conversion formula to change cubic inches to metric cc's:

$$\textbf{Cubic Centimeters (cc's) = Cubic Inches} \times \textbf{16.387}$$

Multiply cubic inches times 16.387 to find the cubic centimeters (cc's).

Apply this formula to convert the calculated standard cylinder volume from our example problem (15.69 cubic inches) to Metric cc's. You can round the result to one decimal place (tenths of a cc).

$$\textbf{Cubic Centimeters = Cubic Inches} \times \textbf{16.387}$$

$$\textbf{Cubic Centimeters = 15.69} \times \textbf{16.387 = 257.1 cc's (rounded result)}$$

Subtract the measured water volume (201.5 cc's) from the calculated standard cylinder volume (257.1 cc's) to find the dome volume (E) for our example engine:

$$\textbf{257.1 - 201.5 = 55.6 cc's (answer)}$$

The example piston has a net dome volume (E) of 55.6 cc's.

Plug the piston dome volume (E) into the formula:

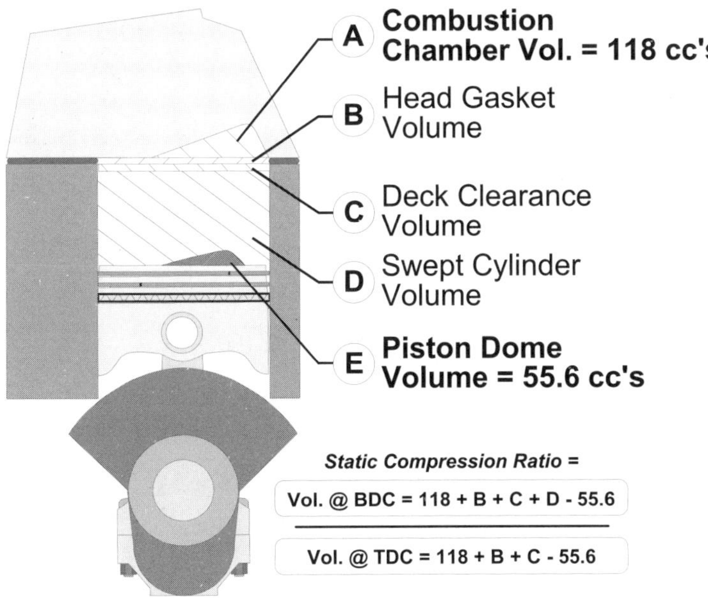

The piston dome volume (E) has been measured and added to the static compression ratio equation.

Calculating Head Gasket Volume (B):

Composition head gaskets usually have the compressed head gasket volume (B) printed on the package in cc's. This is also true of copper head gaskets if they have an irregular shape (valve relief cutouts). If the hole in a copper head gasket is round, you will have to measure the thickness and hole diameter, then calculate the head gasket volume (B). Apply the formula for the volume of a cylinder, with the conversion into cubic centimeters (cc's).

Example:

Determine the copper head gasket volume (B) for the example 502 cubic inch GM racing engine. The measured bore is 4.47" and the thickness is .051".

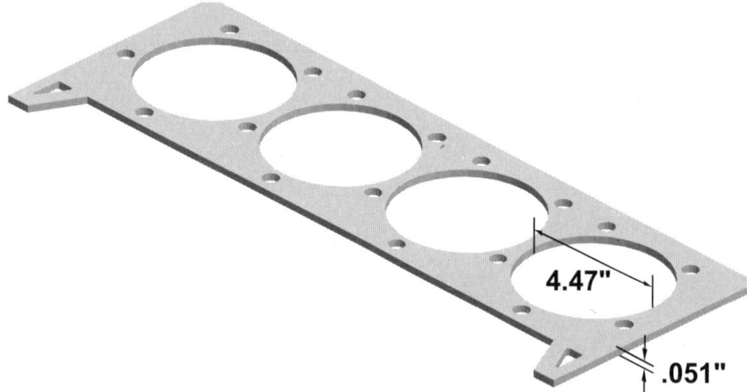

If the gasket is copper with a round hole, measure the thickness with a 1" micrometer and the hole diameter with a dial caliper. Apply the formula for the volume of a cylinder to determine the head gasket volume (B).

Use the cylinder volume formula, but multiply by the cc correction factor (multiply by 16.387) to determine the volume added to the top of the cylinder in cc's by the head gasket (B). The bore is the same as the engine bore (4.47"). The stroke is the compressed thickness of the head gasket (.051").

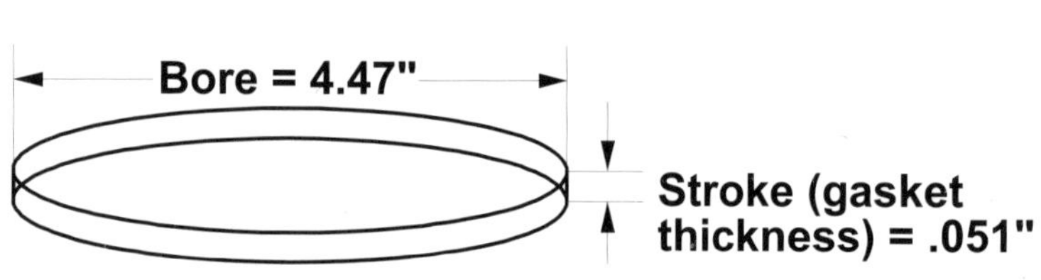

Use the cylinder volume formula, but multiply by 16.387 so that the answer is expressed in cc's instead of cubic inches. This is the volume added by the thickness of the head gasket (B).

$$\textbf{Head Gasket Volume (B)} = \textbf{bore}^2 \times \textbf{stroke} \times .7854 \times 16.387$$

$$\textbf{Head Gasket Volume (B)} = 4.47 \times 4.47 \times .051 \times .7854 \times 16.387$$

$$\textbf{Head Gasket Volume (B)} = 13.1 \textbf{ cc's (rounded result)}$$

The calculated head gasket volume (B) is 13.1 cc's.

Plug the head gasket volume (B) into the formula:

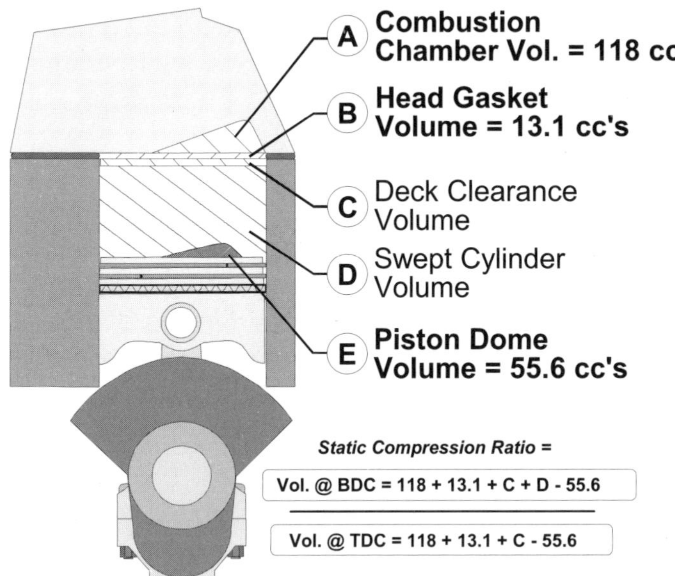

The head gasket volume (B) has been calculated, converted to cc's, and added to the static compression ratio equation.

Calculating Deck Clearance Volume (C):

Like the head gasket volume, the deck clearance volume is a simple mathematical calculation. It must also be expressed in cc's, so be sure to multiply by 16.387.

Example:

Determine the deck clearance volume (C) for the example 502 cubic inch GM racing engine. The bore for this engine is 4.47" and the deck clearance is .014".

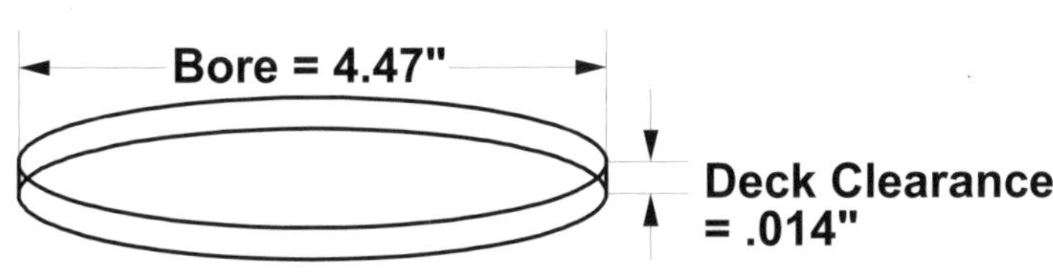

Use the same cylinder volume formula that you used for the head gasket volume to calculate the volume added by the deck clearance (C). The result must be expressed in cc's.

$$\textbf{Deck Clearance Volume (C)} = \textbf{bore}^2 \times \textbf{stroke} \times .7854 \times 16.387$$

$$\textbf{Deck Clearance Volume (C)} = 4.47 \times 4.47 \times .014 \times .7854 \times 16.387$$

$$\textbf{Deck Clearance Volume (C)} = \textbf{3.6 cc's (rounded result)}$$

The deck clearance volume (C) is 3.6 cc's.

Plug the deck clearance volume (C) into the formula:

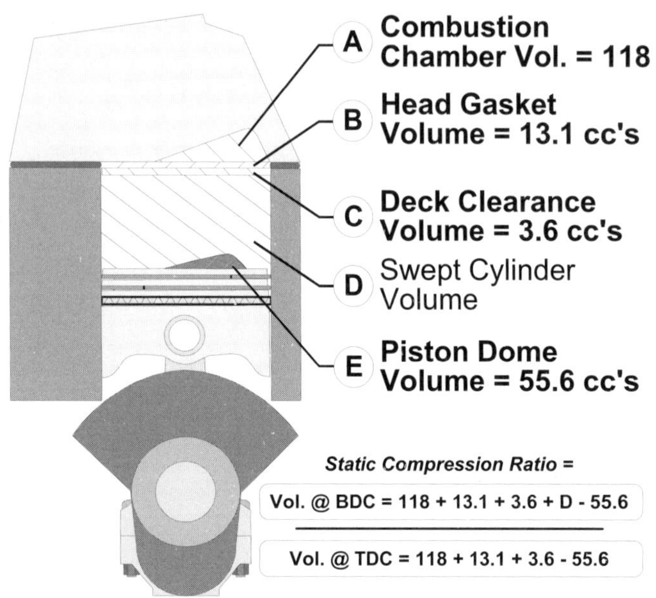

The deck clearance volume (C) has been calculated, and added to the static compression ratio equation. All these volumes are expressed in cc's.

Calculating the Swept Cylinder Volume (D):

Calculate the volume for one cylinder and express it in cc's (multiply by 16.387). This is the final unknown in the static compression ratio formula.

Example:

Calculate the swept cylinder volume for the example 502 cubic inch GM racing engine. The bore of this engine is 4.47" and the stroke is 4.000".

$$\textbf{Swept Cylinder Volume (D)} = \textbf{bore}^2 \times \textbf{stroke} \times \textbf{.7854} \times \textbf{16.387}$$

$$\textbf{Swept Cylinder Volume (D)} = \textbf{4.47} \times \textbf{4.47} \times \textbf{4} \times \textbf{.7854} \times \textbf{16.387}$$

$$\textbf{Swept Cylinder Volume (D)} = \textbf{1028.6 cc's (rounded result)}$$

The calculated cylinder volume (D) is 1028.6 cc's.

Plug the swept cylinder volume (D) into the formula:

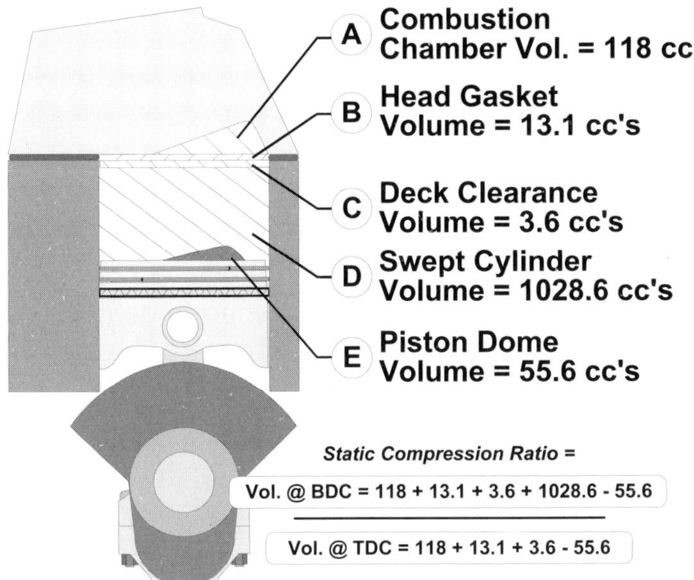

The swept cylinder volume (D) has been calculated, converted to cc's, and added to the static compression ratio equation.

All of the variables are now known and plugged into the formula. You may now solve the equation to determine the static compression ratio of the engine.

Example:

Calculate the static compression ratio for the example engine. You may round your answer to the nearest tenth.

First, perform the addition and subtraction for the volumes at BDC and TDC, then divide the number on the top by the number on the bottom.

$$\textbf{Static Comp. Ratio} = \frac{\textbf{Volume @ BDC} = 118 + 13.1 + 3.6 + 1028.6 - 55.6}{\textbf{Volume @ TDC} = 3.6 + 13.1 + 118 - 55.6}$$

$$\textbf{Static Comp. Ratio} = \frac{1107.7}{79.1} = \frac{14.0}{1} \textbf{ (rounded answer)}$$

Answer to Example Static Compression Ratio Problem:
The engine has a static compression ratio of 14:1. This meets the target ratio exactly.

Correcting Static Compression Ratio:

Raising the Static Compression Ratio - If the measured static compression ratio is too low, there are several ways to raise it:

- Mill the Cylinder Head Surfaces - This reduces the combustion chamber volume.
- Mill the Block Deck Surfaces or Install a Thinner Head Gasket - Be very careful if you choose one of these ways to increase the static compression ratio—material milled from the block deck surfaces or thinner head gaskets reduce the total deck clearance. Never reduce the total deck clearance below the minimum required to maintain both piston-to-valve clearance and piston deck clearance.
- Use Different Pistons or Heads - If the static ratio is very low (more than one number), you may need to use pistons with a greater dome volume or heads with smaller combustion chamber volumes.

This cylinder head is about to be milled to reduce the volume of the combustion chambers. Some cylinder head manufacturers supply information that tells the machinist how much to remove to obtain the right volume in cc's.

Lowering the Static Compression Ratio - If the measured static compression ratio is too high, you may lower it by the following methods:

- Mill the Piston Domes - Shorter domes promote better breathing and improve flame travel. If you already have enough piston-to-valve clearance, a good way to reduce the static compression ratio is to have material milled off the top of the piston domes. The machinist weighs the piston before and after milling, then applies a standard ratio for aluminum weight-to-volume to determine how much the dome volume has been reduced. If your piston-to-valve was a little on the tight side, you can lower the static compression ratio a little by deepening the valve reliefs.
- Install a Thicker Head Gasket - This is not normally a good choice because it may increase the total deck clearance beyond specifications and reduce combustion efficiency.
- Increase the Combustion Chamber Size - An experienced head porter can remove material from the combustion chambers to increase the volume.
- Use Different Pistons or Heads - If the static ratio is very high (more than one number), you may need to use pistons with a smaller dome volume or heads with larger combustion chamber volumes.

Degreeing-In the Camshaft

New racing camshafts have a *cam card* included that shows the specifications for that camshaft. *Degreeing-in* the cam means verifying that the valve timing and lift are close to the specifications printed on the cam card. There are several good reasons to degree-in a camshaft including:

- Checking for Mislabeled Camshaft - You may have purchased a camshaft that was mislabeled or placed in the wrong box.
- Verifying Valve Events - For most applications, it is reasonable to expect that the actual valve opening and closing events are within two degrees of the specifications printed on the cam card and within a few thousandths of the listed lobe lift.
- Checking Camshaft Phasing - The actual lift and duration may be correct, but the camshaft *phasing* may be wrong if the sprocket locating dowel is positioned incorrectly. This doesn't necessarily mean that you must return the camshaft—you may be able to correct the phasing problem. Also, racers and engine builders sometimes find that a particular camshaft works better if it is advanced or retarded a degree or two from the manufacturer's recommended location.

These are the steps for degreeing-in a camshaft:

1. *Install the camshaft*
2. *Install the crank, piston & rod assembly, and cam drive assembly*
3. *Mount and adjust the degree wheel & pointer*
4. *Install #1 lifters and dial indicator*
5. *Determine valve opening location, lobe lift, & valve closing location*
6. *Calculate & correct the camshaft phasing*

Step #1, Install the Camshaft:

Apply oil to the cam journals and lobes. Rotate and slide the camshaft into the block. Support and rotate the camshaft as you install it.

Carefully slide the camshaft into the block. Avoid creating nicks or scratches on the cam bearings.

Step #2, Install the Crank, Piston & Rod Assembly, and Cam Drive Assembly: Clean the engine block and crankshaft. Lubricate the main bearings and install the crankshaft.

Carefully place the crankshaft onto the oiled main bearings.

Lubricate and install the main caps, then tighten the bolts or nuts enough to seat the caps. Apply some motor oil on the #1 cylinder wall, and then stabilize the #1 piston in the bore by wrapping the ring grooves with an even layer of masking tape. Install the piston & rod assembly with rod bearings. Lubricate and snug the rod cap enough to seat it.

Install the front plate and cam thrust hardware with two nuts. Follow the instructions supplied with your cam drive kit. If a thrust plate is used, be sure to check the installed thrust clearance (end play). Set up a dial indicator as shown below and gently push the cam as far as it will go in one direction. Zero the dial, and push the cam the opposite way. The dial reads the cam thrust clearance. Make this measurement several times to be sure it is repeatable and accurate.

The dial indicates that the cam thrust clearance is .005". Change thrust shims as needed to obtain the clearance recommended by the manufacturer.

Install the crank sprocket (or pulley), chain (or belt), and cam sprocket (or pulley) as a unit. The timing marks must be aligned as shown below.

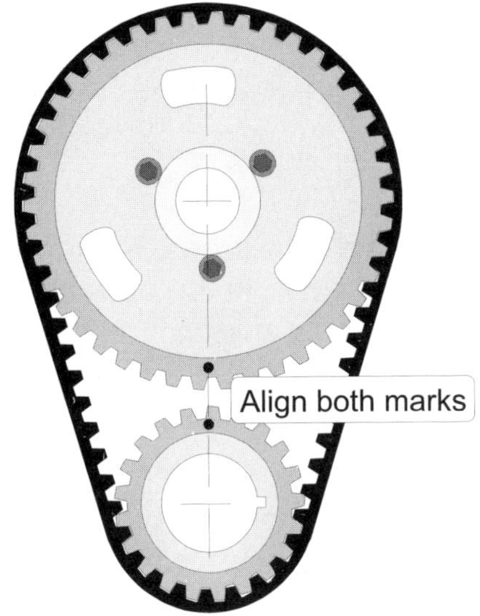

Rotate the cam and crank as needed to install the cam drive assembly as shown. Use a straight edge to be sure you are not off one tooth.

IMPORTANT! Some cam drive assemblies have other markings on the sprockets and additional keyways to change the cam phasing. Be sure to refer to the directions and use the standard "0" alignment marks.

Step #3, Mount and Adjust the Degree Wheel & Pointer:

A *degree wheel* is a round plate that has degree markings to 180° on either side of TDC and/or for all 360° of crankshaft rotation. Most degree wheels mount to a crank turning socket. Install the socket first, and tighten the set screw. Install the degree wheel on the crank turning socket and tighten the knurled nut securely. Attach a pointer to a fixed location on the block.

Install the crank turning socket and degree wheel onto the crankshaft snout. Be sure the woodruff key is in place and that you are using the correct socket. The degree wheel will keep precise track of the crankshaft position as you rotate the crankshaft.

To adjust the degree wheel, rotate the crankshaft until the #1 piston is at TDC. Move the pointer or degree wheel so that the reading is zero degrees.

> ***NOTE:*** Piston movement slows down significantly near TDC. This effect is sometimes referred to as *piston dwell*. Near the top, a degree or two of crankshaft rotation makes very little measurable difference in piston location. This makes it more difficult to determine when #1 piston is exactly at TDC.

To overcome errors related to piston dwell, find TDC by using a standard piston *checking depth*. Position the #1 piston so that it is down in the bore an exact distance both before and after TDC. Then rotate the crankshaft until it is exactly halfway between these locations.

One way to create a checking depth is by using a *piston stop*. A piston stop is a metal bar that bolts across the block deck and mechanically stops piston travel. Although some builders use a piston stop, we feel that using a dial indicator to find a standard checking depth will provide you with a more accurate TDC adjustment. It also eliminates the possibility of denting the soft aluminum piston.

First, you must make a rough TDC adjustment. Mount a dial indicator on a *deck bridge* and position it over the #1 piston. The piston rocks on its pin, so apply pressure in one direction so that you have repeatable readings. Use a long bar to engage the crank turning socket, and rotate the crankshaft until you find the high point in the piston travel (TDC). Zero the dial indicator, then adjust the degree wheel or bend the pointer as required to indicate 0° (TDC).

The dial indicator mounted in a deck bridge shows you when the piston is close to the high point in its travel (TDC).

For this example, we will use a standard piston checking depth of .050". Rotate the crankshaft clockwise until the piston approaches TDC. As you do this, apply pressure to the piston in the same direction as you did before to take out the piston rock. Stop rotating when dial reads exactly .050" before TDC. Note and record the reading on your degree wheel. You can apply a piece of masking tape to the wheel if you wish.

Now, turn the crankshaft and take out piston rock until the piston has passed TDC and is exactly .050" below TDC. Note and record or mark the degree wheel reading with masking tape.

Rotate the crankshaft until the piston is at .050" before top dead center (BTDC). Mark this location on a piece of masking tape.

Rotate the crankshaft until the piston is at .050" after top dead center (ATDC). Mark this location on a piece of masking tape.

Rotate the crankshaft until it is exactly halfway between the two degree markings. Adjust the degree wheel or pointer until they indicate "0" (TDC). Your degree wheel will now read crankshaft position accurately. Recheck your measurements.

To position the crankshaft at #1 TDC, rotate it exactly halfway between the two marks.

Without moving the crankshaft, adjust the degree wheel or pointer until "0" (TDC) is indicated.

Step #4, Install #1 Lifters and Dial Indicator:

Lubricate the lifters, and slide them into the lifter bores for #1 cylinder. If the lifters are roller tappets, be sure to install the link that prevents lifter rotation.

Identify the #1 intake lifter. If the pistons have valve reliefs, look for the lifter that corresponds to the larger (intake) valve relief on the piston. You can also determine the order of lifter bores by inspecting the valve layout on the cylinder head.

Mount the dial indicator so that it is in straight contact with the #1 intake lifter. Rotate the crankshaft, and adjust the dial so it reads zero when the lifter is all the way down (on the base circle).

Install the dial indicator so the plunger is in direct line with lifter operation. Use an extension or pushrod to reach the lifter. Zero the dial when the lifter is on the cam base circle.

Step #5, Determine Valve Opening Location, Lift, & Closing Locations:

The specifications are on a card that is shipped with your camshaft. These are the cam card specifications for our example camshaft for a 502 CID racing engine:

Specifications	Intake	Exhaust
Open @ .050"	29° BTDC	95° BBDC
Lobe Lift	.512"	.470"
Close @ .050"	75° ABDC	33° ATDC
Duration @ .050"	284°	308°
Lobe Separation 117°		
Install Cam at 113° Intake Centerline		

NOTE: Due to the slack in timing chains or belts, you must always approach locations when degreeing-in the cam by turning the crankshaft <u>clockwise</u> (the same way it rotates when the engine is running). If you turn the crankshaft too far, turn it back some distance, and get a "running start" at it again with a clockwise rotation. This ensures the accuracy of your degree measurements.

<u>Intake Open</u> - Turn the crankshaft clockwise until the dial indicator shows that the intake lifter has risen to the .050" checking height shown on the cam card. Write down the degrees BTDC (before TDC) indicated on the wheel.

Turn the crankshaft until the intake lifter rises .050" off the cam base circle. The degree wheel indicates that the intake valve opens at 26° BTDC (before TDC).

<u>Intake Lobe Lift</u> - Rotate the crankshaft slowly clockwise. The reading on the dial indicator will increase steadily as the lifter rises. When the dial reading begins to decrease, rotate the crankshaft back & forth until you find the highest reading.

Turn the crankshaft until you obtain the highest reading on the dial. Count the number of full revolutions; each is equal to .100".

In this case, the needle made five complete turns and indicates an additional .012". This is a total reading of .512". Record the intake lobe lift.

Intake Close - First, turn the crankshaft slowly clockwise until the dial indicator shows that the intake lifter is the checking height (.050") from the fully closed position. If you pass the location and reach the base circle (zero dial reading), turn the crankshaft counter clockwise beyond the .050" reading, and approach it slowly in a clockwise direction.

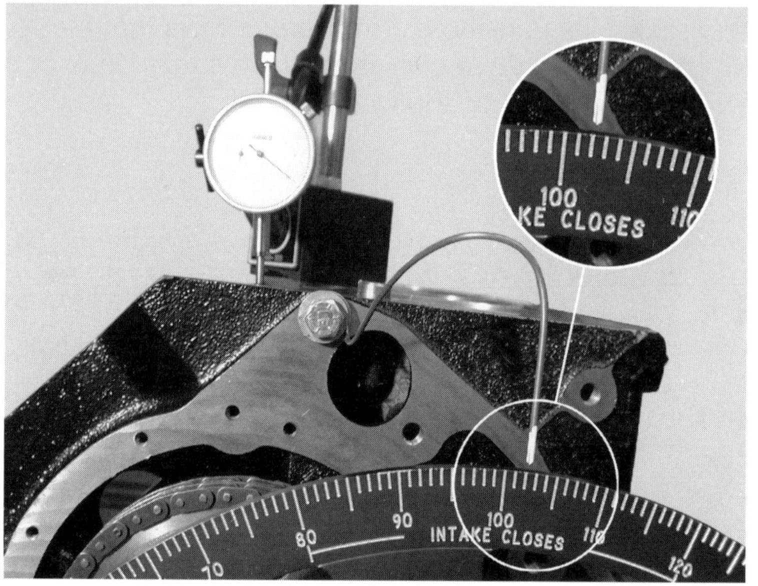

Turn the crankshaft until the intake lifter is .050" from fully closed. The degree wheel reads 102°, but this is in degrees BTDC, not degrees ABDC as shown on the cam card. You must convert this reading to degrees after bottom dead center in order to compare it with the cam card specs.

Some degree wheels have multiple scales so that you can make a direct reading of degrees ABDC. The degree wheel in our example does not. Although there is a mathematical way to change the indicated degrees BTDC into ATDC (subtract the reading from 180°), there is an easier way that eliminates the math. Count the full ten degree marks past the 180° (BDC) location as shown below, then add the partial degree remainder to make your final intake close reading in degrees ABDC.

Count by 10's as shown here to determine the indicated intake close location in degrees ABDC. There are 70° plus a remainder of 8° for a final reading of 78° ABDC. Record the intake close result.

<u>Exhaust Open</u> - Remove the dial indicator from the intake lifter, and remount it on the exhaust lifter. Rotate the crankshaft and zero the dial when the lifter is on the base circle (all the way down). Turn the crankshaft slowly clockwise until the dial indicator shows that the exhaust lifter has risen to the checking height of .050". Write down the degrees shown on the wheel.

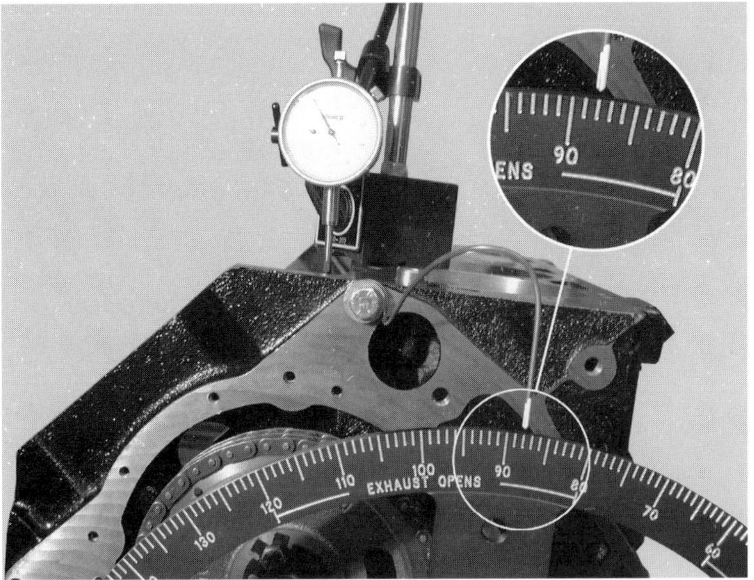

Turn the crankshaft until the exhaust lifter rises .050" off the cam base circle. The degree wheel reads 88°, but this is in degrees ATDC, not degrees BBDC as shown on the cam specs. You must convert this reading to degrees before bottom dead center in order to compare it with the cam card specs.

As with the previous intake close measurement, this degree wheel has no direct reading for degrees BBDC. Count the full ten degree marks past the 0° (TDC) location as shown below; then add the partial degree remainder to make your final exhaust close reading in degrees BBDC.

Count by 10's as shown below to determine the indicated exhaust open location in degrees BBDC. There are 90° plus a remainder of 2° for a final reading of 92° BBDC. Record the exhaust open result.

Exhaust Lobe Lift - Rotate the crankshaft slowly clockwise. The reading on the dial indicator will increase steadily as the lifter rises. When the dial reading begins to decrease, rotate the crankshaft back & forth until you find the highest reading. Record the exhaust lobe lift.

Turn the crankshaft until you obtain the highest reading on the dial. Count the number of full revolutions; each is equal to .100".

In this case, the needle made four complete turns and indicates an additional .071". This is a total reading of .471". Record the exhaust lobe lift.

Exhaust Close - Turn the crankshaft slowly clockwise until the dial indicator shows that the exhaust lifter is the checking height (.050") from the fully closed position. Write down the degrees shown on the wheel.

Turn the crankshaft until the exhaust lifter is .050" from being closed. The degree wheel reads 36.5° ATDC.

This degree wheel reads degrees after TDC, so no conversion is needed. Record the exhaust close event (36.5° ATDC @ .050") with your other measurements.

Step #6, Correct the Camshaft Phasing:

These are the recorded measurements for our example camshaft:

Event	Intake (actual)	Exhaust (actual)
Open @ .050"	26° BTDC	92° BBDC
Lobe Lift	.512"	.471"
Close @ .050"	78° ABDC	36.5° ATDC

Before you can compare these results with the cam card specifications, you must do a little math to determine *duration* and *intake lobe centerline*.

Calculate Duration - Duration is the total time in crankshaft degrees that the valve is open at the specified checking clearance (.050" in this example). Total duration is the sum of the open location, 180° (the distance from TDC to BDC), and the closing location.

$$\textbf{Duration} = \textbf{Open Degrees} + \textbf{180}^\circ + \textbf{Close Degrees}$$

Apply this formula to our sample camshaft measurements:

$$\textbf{Duration} = \textbf{Open Degrees} + \textbf{180}^\circ + \textbf{Close Degrees}$$

$$\textbf{Intake Duration} = \textbf{26}^\circ + \textbf{180}^\circ + \textbf{78}^\circ = \textbf{284}^\circ \text{ @ .050" (answer)}$$

$$\textbf{Exhaust Duration} = \textbf{92}^\circ + \textbf{180}^\circ + \textbf{36.5}^\circ = \textbf{308.5}^\circ \text{ @ .050" (answer)}$$

The measured intake duration is 284°, and the measured exhaust duration is 308.5° This is very close (within .5°) of the cam card specifications.

Calculate Intake Lobe Centerline - The actual intake and exhaust opening/closing events may vary a couple of degrees or more from the cam card specifications. If the measured events are close to specs (within 2°), you can install the cam and correct any error in phasing. This is determined by measuring the distance from the centerline of the intake lobe to TDC (often called *intake centerline*). The diagram below shows how the intake centerline is determined.

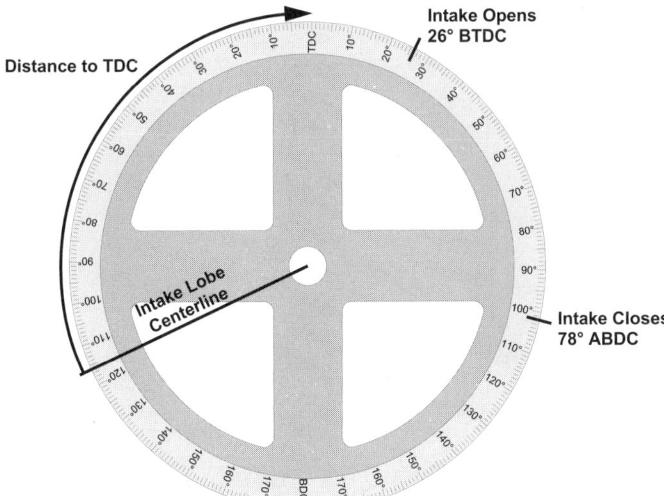

If the camshaft duration is close, check the phasing. First, find the center of the intake lobe by dividing the total intake duration (284°) by two.

To reference this lobe centerline to TDC, you must subtract the degrees that the intake opens before top dead center (in this example, subtract 26° BTDC).

This is how the intake lobe centerline calculation looks when expressed as a mathematical formula:

$$\textbf{Intake Centerline} = \frac{\textbf{Duration}}{\textbf{2}} - \textbf{Intake Open Degrees BTDC}$$

Now, plug in the numbers from our example camshaft into the formula:

$$\textbf{Intake Centerline} = \frac{\textbf{284}^\circ}{\textbf{2}} - \textbf{26}^\circ\,\textbf{BTDC} = \textbf{116}^\circ\,\textbf{(answer)}$$

The example camshaft has an intake centerline of 116°.

Refer to the camshaft specifications chart on page 302. The measured cam duration is very close to the cam card specifications (within .5°), but the cam phasing is wrong. This camshaft was supposed to be installed at a 113° intake centerline, but our measurements and centerline calculation show the actual intake centerline to be 116°. This means that the intake lobe is 3° *farther* from TDC, so the camshaft is *3° retarded* from the recommended installed position.

Verify the Camshaft Lobe Separation - It is possible that you could have a camshaft that has the lobes ground with the right lift and duration, but was ground with the wrong lobe separation. Before you correct camshaft phasing, it's important to check the lobe separation. Calculate the exhaust centerline in the same way that you did so for the intake centerline:

$$\textbf{Exhaust Centerline} = \frac{\textbf{Duration}}{\textbf{2}} - \textbf{Exhaust Open Degrees ATDC}$$

Now, plug in the numbers from our example camshaft into the formula:

$$\textbf{Exhaust Centerline} = \frac{\textbf{308.5}^\circ}{\textbf{2}} - \textbf{36.5}^\circ\,\textbf{ATDC} = \textbf{117.75}^\circ\,\textbf{(answer)}$$

The example camshaft has an exhaust centerline of 117.75°.

Now, determine the lobe separation. Use the formula below:

$$\textbf{Lobe Separation} = \frac{\textbf{Intake Centerline} + \textbf{Exhaust Centerline}}{\textbf{2}}$$

$$\textbf{Lobe Separation} = \frac{\textbf{116}^\circ + \textbf{117.75}^\circ}{\textbf{2}} = \textbf{116.875}$$

The lobe separation as listed on the cam card was 117°. The actual separation as measured by degreeing in the cam is 116.875°, only .125°, or just one-eighth of a degree from specification—easily close enough to warrant the installation of this camshaft in your engine. If the measured lobe separation is a degree or more from specification, it cannot be corrected and must be replaced. Contact the cam manufacturer for their return policies and information.

To correct camshaft phasing, the cam drive assembly must be set to *advance the camshaft 3°*. This means that the camshaft must be turned 3° clockwise from its current position.

Phasing the camshaft is a snap if you have a belt drive. Simply loosen the adjustment bolts, rotate the inner hub until the indicator reads 3° advance, and retighten the bolts.

If you have a chain & sprocket drive, you can buy an offset woodruff key for the crankshaft snout, but the offset weakens the key. You can also buy a crank sprocket that has additional keyways and alignment marks. We prefer to install the crank sprocket at 0 and install a cam degree kit that contains uses an offset bushing that relocates the cam sprocket. Be sure to follow the installation instructions carefully with either system.

With the offset bushing system, you must drill all four holes (three bolt holes and one bushing hole) to 13/32". The bushings are color-coded and come in one degree increments from 0° to 8°. Install the offset bushing of the right type to make the needed correction. Make sure that you have the offset bushing installed to move the camshaft in the right direction (3° clockwise for our example). Run through the valve opening numbers again to be sure the cam phasing is correct.

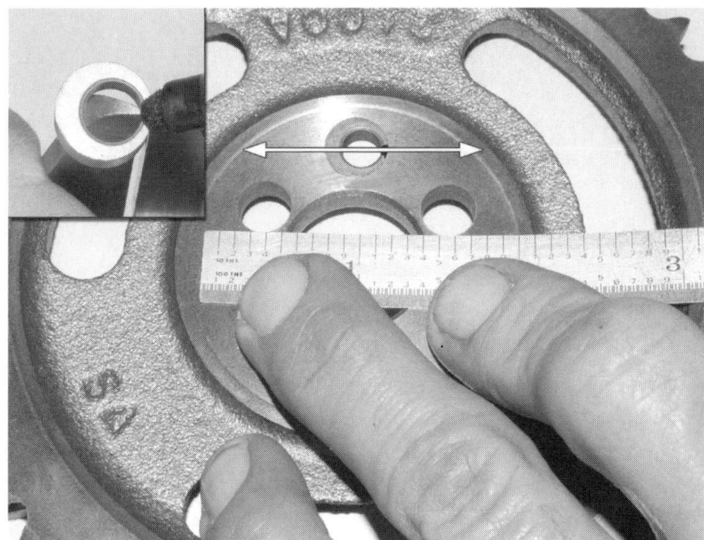

Offset bushings are available to correct camshaft phasing for many chain & sprocket cam drives (see insert on upper left). Be sure that the thick-to-thin centerline of the bushing is parallel with the bolt holes as shown here.

Measuring Piston-to-Valve Clearance

Inadequate piston-to-valve clearance is one of the most common causes of catastrophic engine failure. Never run a racing engine without verifying this important measurement.

Some racers use a clay impression method for checking piston-to-valve clearance. A pancake of clay is placed on the piston, then the engine is partially assembled. Rotating the crankshaft causes the valves to push into the clay, then the resulting impression is examined and measured. Using clay to measure piston-to-valve does not provide very accurate results and fails to address important clearance issues such as radial valve clearance and parallelism.

We use only precision measuring tools for a reliable measurement, then locate valve centers and angles. This ensures correct piston-to-valve clearances so that valves and pistons are unlikely to collide and damage parts. Follow these steps for measuring piston-to-valve clearance:

1. *Check the piston dome-to-combustion chamber clearance*
2. *Install the #1 piston & rod assembly, camshaft, and degree wheel*
3. *Mark the valve guide centers on the pistons*
4. *Degree-in the camshaft*
5. *Measure the valve relief angles*
6. *Check the radial valve clearance*
7. *Assemble the valve train components on #1 cylinder*
8. *Measure the piston-to-valve clearance*

Step #1, Check the Piston Dome-to-Combustion Chamber Clearance:

This check ensures that there is no interference between the piston domes and the combustion chambers. Apply a machinist's dye to the deck surface of the cylinder head; then attach the head to the block with two head bolts. Reach from the underside of the engine and scribe a mark around the circumference of the cylinder.

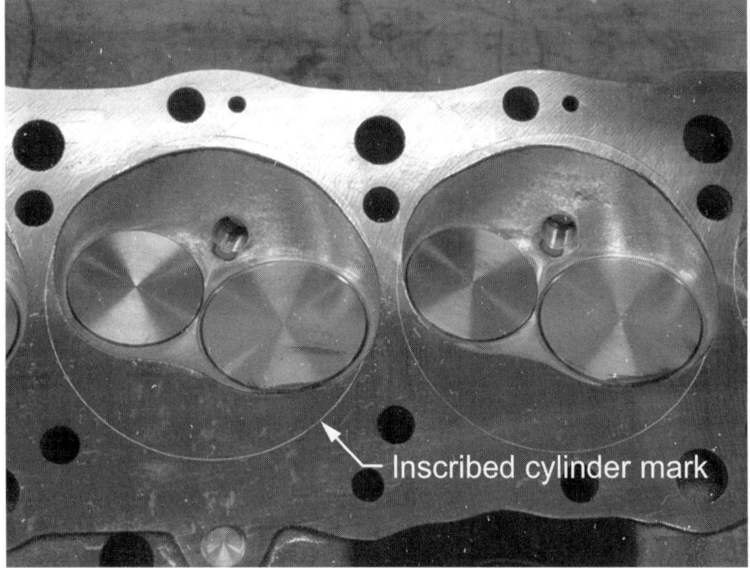

This inscribed mark on the cylinder head allows you to check the fit of the piston dome with the shape of the combustion chamber.

Remove the head and lay it on a bench. Link two pistons together with a wrist pin to keep them parallel as shown in the figure below. Visually center the piston pair with the inscribed cylinder lines.

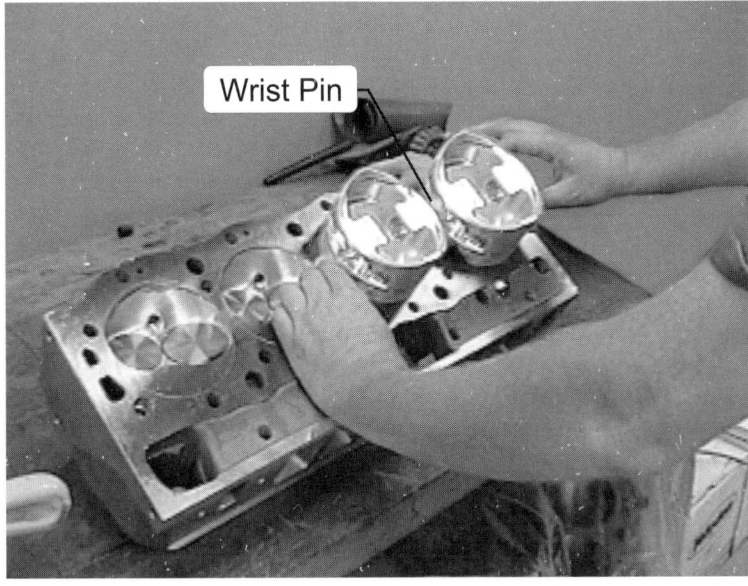

To check the dome-to-combustion chamber clearance, place the linked piston pair with the domes in the combustion chambers. Center the tapered piston tops within the inscribed cylinder lines.

Slide the pistons in all directions. The tapered top of each piston must be able to move to the inscribed cylinder line without interference.

Checking Dome Clearance

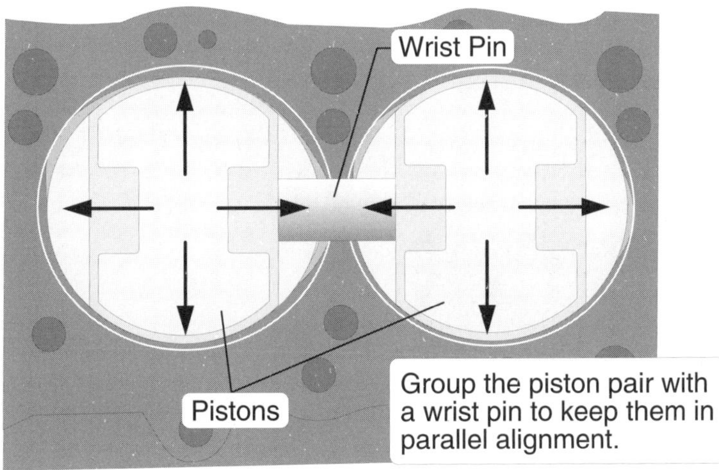

If the piston pair can slide in all directions to the inscribed cylinder lines, there is adequate dome-to-combustion chamber clearance.

Any dome-to-combustion chamber interference must be corrected before you assemble the short block. Locate and mark any areas of interference. Re-contour the piston domes or combustion chambers, or try a different piston/cylinder head combination. Be sure to measure the static compression ratio after you have resolved the dome interference problem.

Step #2, Install the #1 Piston & Rod Assembly, Camshaft, and Degree Wheel:

Apply even layers of masking tape over the ring grooves to keep the piston from rocking in the bore. Clean and install the camshaft, crankshaft, and the #1 piston & rod assembly.

Apply some machinist's dye to the top of the piston. Install and adjust the degree wheel. Refer to the *Degreeing-In the Camshaft* section of this unit for complete degree wheel installation and adjustment procedures.

Install the piston & rod assembly and a degree wheel. Use a dial indicator and a checking depth to be sure the wheel reads accurately.

Step #3, Mark the Valve Guide Centers on the Pistons:

Remove the valves from your cylinder heads, and install them with the head gaskets. You need only use enough bolts to hold them in place. You can make a valve guide marking punch out of round steel stock of the same diameter as the valve stem or cut off the head of an old valve and sharpen the end to a point.

Before you mark the exhaust valve center, rotate the crankshaft clockwise until the #1 piston is at 10° on the degree wheel. It makes no difference if it is before or after TDC. This is the position where exhaust valve clash is most likely to occur.

Rotate the crankshaft clockwise to 10° BTDC.

After turning the crankshaft to the 10° BTDC position, slide the marking punch into the exhaust valve guide and tap it gently with a hammer.

Slide the marking punch into the exhaust valve guide and tap the end of the punch lightly to mark the valve center on the piston dome.

Slide the marking punch into the intake valve guide and tap it gently to mark the intake valve center.

Rotate the crankshaft clockwise to 10° ATDC, then mark the intake valve center.

Step #4, Degree-In the Camshaft:

If you have already degreed-in the camshaft, you may skip this step.

Step #5, Measure the Valve Relief Angles:

It is very important that the valve heads and reliefs are parallel. If the valves and pistons ever do collide, angular contact will bend the valve heads and cause severe engine damage. Parallel contact between valve heads and reliefs limits the damage to valve train components—often to nothing more than a bent pushrod or broken rocker arm.

Remove the cylinder head and slip intake and exhaust *checking valves* into the guides of #1 cylinder. Reinstall the cylinder head with two bolts. You can make your own checking valves out of old intake and exhaust valves:

Checking Valve

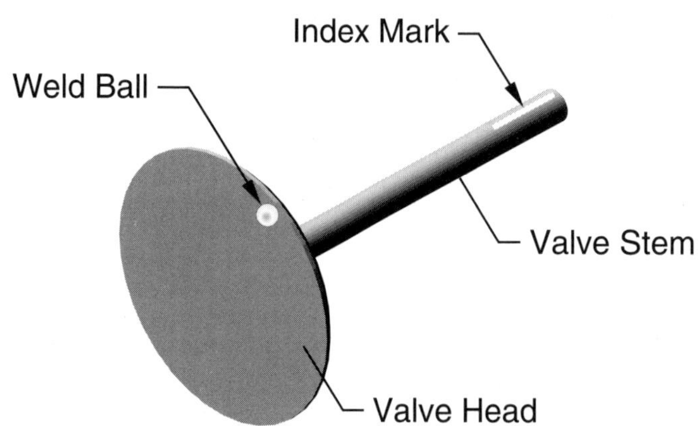

The weld ball rises and falls as it follows the contour of the valve relief in the piston dome. The index mark on the stem indicates the orientation of the ball.

In order to cut the valve reliefs at the correct angle, your machinist needs information that shows the relative tilt between the valve head and valve relief. Make a diagram similar to the one below and record the rise of the valves at 90° intervals as you rotate them.

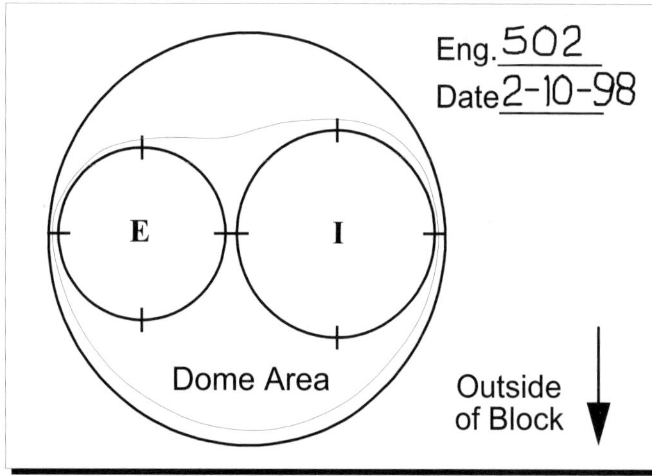

This diagram shows the orientation of the piston valves and dome for #1 cylinder (standing by the left side of the engine). The valve rise readings enable the machinist to cut the reliefs parallel with the valve heads.

Checking the Intake Valve Relief Angle – Pull the checking valves up by the stems and hold them in place so they do not fall into the engine as you turn the crankshaft.

> ***IMPORTANT!*** The checking valves must not be allowed to fall into the cylinder as you rotate the crankshaft. For safety, place rubber O-rings on the valve stems and run them all the way down against the guides with the valves fully closed.

Rotate the crankshaft clockwise until the #1 piston is at 10° ATDC. To be sure the valves don't fall too far into the cylinder, never go past 10° before or after TDC. Push the valves down against the piston—the safety O-rings will slide up the valve stems as you do this.

Hold the checking valves up and rotate the crankshaft clockwise to 10° ATDC. Release the checking valves and push them down until they rest on top of the piston.

Attach a dial indicator so that the plunger rests directly on top of the intake checking valve stem as shown in the photo below. Rotate the intake checking valve until it is at its lowest position and zero the dial indicator.

Set up and the dial indicator as shown here. Adjust it so that it is inline with the valve stem for accurate results. Rotate the valve, and watch the dial. Stop when the checking valve is in the lowest position and zero the dial indicator.

Locate the index mark on the intake checking valve stem, and record it on your diagram as shown below.

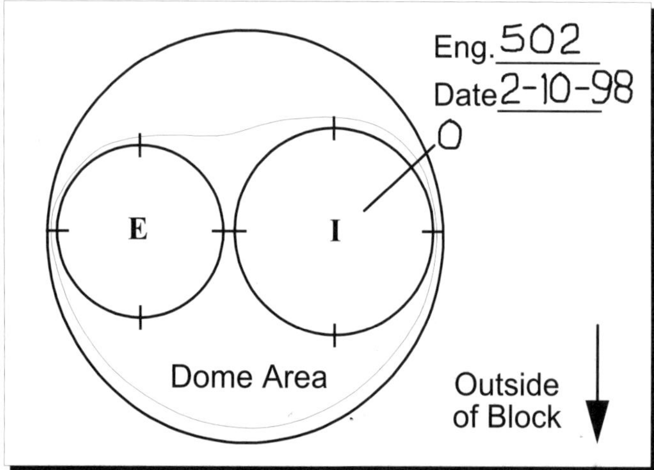

Mark the low point on the diagram with a zero.

Watch the index mark on the intake checking valve stem. Rotate the valve clockwise to the first 90° mark (3 o'clock position), and read the valve rise on the dial indicator. Write the number in thousandths of an inch on the diagram.

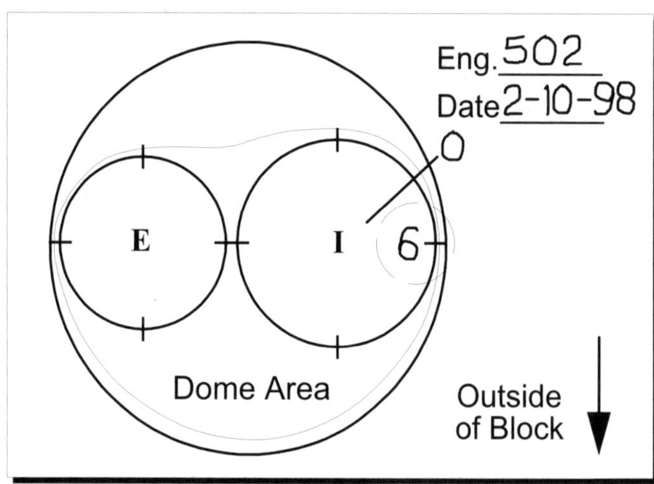

With the intake checking valve in the 3 o'clock position, the dial in this example read .006".

Rotate the checking valve another 90° (6 o'clock position), and write the indicated checking valve rise on the diagram. Repeat this for the 9 and 12 o'clock positions. Make sure the needle on the dial returns to zero when the valve is back in the starting (zero) position.

Checking the Exhaust Valve Relief Angle - Pull the checking valves up by the stems, and hold them in place so they do not fall into the engine as you turn the crankshaft. Slide the safety O-rings down until they contact the valve guides. Rotate the crankshaft counter-clockwise beyond 10° BTDC; then turn it clockwise until the #1 piston is at 10° BTDC.

Hold the checking valves up, and then rotate the crankshaft until the degree wheel reads 10° BTDC. Release the checking valves and push them down until they rest on top of the piston.

Attach the dial indicator so that the plunger rests directly on top of the exhaust valve stem. Rotate the exhaust checking valve until it is at its lowest position, and zero the dial indicator.

Watch the index mark on the exhaust checking valve stem. Rotate the valve clockwise to the first 90° mark, and read the valve rise on the dial indicator. Write the number in thousandths of an inch on the diagram. Repeat this for each 90° mark. Your completed diagram will look something like this:

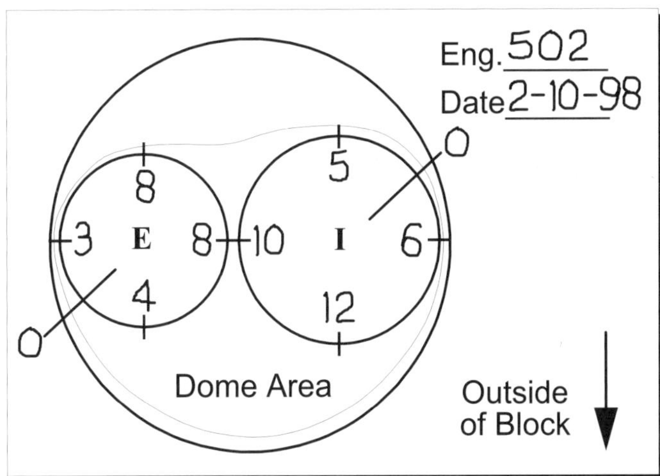

A machinist can translate these readings into valve angle settings. This ensures the correct piston-to-valve clearance and parallel contact to minimize damage should the valves and pistons ever collide.

Step #6, Check the Radial Valve Clearance:

Inscribe the circumference of the valves into the piston dome to be sure the valve heads have the required .050” to .060” radial clearance with the reliefs. First, remove the cylinder head; then set a pair of dividers to the radius of the intake valve.

The radius is half the valve diameter. Measure the valve head with a dial caliper.

Example:

The measured intake valve diameter for your engine is 2.25”. What is the valve radius?

$$\textbf{Valve Radius} = \frac{\textbf{Diameter}}{\textbf{2}} = \frac{\textbf{2.25"}}{\textbf{2}} = \textbf{1.125" (answer)}$$

The radius of this intake valve is 1.125”.

Adjust a dial caliper to the intake valve radius; then set the dividers to the jaw size of the caliper.

NOTE: You can skip using dividers if you wish and use the ID ends of the caliper to inscribe the valve circle on the piston.

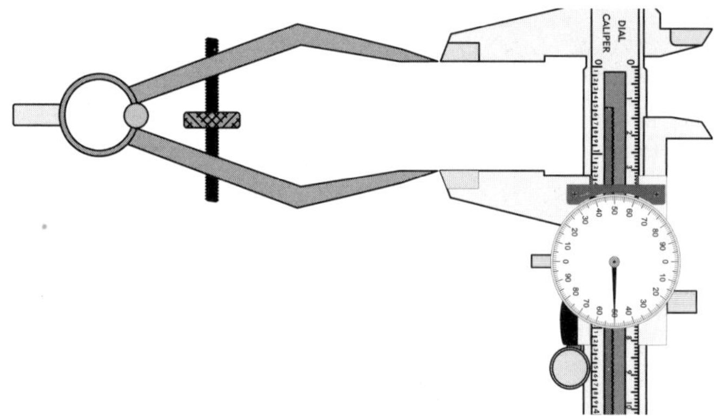

For the example, set the dial caliper jaws to 1.125”. Use the jaws as a reference, and adjust the dividers.

Place one side of the dividers in the valve center punch mark in the piston dome (created on *Step #3*), and sweep the other side in a circle to inscribe the valve outline.

Inscribing Valve Outline

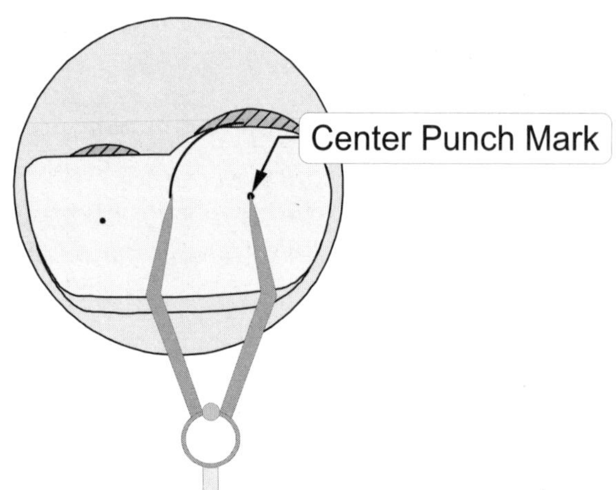

Inscribe the intake valve outliner with the dividers.

Measure the radial clearance between the inscribed valve lines and the valve reliefs with a dial caliper. There should be .050” to .060” radial clearance to prevent contact when the pistons rock near TDC.

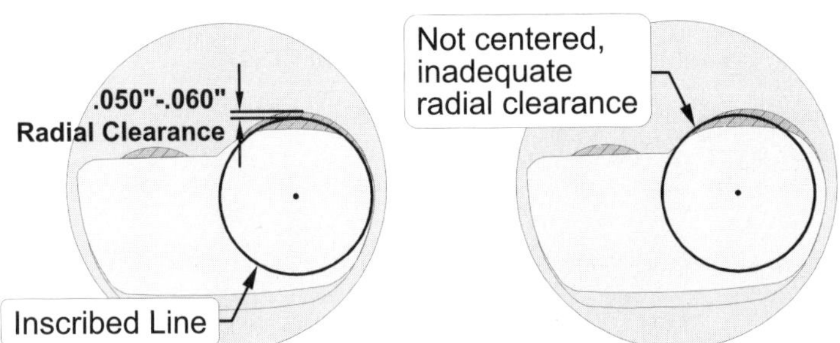

Measure the radial valve clearance from the valve relief to the inscribed line.

Repeat this procedure for the exhaust valve. A machinist can correct any radial valve clearance problems during the relief cutting procedure.

Step #7, Assemble the Valve Train Components on #1 Cylinder:

Remove the cylinder head, and install the valves, springs, and retaining hardware.

IMPORTANT! A valve spring compressor must be used to install the valves in the cylinder heads. This is a dangerous procedure that should only be performed by an experienced technician. Always wear appropriate eye protection when using a valve spring compressor.

Install the cylinder head and head gasket with a few bolts. Install the lifters, pushrods, and rocker arms for #1 cylinder. Adjust the *valve lash*. Refer to your cam card for the correct intake lash specification. Rotate the crankshaft until the intake lifter is on the base circle (valve closed). Adjust the intake rocker arm until the correct size feeler gauge slides between the rocker arm and valve with slight drag.

After setting the intake valve lash, set the exhaust valve lash. Rotate the crankshaft until the exhaust lifer is on the base circle, and use the correct feeler gauge for exhaust valve lash.

Adjust the valves to the correct lash specification. This information should be included on the cam card that was supplied with your camshaft.

Step #8, Measure the Piston-to-Valve Clearance:

Exhaust Piston-to-valve Clearance - Rotate the engine clockwise until the degree wheel indicates that the #1 piston is at 10° BTDC on the *exhaust stroke*. Slowly turn the crankshaft until the exhaust rocker begins to move (exhaust open). Continue rotating the crankshaft until the degree wheel reads 10° BTDC. If you have the crank in the correct location, both valves will be open (overlap period).

Exhaust piston-to-valve clearance must be checked with the #1 piston at 10° BTDC.

Install the dial indicator so that the plunger rests on top of the exhaust valve spring retainer and in-line with the exhaust valve stem. Zero the dial. Tighten the rocker arm adjustment nut until you feel the valve contact the piston. Check to be sure that the rocker assembly has not bottomed on the stud. The dial reading is the exhaust piston-to-valve clearance. Record this reading and loosen the rocker arm.

Slowly tighten the rocker arm nut until the valve gently contacts the piston. You will feel the wrench bind when this happens. Record the exhaust piston-to-valve clearance.

Intake Piston-to-Valve Clearance – Slowly rotate the engine clockwise just past TDC until the degree wheel indicates 10° ATDC. At this point, you are on the *intake stroke*.

Intake piston-to-valve clearance must be checked with the #1 piston at 10° ATDC.

Install a dial indicator so that the plunger rests on top of the intake valve spring retainer. Make sure the plunger is in-line with the intake valve stem. Zero the dial.

Tighten the rocker arm adjustment nut until you feel the valve contact the piston. Again, check to be sure that the rocker arm assembly has not bottomed on the stud. The dial reading is the intake piston-to-valve clearance. Record this reading, and loosen the rocker arm.

A good rule of thumb for intake piston-to-valve clearance is total deck clearance plus .010". A good rule of thumb for exhaust piston-to-valve clearance is at least 1.6 to 2 times the intake clearance. These are the piston-to-valve clearance specifications we use for the majority of applications:

Common Intake Piston-to-Valve Clearance = .060"-.065"

Common Exhaust Piston-to-Valve Clearance = .120" minimum

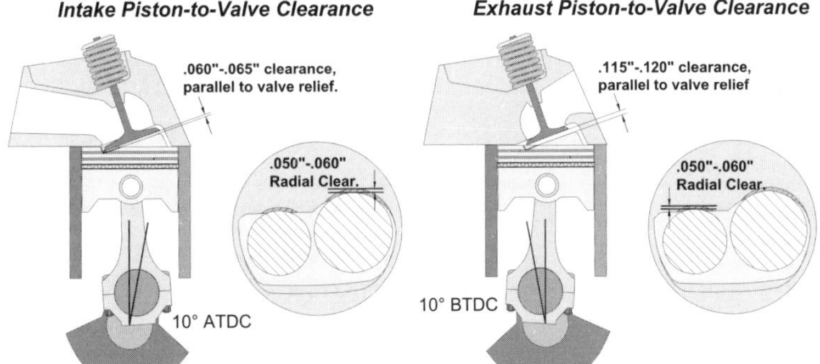

Before you assemble any racing engine, make sure you meet all of these specifications for piston-to-valve clearances.

If the piston-to-valve clearances are incorrect, have the valve reliefs in your pistons cut by an experienced machinist. Always recheck static compression ratio and piston-to-valve clearances after the pistons have been cut.

Critical Engine Measurements Chart

This handy chart shows all of the important engine measurements that we prefer for most applications. Be sure all your components meet the correct specifications prior to engine assembly:

#	*Measurement*	*Normal Range*
1	cam lift	card spec. ±.005"
2	cam int./exh. deg. open/close	card spec. ±2°
3	cyl. bore diameter	±.0005"
4	cyl. out-of-round	±.0002"
6	cyl. taper	±.0002"
7	block main bore dia.	±.0002"
8	main bore align.	.0015"
9	cam bore dia.	±.0005"
10	cam bore align.	±.0015"
11	cam thrust, w/thrust washer	.010"-.012"
	cam thrust, w/thrust bearing	0"-005"
12	crank straightness	.001" max.
13	crank journal dia.	±.0002"
14	crank thrust clear.	.005"-.012"
15	rod length	±.002"

#	*Measurement*	*Normal Range*
16	total deck clearance	.040"-.050" steel rod
		.055"-.070" alum. rod
17	rod dia., big end	±.0002"
18	rod cheek (side) clearance	.015"-.020" steel rod
		.018"-.025" alum. rod
19	rod bear. oil clear.	.003".004"
20	main bear. oil clear.	.003"-.004"
21	wrist pin to pin bore clear.	.0015" (under 7800 rpm's)
22	Bottom end rod clear. (all)	.060" min.
23	wrist pin to lock clear.	.005" (under 7800 rpm's)
24	piston weight	±. 5 gm.
25	piston-to-wall clear.	.006"-.012" (most)
		.010" (500 pro stock)
26	ring groove depth	.001"-.003"
27	ring vertical clearance	.001"-.004" w/o ports
		.0006"-.002" w/gas ports
28	compression ring end gap (min.)	.004" per in. cyl. dia.
		.030" nitrous ox.
29	piston-to-valve clearance	.060-065" intake .120" exhaust .050"-.060" radial cl.

IMPORTANT! The specifications listed in the chart above are for general informational purposes only. Actual clearance requirements can vary by application. Always consult your engine builder and the racing component manufacturers for specific recommendations.

Review Questions

1. What is engine displacement? In what units are American racing engine displacements usually expressed? What does "CID" mean?

2. What is the formula for the engine displacement? Apply the engine displacement formula to determine the displacement of a V8 engine with these specifications:
   - Bore = 4.000"
   - Stroke = 3.00"

3. Why is it important to calculate your racing engine displacement accurately? Describe two ways to change engine displacement. Which way is usually more desirable for a class like NHRA Pro Stock?

4. Identify the engine volumes in the figure below that affect static compression ratio.

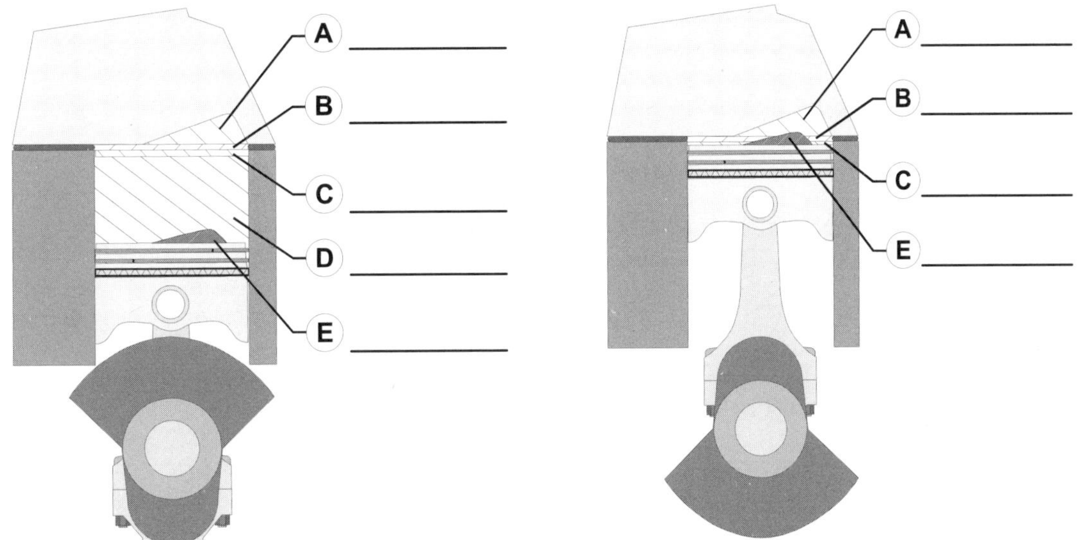

5. How do you decide what the static compression ratio of a racing engine should be? Calculate the static compression ratio of an engine with the following specifications:

Bore = 4.5"
Stroke = 4.125"
Deck Clearance = .025"

Head Gasket Thickness = .030"
Comb. Chamber Vol. = 118 cc's
Piston Dome Vol. = 52.5 cc's

6. Why should you purge the air from the spout at the base of the buret? What a meniscus? Where should you read the water level in a buret?

7. What is the purpose of applying tape to the top of a piston when preparing to measure piston dome volume? Why should the piston be installed high in the cylinder instead of at BDC? How can you seal the piston to the cylinder?

8. How do you measure piston dome volume with a buret? Calculate the dome volume for piston with these measurements at 1" below the deck:
   - Bore = 4.000"
   - Measured buret volume = 168 cc's

9. What is the formula for converting English cubic inches to Metric cubic centimeters? Convert 2.4 cubic inches to cubic centimeters (cc's).

10. Calculate the head gasket volume for an engine with these specifications: (convert your answer to cc's)
    - Bore = 4.000"
    - Compressed Gasket Thickness = .040"

11. Calculate the deck height volume for an engine with these specifications: (convert your answer to cc's)
    - Bore = 4.000"
    - Deck Height = .021"

12. What can be done to correct a static compression ratio that is too low? What can be done to correct a static compression ratio that is too high?

13. Describe the procedure for mounting and adjusting a degree wheel to TDC using a dial indicator and a checking depth.

14. What measurement is being performed in the photo below?

15. How can you identify the #1 intake lifter in the block?

16. What do the following acronyms (abbreviations) stand for?

BTDC
ATDC

BBDC
ABDC

17. Describe the procedure for degreeing-in a camshaft. What is a common checking height that is used when measuring cam lift or duration? How can incorrect cam phasing be corrected?

18. What is the technician doing in the figure below? Why is this check so important? Describe the procedure.

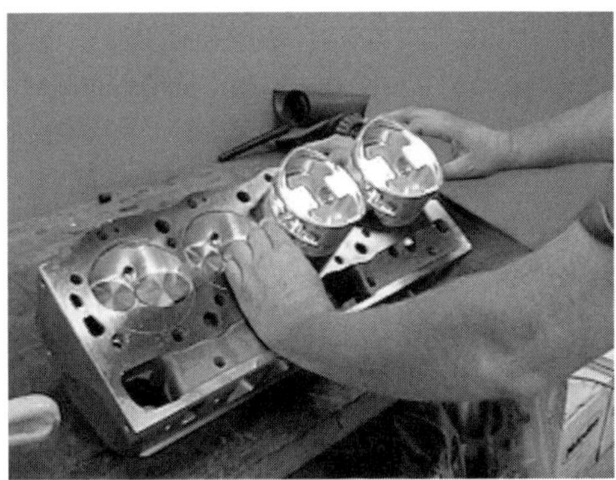

19. Explain how to mark the valve guide centers on the pistons. Where should the crankshaft be when marking the exhaust center? Where should the crankshaft be when marking the intake center?

20. What is the device shown below, and how is it used when checking piston-to-valve clearance? What is the purpose of the weld ball? What does the reference mark tell you?

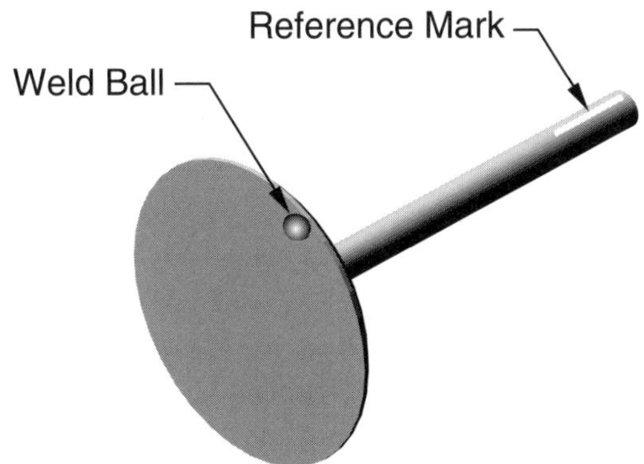

21. What does the diagram below tell the machinist about the piston-to-valve clearance in this engine? What was the crankshaft position when the measurements were made for the intake and exhaust valves?

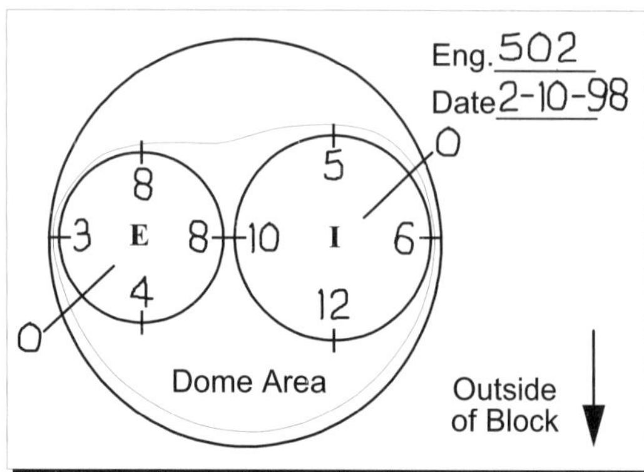

22. What is the radius of an intake valve that measures 2.02" in diameter? How can you mark the valve locations on a piston for measuring radial clearance? What is the minimal radial valve clearance for a racing engine? Is the radial valve clearance acceptable in the figure below? Why or why not?

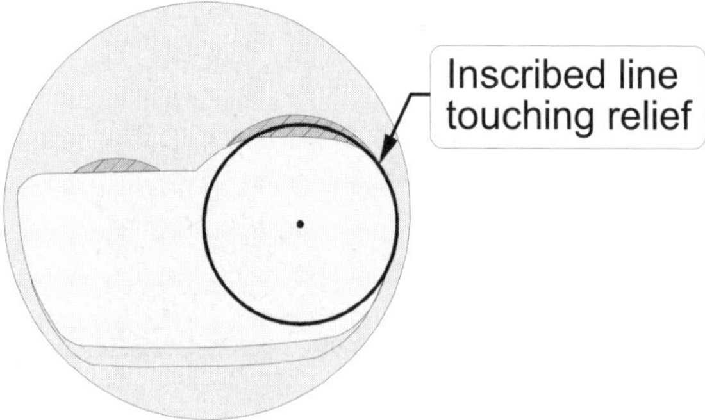

Championship Engine Assembly

Unit VII - Short Block Assembly Procedures

Without a doubt, the assembly phase of racing engine construction is the most fun. At this point, you have spent many hours selecting, cleaning, measuring, and machining the lower engine assembly parts. Now it's time to put it all together.

One tiny mistake at this point can waste a lot of money and undo the many hours that you have invested in building your racing engine. It's very important that you resist the temptation to get into a rush, skip steps, or work to the point of fatigue. Take the time to check and re-check all your work and stop when you need rest.

Before long, you'll have your short block assembled and ready for the upper engine assembly.

Cleanup & Preparation

Although you cleaned the components prior to making measurements, it is likely that there are still dirt and metal particles present. Any dirt in the engine on assembly can damage internal engine parts and scratch cylinder walls. One last thorough cleanup is required to prevent this from happening.

It is very important that you clean all parts with the diligence of a surgeon prior to engine assembly.

Cleaning the Shop Environment:

The shop should be clean and any activities that may stir up dust should cease. This is why we have individual engine assembly rooms that are in a different area from the machining operations.

Don't forget other things that can transfer dirt and grit to engine parts. Clean the workbench, and lay clean paper over the surface. Clean all of your tools and hands as well.

Neatness and cleanliness count when you build a racing engine. Lay paper on the workbench surface, and keep your parts & tools clean and arranged neatly.

Fluids & Sealers:

You will need a number of engine assembly fluids and sealers. These are some of the products we use when we assemble the short block:

1. *Brake Cleaner*
2. *Assembly Lube*
3. *Assembly Oil*
4. *Thread-Tapping Lube*
5. *Motor Oil*
6. *Choke & Carb Cleaner*
7. *Anti-Seize Compound*
8. *Penetrating Oil*
9. *Loctite® Threadlocker*
10. *Loctite® Thread Sealant*
11. *RTV Silicone*

Tools:

These are some of the specialized tools you will need to assemble your short block:

1. *Dial Indicator*
2. *Torque Wrench*
3. *Ring Compressor*
4. *Harmonic Balancer Installation Tool Thread Sealant*

Don't try to build your engine on a workbench or the floor. Invest in a quality engine stand. This allows you to rotate the engine as needed to gain access to the top or underside of the block.

An engine stand puts the assembly at a more comfortable working height. This helps keep the parts clean and makes it a lot easier to put it all together.

Cleaning the Internal Engine Parts:

Clean the engine parts in a solvent-type parts washer, then use an aerosol cleaning solvent such as brake parts cleaner to remove any remaining dirt or oily residue. Use a blow gun to dry the parts. Any bare steel components should be sprayed with a light coat of WD-40 (or equiv.) to prevent the formation of rust.

Clean all internal engine parts in a parts washer; then use an aerosol solvent to remove all oil residue.

IMPORTANT! The use of cleaning solvents can be hazardous. Never use flammable solvents or those that may attack your skin when cleaning engine parts. Always read the warning labels on solvents and adhere to all EPA hazardous waste storage, handling, and disposal requirements.

Assembling the Components

1. *Install all oil gallery plugs*
2. *Install the camshaft*
3. *Install the engine bearings*
4. *Install the crankshaft*
5. *Install the cam drive assembly*
6. *Assemble the pistons & rods*
7. *Install the piston & rod assemblies*
8. *Install the accessory components*

Step #1 - Install All Oil Gallery Plugs:

Apply a small amount of #1 or #2 Permatex sealer to the threads of the oil gallery plugs and install them.

These oil gallery plugs have tapered pipe threads. Apply oil and tighten them securely with a hex key wrench.

Step #2 - Install the Camshaft:

Apply oil to the cam journals and lobes. Flat tappet cams usually require the application of a special break-in lube to the cam lobes. Be sure to obtain this special lubricant from the cam manufacturer. Support the camshaft as you rotate and slide it into the block.

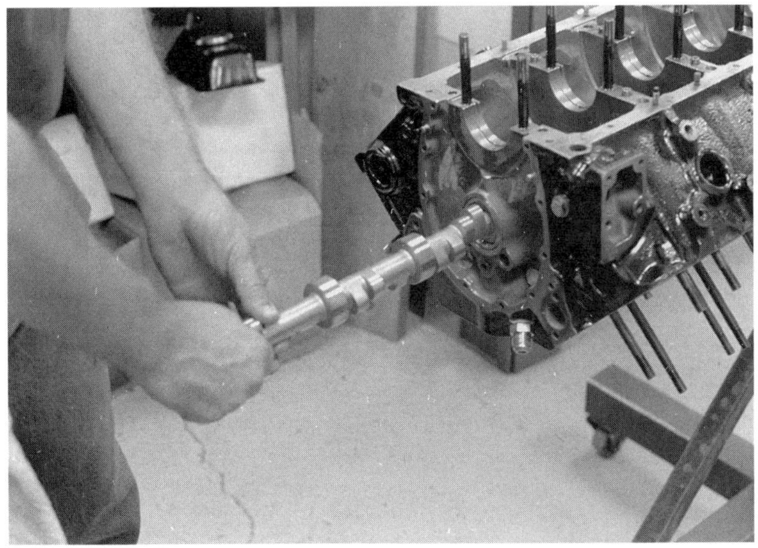

Carefully install the camshaft into the block. Use both hands to guide the lobes through the cam bearings without touching them to avoid scratches.

Step #3 - Install the Engine Bearings:

Install the main bearings. Engine bearing inserts have a locating tab that must engage a slot in the main web for proper alignment in the bore. Be sure to install the half with the oil hole in the engine block.

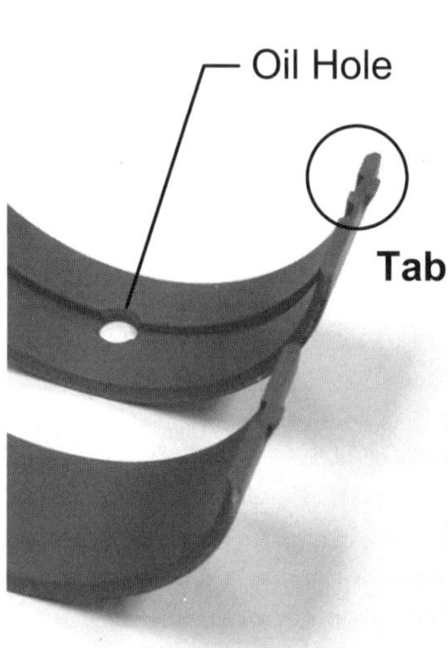

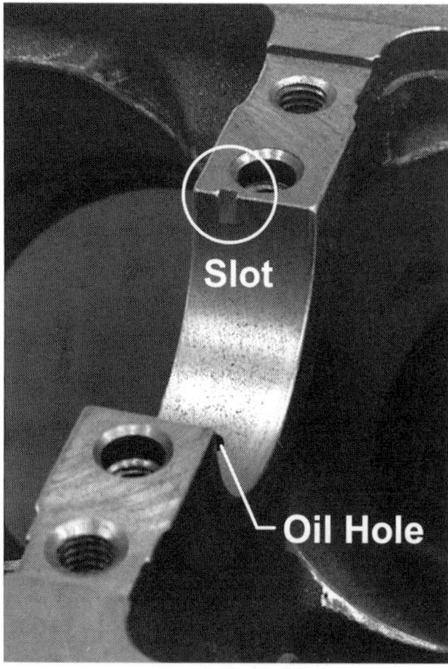

Identify the main bearing insert with the oil hole. Install it so that the alignment tab is engaged with the slot in the bore.

Start the end with the tab; then push the opposite edge down with your fingers. Make sure the insert is fully seated and there is an even amount of crush extending above the mating surface on both sides.

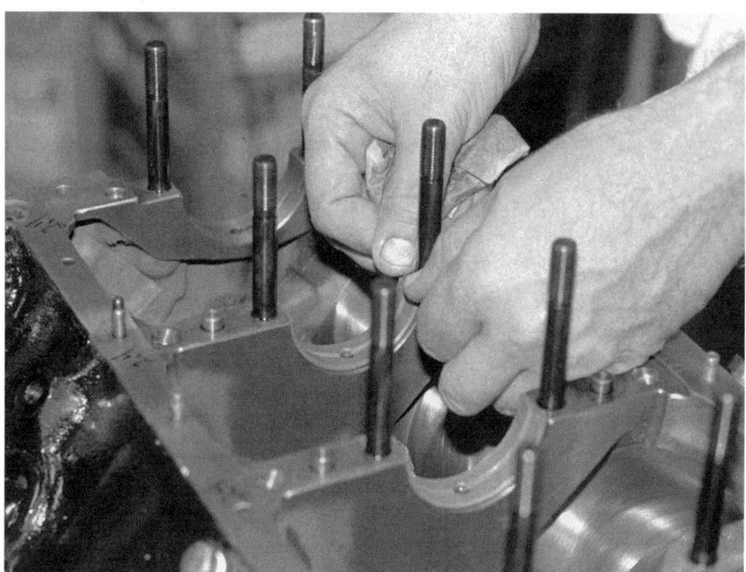

When you install the main bearings, be sure to put the half with the oil hole in the block.

Push the main bearing inserts (half with no oil holes) into the main caps. Make sure the insert is fully seated and there is an even amount of crush extending above the cap mating surface on both sides.

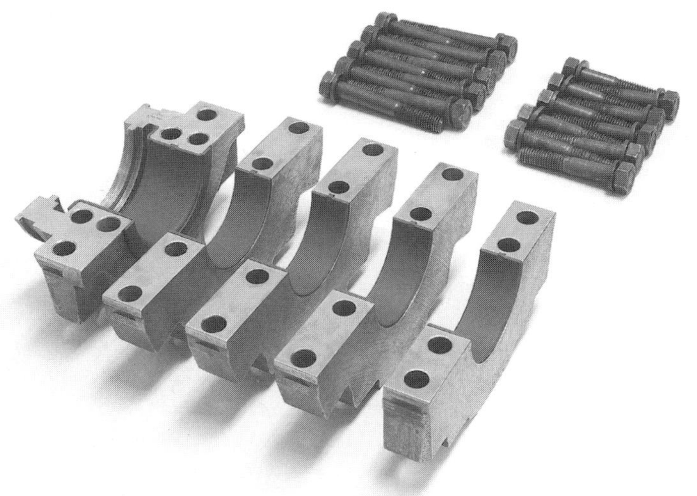

Install the bearing inserts in the main caps. Note that these bearings have no oil holes.

Apply motor oil to the threads of the main cap bolts (or studs). Install the caps on the engine block in the correct order and facing the right way. It is extremely important to follow this rule whenever you install main caps.

Never mix the main bearing caps during engine assembly and never install a bearing cap backwards. Incorrect installation of of bearing caps causes misalignment and places the crankshaft in a bind.

The reason that it is so important not to mix main caps or install them backwards is that the block is align bored with all caps in place. Because of normal machining tolerances, each cap is slightly different in dimension and will fit properly only in the original position. To avoid confusion, main caps are numbered, front to rear.

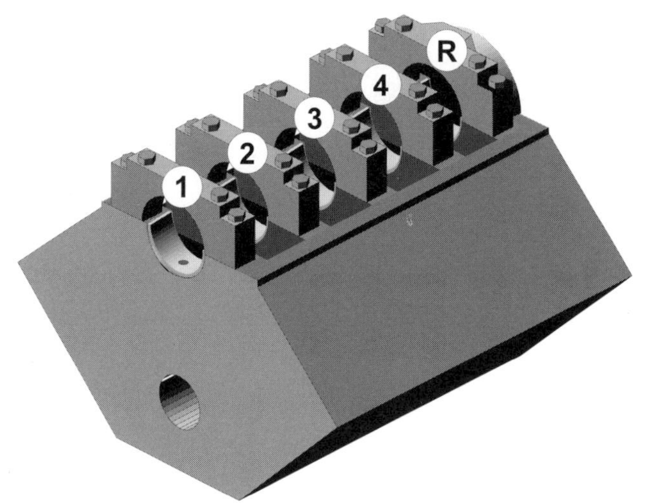

Main caps must always be installed in the original position. They are numbered front to rear as shown. The rear main cap is larger because it contains the rear main seal.

If a main cap is installed backwards, the result will be severe engine damage. Of the five main caps on a GM V8 racing engine, only the larger #5 rear main cap is made so that it cannot be installed backwards. Follow this simple rule to ensure that the other four main caps are installed correctly:

Engine bearing inserts must be installed tab-to-tab. The arrows stamped on main caps may be difficult to see clearly. Make sure that both insert tabs are on the same side as you install the caps.

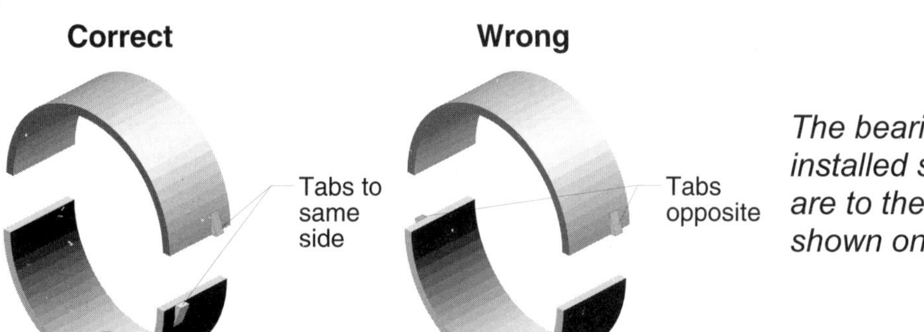

The bearing caps must be installed so that the tabs are to the same side as shown on the left.

Many, but not all main caps have numbers and arrows stamped into them at the time of manufacture. When you point the arrows on the main caps to the front of the engine, it should place the tabs of the inserts to the same side, but always double check to be sure of the bearing tab orientation. The photo below shows the correct position and orientation of the main caps.

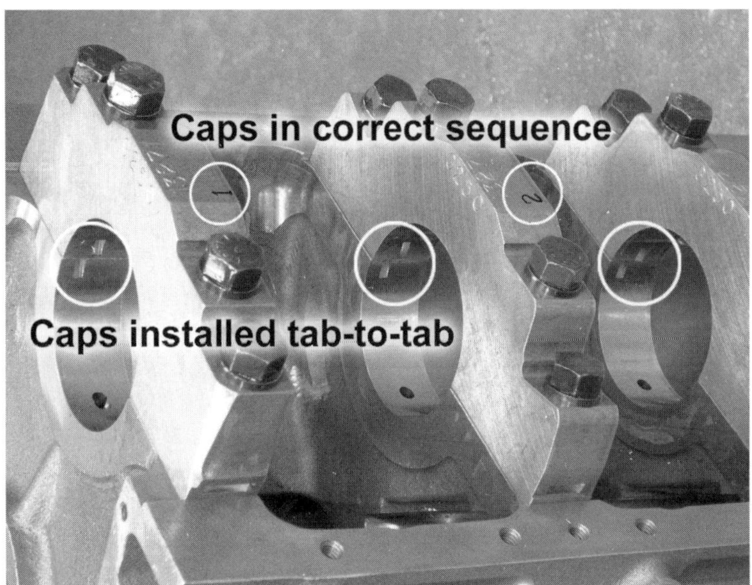

Main caps must be placed in the right order and aligned correctly as shown here.

NOTE: The caps on this block have no arrows and must be aligned by the tab locations (tab-to-tab).

NOTE: The type of lubricant that you apply to bolts has a large effect on bolt tightness at a given torque. Check the manufacturer's recommendations for fastener lubricant and tightening procedures.

Apply lubricant to main cap bolt threads and under the heads. Align the sides of the cap with the block webs by feel, and then gently tap it into the register (machined recess) in the block. Use a dead blow hammer and tap evenly and gently, working from side to side. Start the bolts with your fingers. Torque the cap bolts to the recommended specification in three approximately equal steps. Tighten the inner fasteners on 4-bolt mains first, then the outer bolts. This helps pull the cap down evenly.

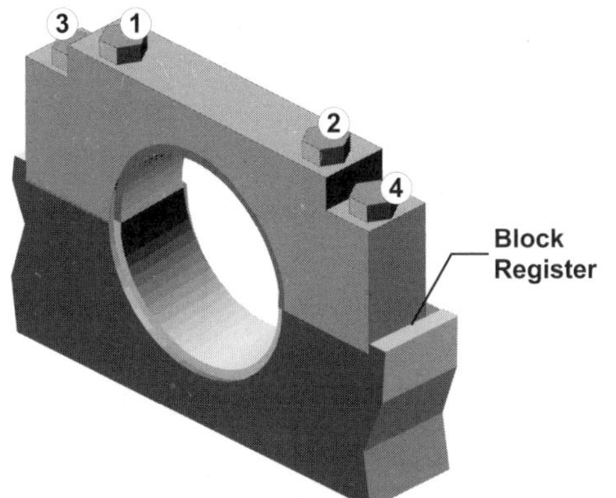

Tap the cap into the register; then install the inner bolts first (#1 & #2). Tighten the outer bolts (#3 & #4). This ensures that the cap is pulled down evenly.

Check the main bearing oil clearances. Adjust an outside micrometer to the first crankshaft main journal diameter, then set the lock. Place a bore gauge into the micrometer and adjust the dial to read "0". The bore gauge dial will now indicate the bearing oil clearance when you place it in the #1 main bearing. You must check the clearance vertically, at 90° to the cap parting line. Gently rock the bore gauge up and down and record the tightest reading. Check the bearing in several places to be sure there is no taper.

Repeat this procedure for all five main bearings. If any bearing oil clearances are out of specifications, you will need to determine the cause. Don't forget our rule about engine clearances—a little loose is always better than too tight!

This long bore gauge is made to reach all main bearings. Record the vertical oil clearance for each bearing. Rock the gauge up and down, and record the tightest reading. Also check the bearings for taper.

Install the rod bearings in the rods and caps and even up the crush. Be sure you install the rod caps on the correct rods and in the right direction (tab-to-tab).

Match the numbers on the rods and rod caps. Make sure you are aligning the caps tab-to-tab.

Check the rod bearing oil clearances. Adjust an outside micrometer to the #1 rod journal diameter; then set the lock. Place a bore gauge into the micrometer, and adjust the dial to read "0". The bore gauge dial will now indicate the bearing oil clearance when you place it in the #1 rod bearing. As with main bearings, you must check the clearance vertically, at 90° to the cap parting line. Gently rock the bore gauge back and forth, and record the tightest reading. Check the bearing in several places to be sure there is no taper.

Repeat this procedure for all of the rod bearings. If any bearing oil clearances are out of specifications, you will need to determine the cause. Be especially careful that none of the bearings are too tight.

Rod bearing oil clearances are also critical. With the rod caps installed, measure the bearing oil clearance of each at 90° to the parting line.

Step #4 - Install the Crankshaft:

Remove the main caps, and place them in order on a clean work bench. Install the rear main seal. The rear main seal in a GM racing engine may be a one or two piece neoprene rubber style. Install the rear main seal in the block and rear main cap now if it is a two-piece type. The seal halves have an angled lip that must face into the engine in order to seal.

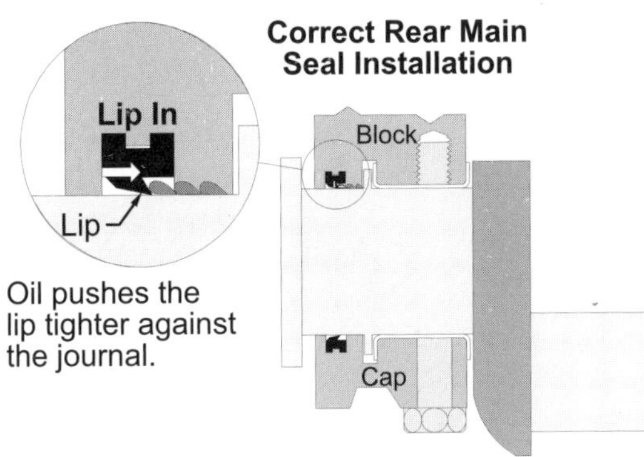

Be very careful to install the rear main seal the right way. If the lip points in as shown on the left, it can seal oil effectively.

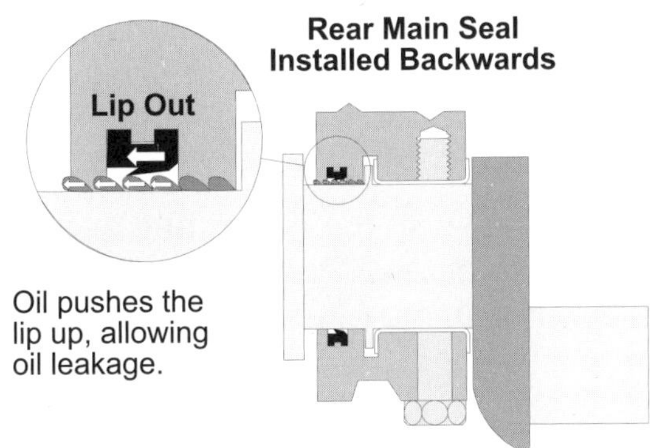

If you install all or part of the rear main seal backwards (lip out), it may leak, particularly if you are not running a crankcase vacuum system.

Apply some RTV silicone sealer to the rear main seal groove in the block; then push the seal in place. Double-check the seal direction to be sure it is installed correctly. Apply racing motor oil to the main bearings. Carefully lower the crankshaft onto the bearings. Watch your fingers, and keep the crank level as you install it.

Carefully place the crankshaft onto the oiled main bearings.

On a GM V8 racing engine, the rear (#5) main cap contains the thrust bearing. The rear main cap has no alignment dowels and can be shifted slightly during installation. This causes misalignment of the thrust bearing insert halves.

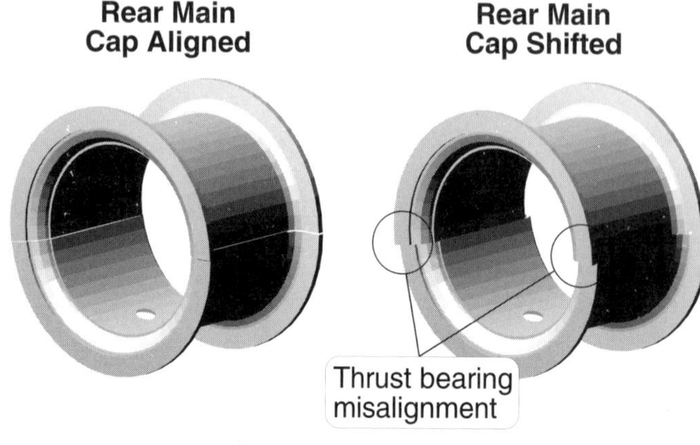

If the rear main bearing cap is shifted, the thrust bearing halves will not be aligned. This reduces the crankshaft thrust clearance and causes uneven bearing wear.

To be sure that the rear main cap is aligned, make two crankshaft thrust clearance measurements; one without the thrust (rear) main cap installed and another after cap installation and final torquing. If the second reading is less than the first, the rear main cap is misaligned and must be loosened, repositioned, and tightened again until both thrust measurements are the same.

Mount a dial indicator so that the plunger is in line with the crankshaft and contacts the rear crankshaft flange as shown in the photo below. Push the crankshaft with your fingers one way, and then zero the dial. Push it the other way, and note the new reading. For accuracy, repeat this measurement several times to be sure you get the same results each time.

Check the crankshaft thrust clearance with no bearing caps in place as shown here. Most racing engines require between .005"-.008". If the thrust clearance is not correct, additional machine work or a different thrust main bearing may be required.

Double-check to be sure you have put the correct bearing inserts into the main caps and that the rear main bearing seal is facing the right way. Lubricate the main journals and bearings; then install the first four main caps. Seat each cap by gently with a soft-face hammer. Apply the recommended lubricant to the main bolt threads and to the underside of each bolt head.

Apply a small amount of RTV silicone sealer to the rear main seal mounting groove; then push the seal in place. Double-check to be sure you have installed the seal correctly. Apply a small amount of RTV silicone sealer to the rear main seal mounting groove.

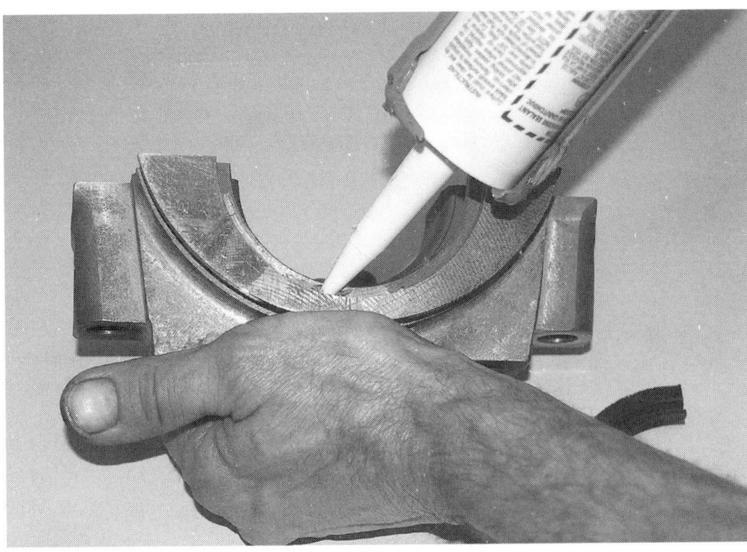

Apply a small amount of RTV silicone sealer to the rear main seal mounting groove.

Offset the seal a little from the parting line of the main cap as shown below. This ensures seal alignment and minimizes the chance of the seal becoming pinched between the block and the cap during installation. Remove any excess silicone that oozes out from under the seal as you press it in place. Then apply an assembly lubricant or racing motor oil to the rear main seal.

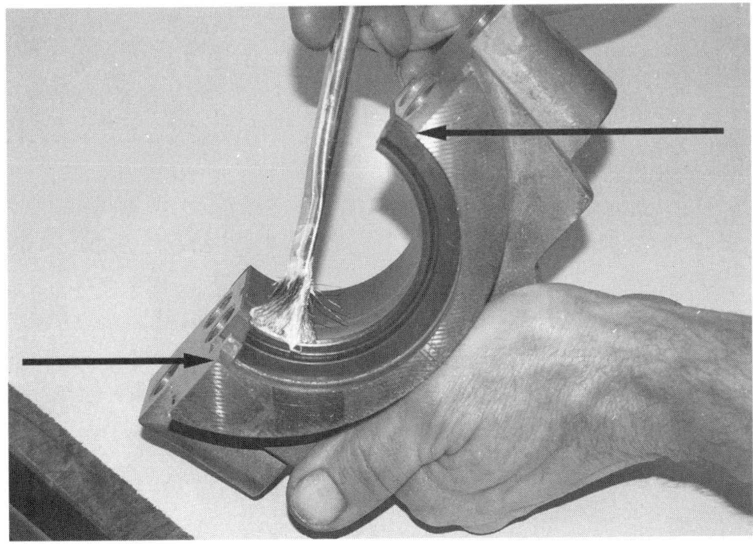

Note that the seal has been installed rotated offline a small amount so that the two seal halves will be in perfect alignment. Apply lubricant to the rear main seal lip. Apply racing motor oil to the bearing and crank journal as shown here.

Install the rear main cap. Push the crankshaft as far as it will go in one direction (in or out); then slide the rear main cap along the crank thrust surface until it contacts the block. Gently seat the cap with a soft-face hammer; then lubricate and install the bolts with your fingers.

Always tap the cap in place with a soft-face hammer to seat it first. Then start the bolts with your fingers to prevent thread damage.

Torque the rear main cap bolts to the recommended specifications. Recheck the crankshaft thrust to be sure the rear main thrust bearing halves are aligned.

If the measured thrust clearance is the same with the thrust main torqued as it was with no main caps, the alignment is correct and you can proceed with the engine assembly.

If the torqued-cap thrust clearance is now less than it was with no cap installed, the cap is offset and the thrust bearing halves are misaligned. Loosen the main cap bolts a little and drive the crankshaft in both directions using an aluminum drive tool to protect the crankshaft snout and flange from damage. Then retighten the bolts and check to be sure you now have the correct crank thrust clearance.

Oil and install the front four main caps and bolts. Always seat the cap into the register first by carefully tapping on it with a hammer. Remember, all caps <u>must</u> be in the correct numbered sequence and with the bearings tab to tab. Follow the recommended bolt torque specifications. Tighten them to 1/3 of the final torque. Tighten the inner bolts first, then the outer ones. Repeat this at 2/3 of the final torque, then again at full torque specifications.

Always torque main cap bolts in three increments. Don't jerk the torque wrench; pull it steadily until the desired torque is achieved.

Re-torque the rear main cap bolts, and check the crankshaft thrust clearance again.

NOTE: If you find that the thrust clearance has diminished, you'll have to loosen the caps one at a time to find out which one is causing the problem. In some cases, the bearings may be interfering with the filet radius at the sides of the main journals. For additional information about these issues, review *Unit III - Short Block Component Selection & Preparation, Checking for Interference.*

Step #5 - Install the Cam Drive Assembly:

NOTE: The following steps show the installation of a particular type of belt drive system. Chain-drive systems require different procedures. New racing camshaft drive systems come with detailed installation instructions. Be sure to read and follow those instructions carefully.

IMPORTANT! Neoprene rubber seals require oil but Teflon® seals require no lubricant. Be sure the seal lip points to the inside of the engine.

It's a good idea to remove the cam spider key from the cam hub before installing the thrust plate to prevent seal damage. Install the thrust shim & thrust plate hardware with at least two nuts.

Install the front cover with RTV silicone and gasket. Apply a small, consistent bead of RTV silicone sealer around the front cover flange of the block to ensure a good seal. Place the front cover gasket on the block; then apply another small bead of RTV silicone sealer. Start all the timing cover bolts with your fingers and then tighten them evenly.

Install the front timing cover.

Check and adjust the cam thrust clearance as previously described in *Unit VI - Short Block Pre-Assembly Measurements, Degreeing-In the Camshaft, page 298* in this book. Once the cam thrust clearance is correct, remove the retaining nuts and slide the thrust plate slightly away from the cover. Apply a bead of RTV sealer around the OD of the thrust plate and slide the thrust plate back against the cover.

Spread the RTV sealer you placed around the OD of the thrust plate wide enough to seal with the cover. Apply the excess RTV sealer from your finger to the threads of each stud and start all the nuts with your fingers before tightening them evenly.

When applying the RTV sealer to the thrust plate, avoid getting sealer behind the plate, as this will add stack to the thrust shims. Note that the key has been removed from cam hub to avoid seal damage.

If you installed a new crankshaft, it may be necessary to install a woodruff key into the keyway slot for the pulley. Drive the key into the slot carefully using a hammer and brass drift punch. Apply RTV sealer to the crank key and the inner chamfer of the crank pulley hub to seal oil and vacuum.

Slide the crank pulley on the snout of the crank and carefully tap the inside hub of the crank pulley with the installation tool provided with the kit until fully seated. Using a feeler gauge, measure the clearance between the back of the pulley and the front cover plate to insure a minimum clearance of .020". Compare this to the manufacturer's specifications and make any required corrections.

NOTE: For additional information about checking and correcting crank pulley clearance, see *Unit IV - Upper End Component Selection Camshafts & Lifters, Belt Drives, page 204.*

The drive pulley and cam thrust plate have been installed. Check to be sure the crank pulley to front cover clearance is correct.

NOTE: The camshaft must be degreed-in before performing the following steps. Follow the steps in *Unit VI - Short Block Pre-Assembly Measurements, Degreeing-In the Camshaft* and install the cam drive system with the corrected phasing.

Install the cam spider key. Rotate the crankshaft and camshaft so that the timing marks are aligned. Install the cam pulley and belt as a unit, making sure that keys are in place.

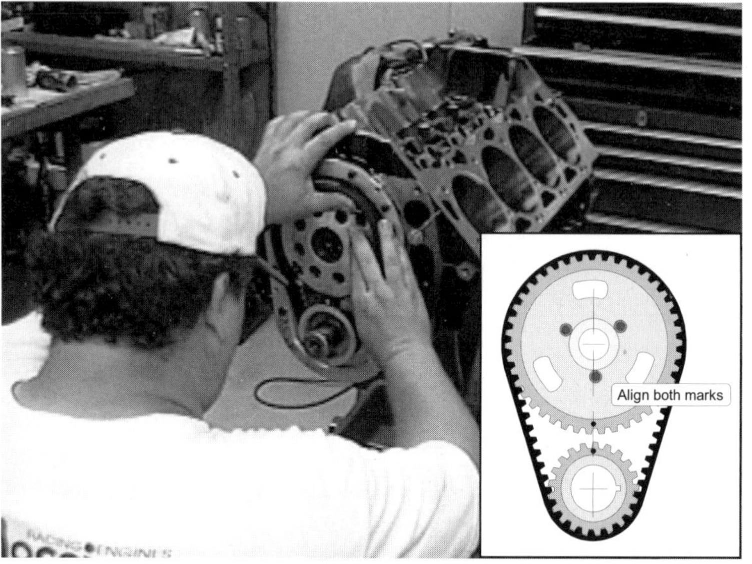

Install the cam pulley and belt with the timing marks aligned. A typical alignment for cam drive systems is shown in the inset picture.

NOTE: The installation and mark alignment procedures vary with different styles of cam drive systems. If you are installing a chain-drive with correction for camshaft phasing, be sure you selected the right keyway and corresponding alignment mark. With this type of sprocket, we prefer to always use the "0" alignment and make the camshaft phasing corrections by installing a cam bushing kit. See *Unit VI - Short Block Pre-Assembly Measurements, Degreeing-In the Camshaft, Correcting Camshaft Phasing* for additional information.

Note that this crank sprocket for a chain-drive has three different keyways identified by three different symbols. Follow the manufacturer's installation instructions and be sure you are using the correct keyway and alignment symbol.

Apply a thread locking agent to the threads of the cam bolts. Torque the cam bolts to the recommended specifications.

Torque the cam pulley bolts to the manufacturer's listed specification. A ratchet and socket are being used here to prevent the crankshaft from rotating as the cam bolt is being torqued.

If you are installing a chain & sprocket drive, install the cam button as shown below before you torque the cam bolts. The cam button limits camshaft thrust by contacting the front timing cover if the camshaft tries to "walk out" of the block. Be sure to follow the manufacturer's directions for checking the final installed cam thrust clearance.

To keep the camshaft from "walking out" of the block, install the cam button. Torque the bolts to the manufacturer's specifications..

NOTE: Camshaft phasing affects piston-to-valve clearance. After you have installed the cam drive with the corrected phasing, you must recheck the piston-to-valve clearance when you complete the engine assembly. *See Unit VI - Short Block Pre-Assembly Measurements, Measuring Piston-to-Valve Clearance* for information.

Step #6 - Assemble the Pistons & Rods:

Clean the rods and pistons thoroughly with solvent and blow the parts dry. Piston domes must be orientated to the outside of the block in order to fit the combustion chambers of the cylinder heads. If you are using new connecting rods, be sure to inscribe them with the corresponding cylinder numbers as you install the piston and rod assemblies. Use an electric pencil for this, not number stamps which can distort the rod bore. Make sure you install the pistons on the rods so that the deep chamfers of each will be toward the fillet radius on the crankshaft.

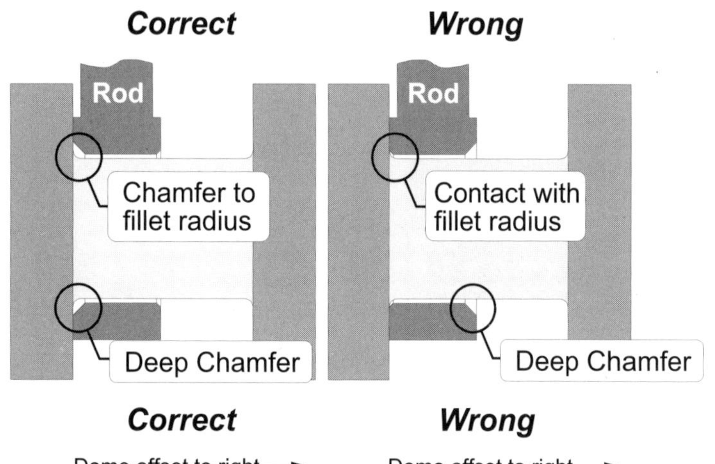

When you install the piston on the rod, turn the rod so that the deeper chamfer is toward the fillet radius on the crankshaft. The bearing will also be offset away from the fillet radius.

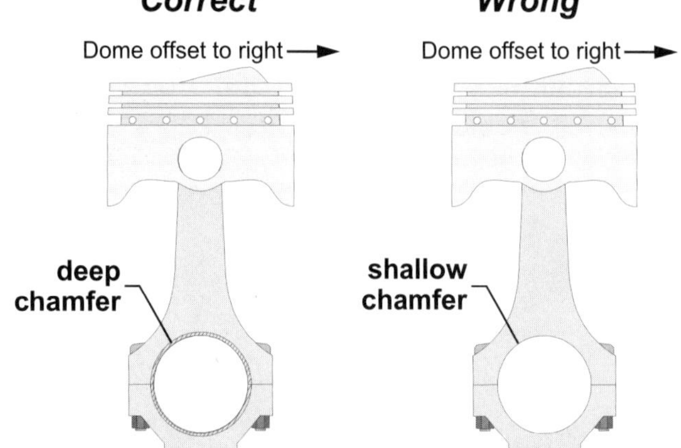

On a GM V8 racing engine, point the piston dome to the right with the deeply chamfered side (fillet radius side) of the connecting rod toward you as shown here.

Install the retaining clips in one side of the piston. Lubricate the wrist pin and pin bore with racing motor oil, and slide the wrist pin through the piston and rod. Install the other retaining clips. Recheck the orientation of the rod chamber and piston dome to be sure it is correct. Repeat this procedure for all eight rods and pistons.

Install the rings on the pistons. Place the oil ring expander into the groove, then install the upper and lower scraper rails. Separate the gaps in each as shown below:

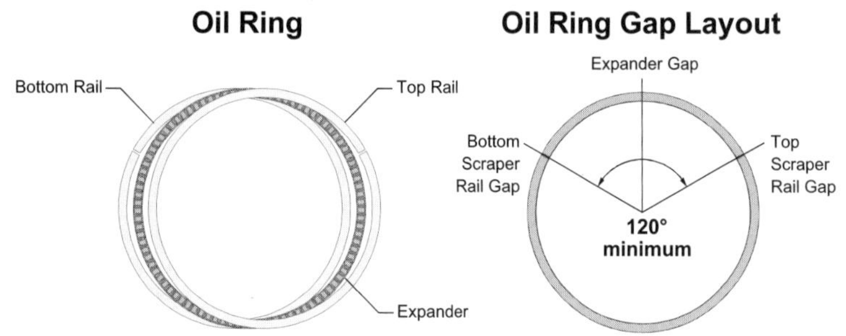

Install the expander, bottom scraper rail, and top scraper rail in that order. Carefully spiral the rings into place with your fingers; then arrange the gaps as shown.

If the oil rings are installed correctly, they should float (slide easily) in the grooves. If you feel a bind in the oil rings, check to see if an expander is overlapped or if you have the wrong ring set for your pistons.

Unlike oil rings, the top two rings have an up and down side. One common method of identification is the use of *pip marks*. A pip mark is a small dimple that indicates which side is up on the ring. Sometimes the 2nd ring has two pip marks instead of one.

Top Piston Ring Pip Marks

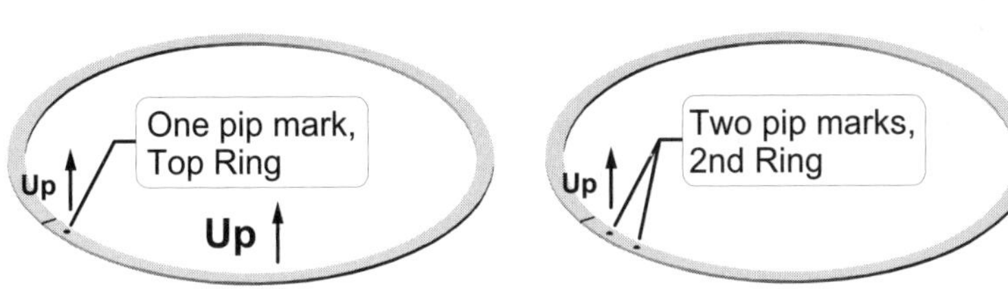

The top two rings may have identifying pip marks that indicate the ring position and direction. Pip marks should always face up.

NOTE: Always refer to the instructions in your ring set to be sure of the correct ring orientation.

Occasionally, we have found rings that had the pip mark cut incorrectly on the bottom side on the ring. We recommend that you also look for the chamfer on the ring ID as shown below to make sure that you are installing the rings correctly.

Ring Cross Sections

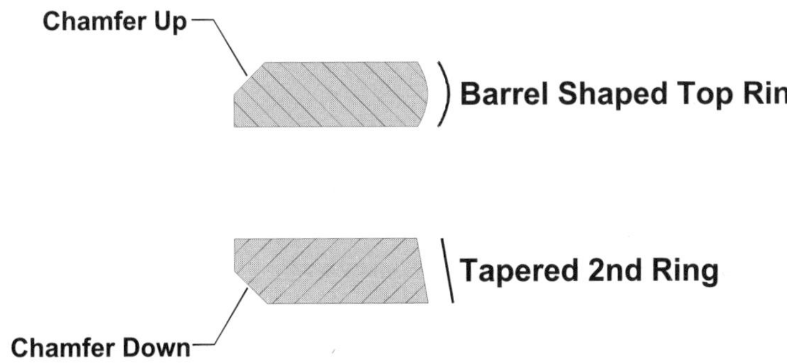

Regardless of what side the pip marks are on, this is the correct orientation for these racing rings. Check your entire set before you install the rings.

A ring expander tool may be used to spread the ring enough to slip it into the groove, but we prefer to install our rings by hand. Install the 2nd ring first. Start one end of the ring in the groove and gently open the ring gap with your thumb until it snaps into the groove.

This technician is hand-installing the top compression ring. Notice how he uses his thumb to gently spread the ring and slip it into the groove. This procedure takes some time and patience to perform correctly.

NOTE: The top two rings are very brittle and will break if they are over-expanded. Spread the ring only enough until it will snap into the groove. Be very careful not to allow the sharp corners at the end gap to gouge the soft aluminum of the piston.

Step #7 - Install the Piston & Rod Assemblies:

Clean the cylinder walls and apply non-synthetic racing motor oil to the cylinder walls and wrist pins.

Wipe the cylinder walls with a clean, lint-free towel. Apply a non-synthetic racing motor oil to the cylinder walls. Apply racing motor oil liberally to the wrist pins.

NOTE: Never use synthetic motor oils on the cylinder walls or the rings will fail to seat. Check with your engine builder for break-in oil recommendations.

Before you install the piston & rod assembly, adjust the top ring gap orientation. Arrange the gaps as shown below.

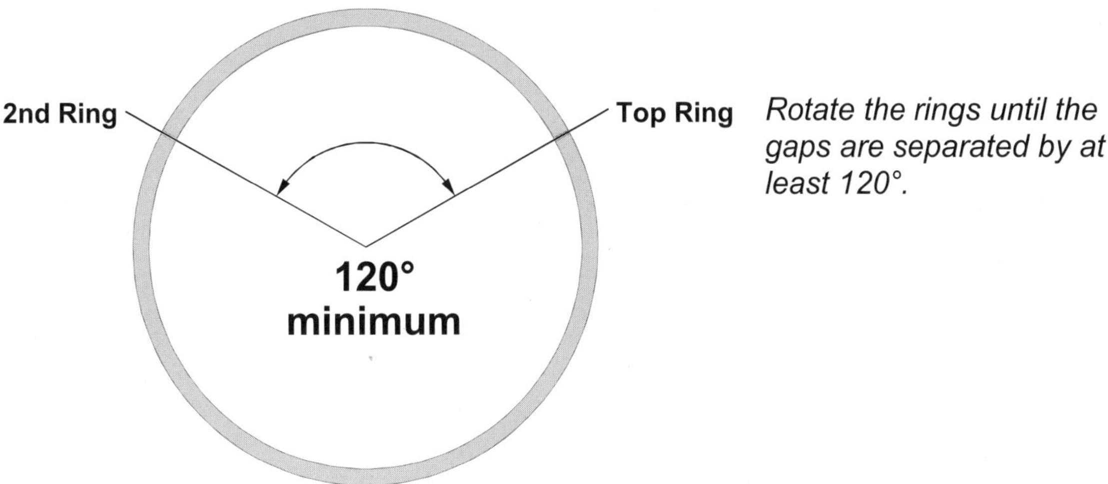

Rotate the rings until the gaps are separated by at least 120°.

Turn the block on the engine stand so that the deck surface is level. Rotate the crankshaft so the rod journal for the first piston is at BDC. Use a quality ring compressor, and slide the piston into the bore as shown below. Make sure the piston dome is to the outside of the block and the deep chamfer on the rod is toward the fillet radius on the crankshaft.

This tapered style ring compressor makes it easy to install the piston & rod assembly. Use your fingers to help get the rings started in the tapered compressor. Don't upset the orientation of the ring end gaps as you do this.

Make sure the rod and piston are oriented correctly, and then slide the first piston & rod assembly into correct bore. Do not allow the rod to scar the crank journal as you perform this step.

Slide the piston in until the ring compressor is seated squarely on the block. Push the piston into the bore with your fingers as shown below. Again, be very careful not to allow the rod to scratch the crankshaft journal.

With the ring compressor installed, push the piston and rod assembly into the cylinder bore. Guide the rod carefully over the crank journal.

Rotate the crankshaft so that the journal is down. Check to be sure the bearing insert is still in place in the connecting rod and that the deep chamfer is toward the crank journal fillet radius. Apply the type of lubricant to the threads and under the bolt head as recommended by the rod or rod bolt manufacturer. Install the cap tab to tab on the connecting rod, and tighten enough to seat the caps.

Install the piston & rod assemblies one at a time, then rotate the crankshaft to be sure the assembly turns smoothly. Rotate the crankshaft so that the rod journal is at BDC for the installation of the next piston & rod assembly. Repeat the installation procedure until all eight piston & rod assemblies have been installed.

IMPORTANT! Any roughness or binding as you turn the crankshaft indicates a serious problem such as an improperly installed oil ring or bearing. Don't take chances! If something doesn't "feel" right, remove the piston, and examine all the parts.

Torque the rod bolts in three approximately equal steps. Use a high quality torque wrench, and pull the bolts smoothly to specifications. Always work back and forth between the two bolts. Avoid using extensions or swivel sockets—these affect torque accuracy. If you need a deeper reach to get to a bolt, use a deep well socket.

IMPORTANT! The type of lubricant that is applied and the torquing procedure affect bolt tightness significantly. Some rod bolts may require the use of a special bolt stretch gauge or "torque-to-yield" method with an angle of bolt rotation. Always follow the manufacturer's specifications for rod bolt tightening, and use only the recommended lubricant.

Torque the rod bolts, working back and forth in three steps. After tightening, see if the rod slides back & forth easily on the journal and that the side of the rod is even at the parting line. With aluminum rods, use a feeler gauge to check for cap misalignment.

After torquing the rods, check the side (cheek) clearance again with a feeler gage. Place the gage between the rod pairs to avoid side loading the bearings.

Step #8 - Install the Accessory Components:

The following are usually installed as part of the short block assembly procedure:

- Oil Pump
- Windage Tray
- Oil Pan
- Harmonic Balancer

Install the oil pump - If this is an internal type pump, install the drive shaft first, then the pump. Install the pickup tube so that the inlet is 1/4"-3/8" above the bottom of the oil pan. We check this with an adjustable square, but you can also make this measurement by placing four small equally-spaced cones of clay onto the pump pickup. Install the pan and push it down until it seats. Remove the pan and check the clay impressions to be sure you have the right clearance.

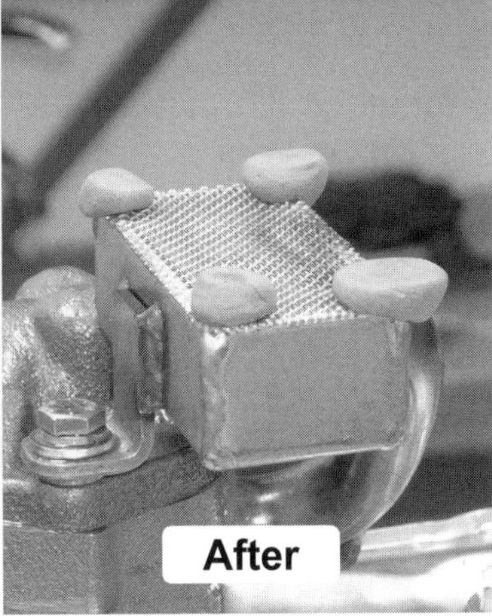

Place four cones of clay onto the pickup, then install the pan. Remove the pan and check the thickness of the compressed cones. They must be 1/4" to 3/8" thick to ensure good oil flow.

The windage tray may bolt onto studded main cap bolts. Install the windage tray and tighten the bolts as required. Rotate the crank assembly, and check for adequate rod clearance to the windage tray.

Many wet-sump type engines can benefit from the installation of a windage tray. Install the tray on the main cap bolt studs.

NOTE: Dry sump systems usually work better without a windage tray. Follow the manufacturer's recommendations for dry sump pan design and component installation.

The windage tray may interfere with the connecting rod bolts, especially on long-stroke engine applications. Rotate the crankshaft assembly as you check for clearance. It's extremely important that you reshape the tray as needed so the rod bolts do not touch.

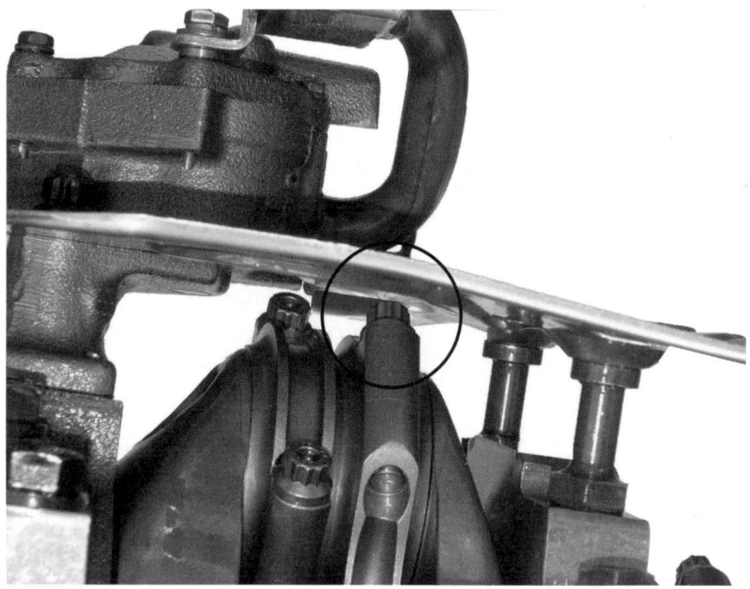

The rod bolts often come extremely close to the windage tray and may actually make contact. You can usually create adequate clearance with careful use of a spoon-type pry bar.

Apply a bead of RTV silicone sealant to the oil pan flange on the engine block. Install the neoprene end seals first, then the side rail gaskets. Apply another bead of RTV silicone on the top of the end seals and gaskets. Install the oil pan and tighten the bolts evenly.

Be very careful not to overtighten the oil pan bolts. Overtightening splits the gasket, distorts the pan flange, and causes leaks.

The harmonic balancer fits very tightly on the crankshaft and may cause damage to the snout when it is pulled off at a later date. Apply anti-seize compound to the crankshaft in the location shown below.

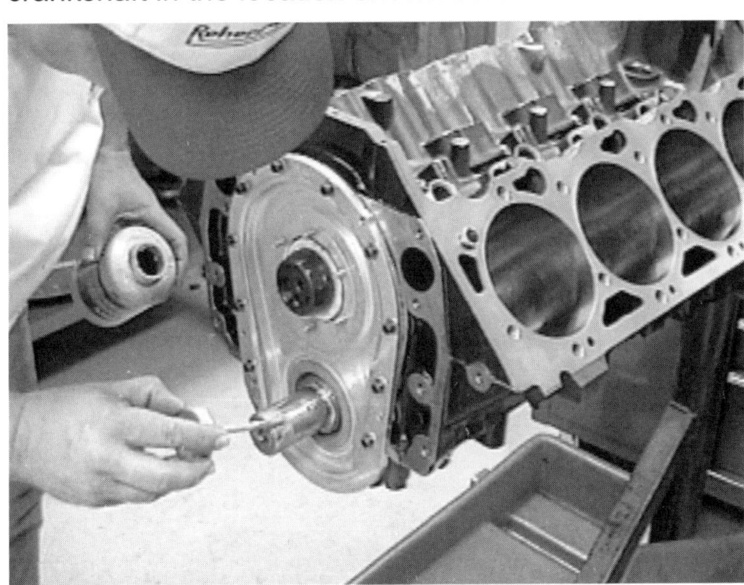

Applying anti-seize compound to the crankshaft snout now can save you a lot of trouble in the future when you disassemble the engine.

Install the harmonic balancer with the correct balancer installation tool as shown below. This special tool engages the threads in the crankshaft snout and has a pressing flange with ball bearings to protect the balancer and crankshaft from damage.

> ***NOTE:*** Never use a bolt to install the balancer or you may pull or damage the threads in the crankshaft snout.

Use one (small) wrench to keep the stud and crankshaft from turning. Use another (large) wrench to press the balancer over the crankshaft snout.

Install the harmonic balancer bolt and washer. Torque the bolt to the crankshaft manufacturer's specifications. Keep the assembly covered until you are ready to complete the upper engine assembly.

> ***NOTE:*** Dirt settles from the air continuously, so be sure to cover any engine parts when you are not working on your engine. You can purchase special plastic engine bags or use trashcan liners to keep dirt off the short block assembly. After you place the bag over the engine, tie or tape the end closed.

Your short block is now assembled and ready for the installation of the upper engine components.

Review Questions

1. Why is it so important to work in a clean shop environment when assembling a short block? Why is it important for your hands and tools to be clean?

2. Name eight fluids & sealers that you will need when you assemble a short block.

3. Name nine types of tools you will need to assemble a short block. Identify the special tools in the photo below:

1. ______________
2. ______________
3. ______________
4. ______________

4. Why is it important to use an engine stand when assembling a short block?

5. Describe the procedure for cleaning the internal engine parts.

6. Describe the procedure for installing the oil gallery plugs. What type of tool is usually required for this?

7. What is a bearing insert tab? Where does the tab go in the main bores? Describe how to install the bearing inserts. Which insert goes into the main cap: the one that is blank or the one with the oil hole?

8. Why must main and rod caps not be mixed during engine assembly? How are main caps numbered? What do the arrows mean on a main cap? What is the rule for orienting bearing insert tabs? What is the torque sequence for 4-bolt main cap bolts?

9. Describe the procedure for measuring main and rod bearing oil clearances.

10. Which figure below ("A" or "B") shows the correct orientation of the rear main seal? What will happen if the rear main seal is installed backwards? Describe the procedure for installing the rear main seal.

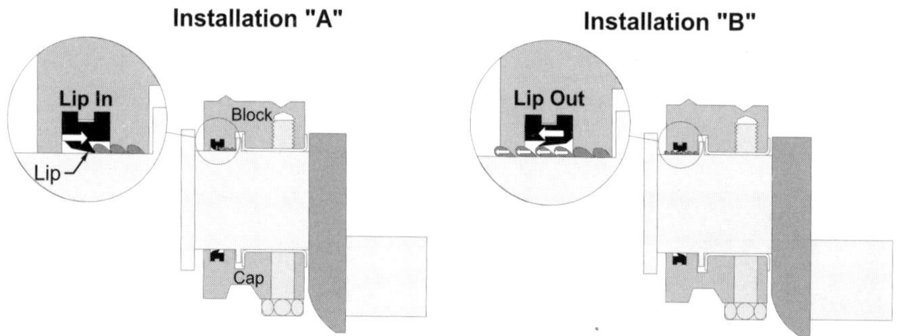

11. Explain how the thrust main must be installed. Describe the procedure for measuring crankshaft thrust clearance. What should you do if there is less clearance after installing the thrust main?

12. Describe the procedure for torquing main bolts (nuts). Why should you avoid using extensions and swivels? How many torquing increments should you use? How can you be sure that a particular main cap has not caused the crankshaft to be in a bind?

13. Describe the procedure for installing the camshaft. What measurement is being performed in the photo below? How is it corrected if it does not meet the manufacturer's specification?

14. Which figure below ("A" or "B") shows the correct orientation of the cam timing marks?

A - Both Marks Down **B - Marks Together**

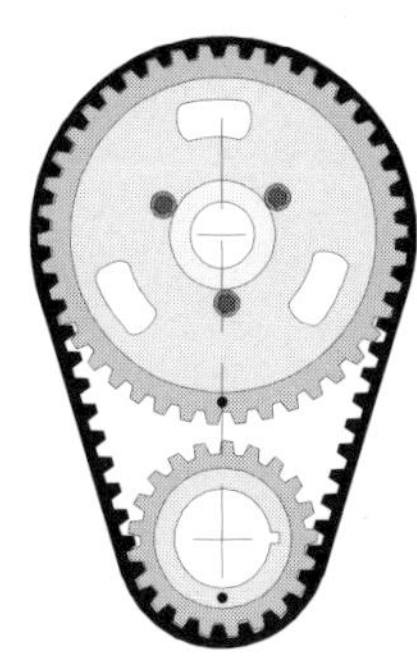

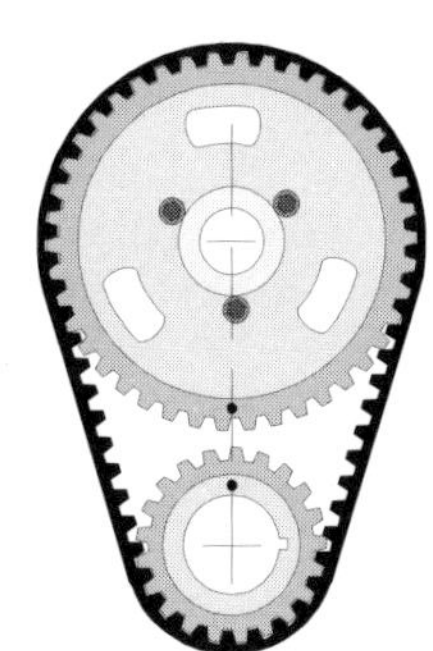

15. Which figure below ("A" or "B") shows the correct orientation of the rod chamfer?

A **B**

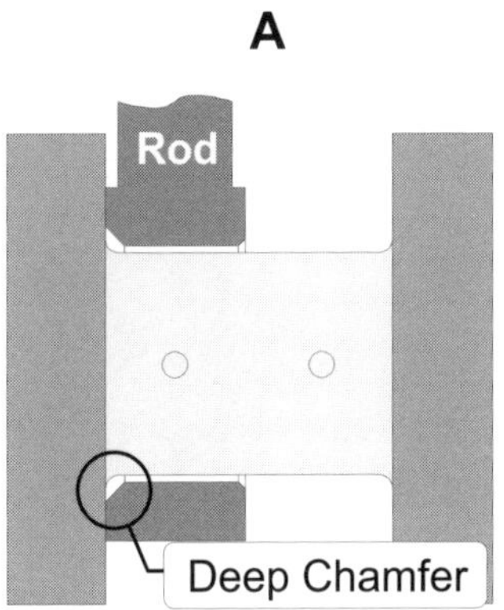

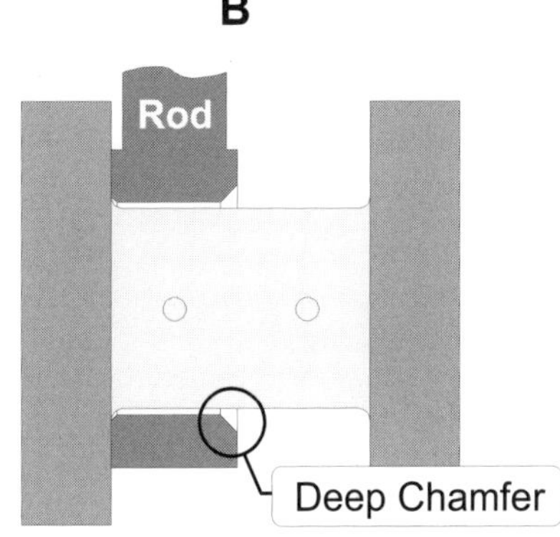

16. Which figure below ("A" or "B") shows the correct orientation of piston domes?

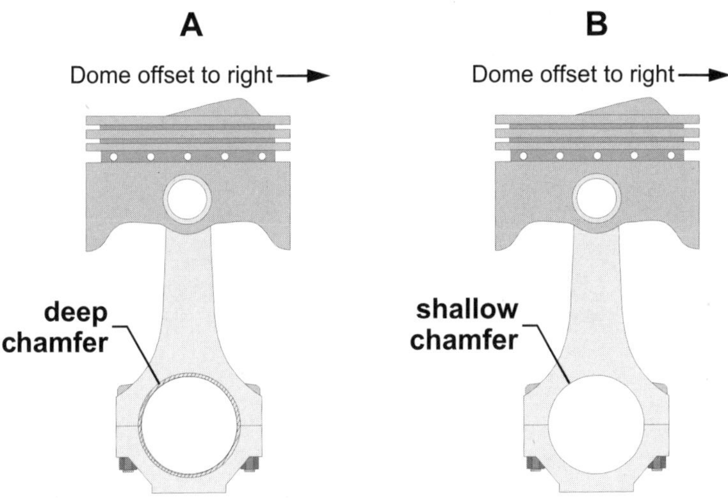

17. Which figure below ("A" or "B") shows the correct orientation of the oil ring gaps? Describe the ring installation procedure. What tool is used to install the rings? What does a "pip" mark on a top ring mean?

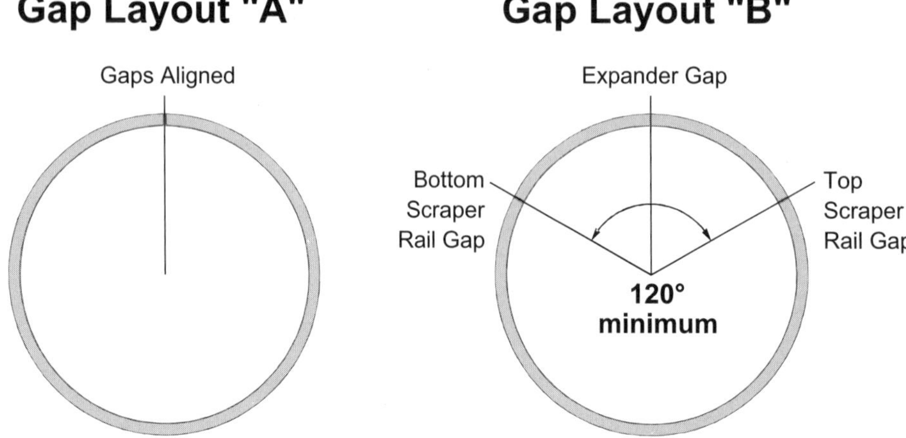

18. Which figure below ("A" or "B") shows the correct orientation of the top rings by the location of the inside chamfer?

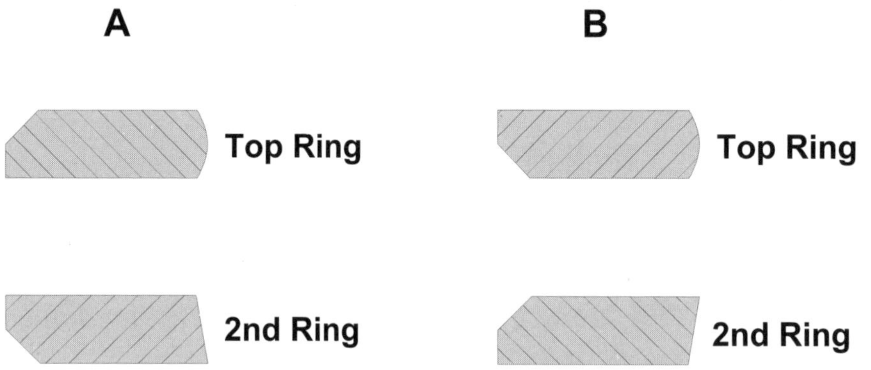

19. Describe the technique for installing rings by hand.

20. Describe the installation of the piston & rod assemblies. What tool is used to compress the rings during the installation? What is the correct orientation of the top ring end gaps? How can you be sure the rod caps are on correctly? What position must the crankshaft be in for each rod & piston installation?

21. How close should the oil pickup be to the bottom of the oil pan? What is the part below? Where does it mount?

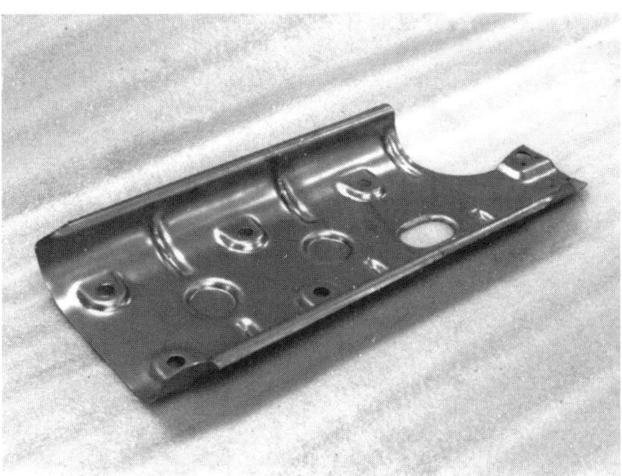

22. Describe the installation of the harmonic balancer. What should you apply to the crankshaft snout before you install the balancer?

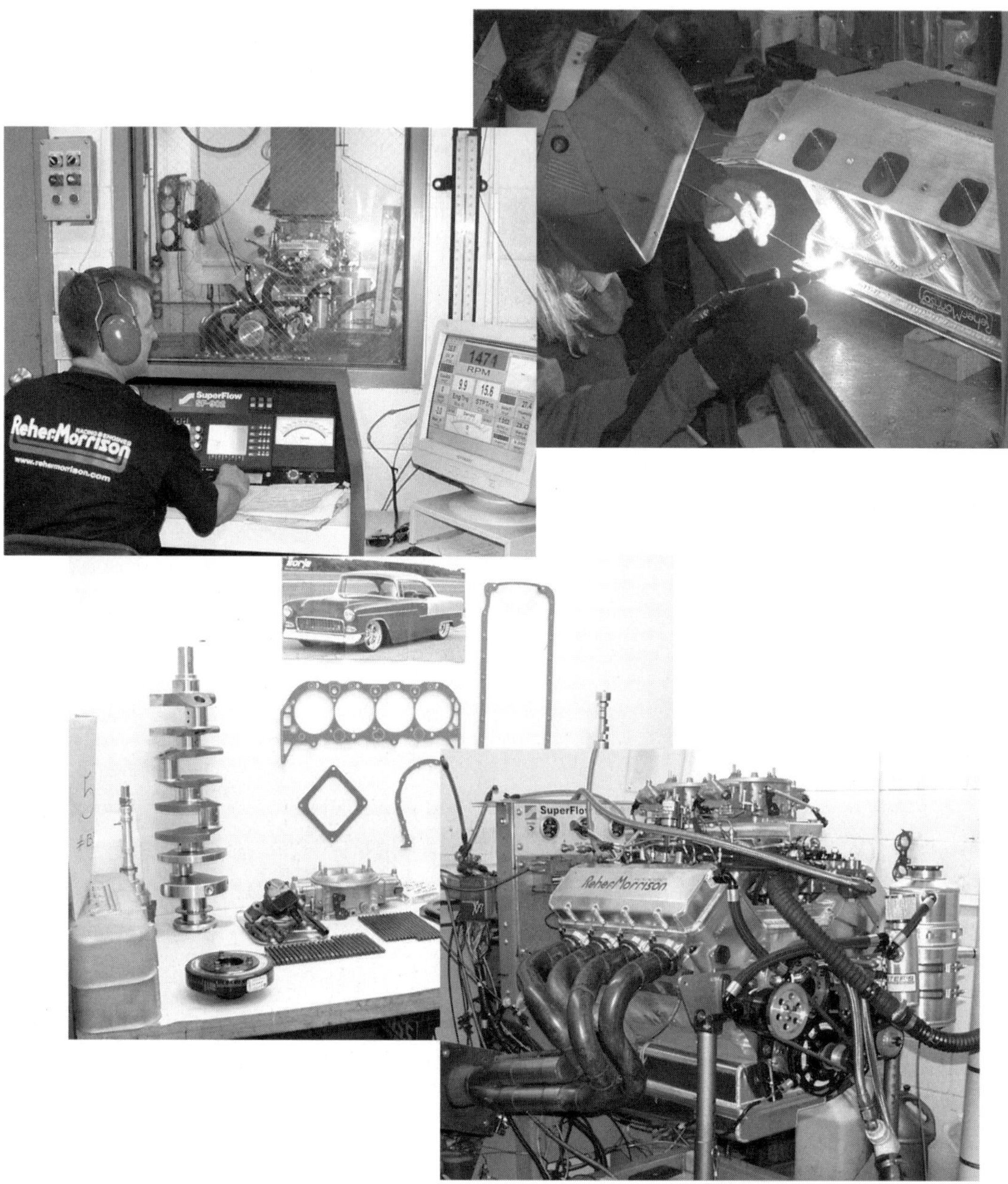
RehenMorrison
SuperFlow
1471
RPM
SuperFlow

Championship Engine Assembly

Unit VIII - Final Engine Assembly Procedures

At this point, you have spent many hours selecting, measuring, and machining parts. The short block is already together—now it's time to complete the engine assembly. It is very important that you don't get into a rush, skip steps, or work past the point of fatigue. Take the time to check and re-check all your work and stop and take a break when you need rest. Soon, you'll hear your engine roar to life and feel the reward for all your efforts.

Before long, you'll have your engine assembled and ready for testing.

Preparation

IMPORTANT! The use of cleaning solvents can be hazardous. Never use flammable solvents near heat or sparks and work in a well-ventilated area. Wear protective gloves and clothing when cleaning engine parts. Read all warning labels on solvents and adhere to all EPA hazardous waste storage, handling, and disposal requirements.

Fluids & Sealers:

You will need a number of engine assembly fluids and sealers. These are some of the products we use when completing the assembly of a racing engine:

1. *Brake Cleaner*
2. *Assembly Lube*
3. *Assembly Oil*
4. *Thread-Tapping Lube*
5. *Motor Oil*
6. *Choke & Carb Cleaner*
7. *Anti-Seize Compound*
8. *Penetrating Oil*
9. *Loctite® Threadlocker*
10. *Loctite® Thread Sealant*
11. *RTV Silicone*

Tools:

There are a number of tools that you will need to perform the upper engine assembly including:

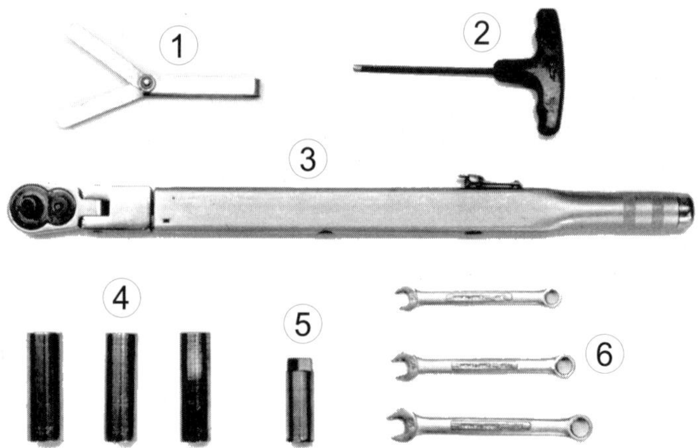

1. *Feeler Gauge*
2. *Hex Key (Allen® Wrench)*
3. *Torque Wrench*
4. *Deep Well Sockets*
5. *Spark Plug Socket*
6. *End Wrenches*

Assembling the Components

1. *Install the cylinder heads*
2. *Install the lifters, pushrods, & rocker arms*
3. *Install the intake manifold*
4. *Prime the oiling system*
5. *Install the distributor, plugs, & wires*
6. *Install the accessory components*

Step #1 - Install the Cylinder Heads:

Head bolts create a lot of stress on the soft ferrous threads in the engine block when they are tightened. We prefer to use studs instead of bolts for high-horsepower applications. Install the studs at this time. Apply a thread locking compound to the block end (coarse) threads, and run them all the way in until they seat.

This special socket has internal jaws that grip the stud. Apply a thread locking compound or sealer if the holes go into the water jacket.

Check to be sure the alignment dowels are in place on the block decks and wipe the surface with a clean rag. Follow the head gasket manufacturer's recommendations for the use of sealers. Some composition gaskets require no sealers or re-torquing after startup. We apply a small amount of RTV silicone sealant around water holes for engines that use copper head gasket and O-rings to prevent water seepage. Place the gasket on the deck surface, with the correct side facing up.

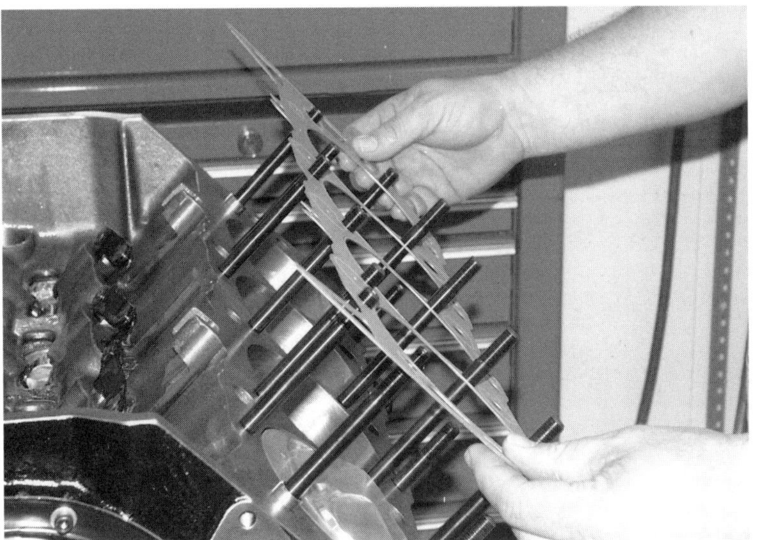

Install one cylinder head at a time. Apply a sealer, if required. Place the gasket on the deck over the alignment dowels with the correct side facing up. This is usually the side with the numbers.

If you are using head bolts and a block with blind holes (do not go through to the water jacket), apply motor oil to the threads and under the heads. If you are using head bolts in holes that do go into the water jacket, you must apply a thread sealant (special head bolt sealer or #2 Permatex) to the threads.

Carefully place the cylinder heads on the block. Make sure the heads mate with the block deck and have engaged the alignment dowels.

Apply sealer to the studs to prevent water leaks, and then install the heads. Take one more look to be sure the head gaskets are installed correctly.

If you are using studs, place the special thick washers over each stud, and thread the nuts onto the studs.

Install the washers and nuts. Be sure to use only the special thick, hardened washers supplied by the stud manufacturer.

The cylinder heads should be torqued in three approximately equal stages and in the right sequence. The middle bolts are always torqued first, working out to the end bolts.

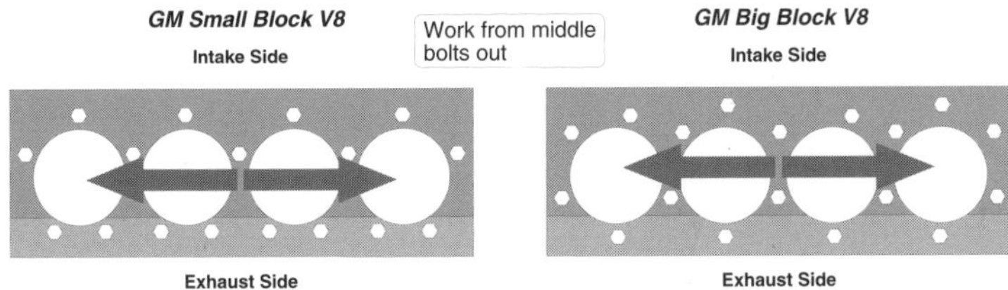

You can obtain the torque sequence from the manufacturer. All sequences begin with the middle bolts and work toward the ends.

Refer to the manufacturer's specifications for head bolt torque. Head bolts of different lengths may require a different torque specification. Begin by setting the torque wrench to about 1/3 of the final torque specification (about 20-25 lb./ft.). Use a deep well socket, and follow the torque sequence.

Pull the torque wrench smoothly to the correct tightness. Count bolts as you work to be sure you have not missed any.

This extension adapter can be used for hard-to-reach head bolts. Make sure it is in line with the torque wrench handle, and adjust the torque reading as recommended by the tool manufacturer to ensure accuracy.

Readjust the torque wrench to about 2/3 of the final value. Repeat the torque sequence. Adjust the wrench for the final torque value, and work through in the same pattern for the final torquing. Perform the same installation procedure for the other cylinder head. Re-check the torque readings on each bolt.

Step #2 - Install the Lifters, Pushrods, & Rocker Arms:

Apply racing motor oil liberally to the lifters and pushrods. Slip the lifters into the bores. If you are using roller tappets, install the lifter pairs with the connecting links. Slip the pushrods into place.

Lubricate the lifters, links, and pushrods, and slip them into place.

Install the rocker arms one at a time. Rotate the engine with a ratchet and crank turning socket until the lifter and pushrod are all the way down on the cam base circle.

WARNING! Never rotate the crankshaft on a racing engine with a breaker bar. The extreme valve spring pressure can cause it to suddenly rotate with great force.

If you are using shaft-type rockers, apply oil to the bolts, and torque them evenly to specifications. With the lifter on the base circle, perform a rough lash adjustment. Adjust the rocker until there is no lash (pushrod just contacts), then back off 1/4 turn to leave some lash.

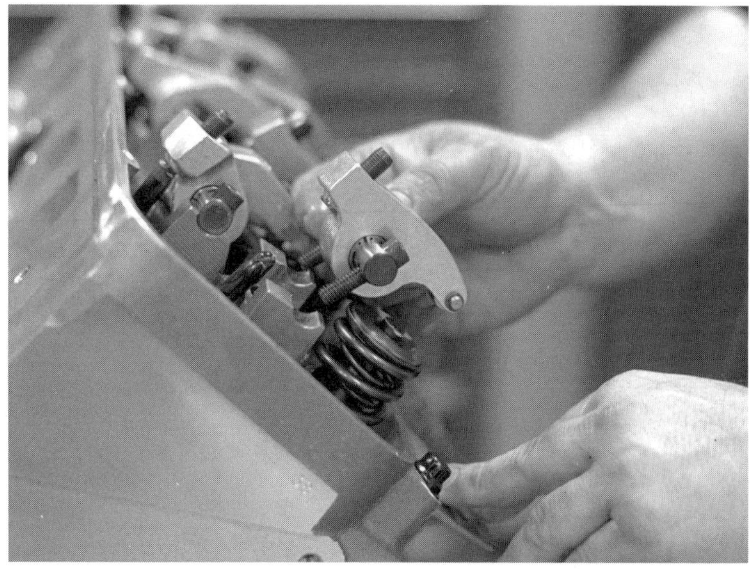

Lubricate the rocker arms, and install them.

If you don't know how to put the lifter on the cam base circle, here's a good way to do it. Crank the engine over and watch the action of the pushrods or rocker arms. Follow this simple rule to be sure the lifters are on the cam base circle when you make the lash adjustments.

Adjust the intake valve when the exhaust valve begins to open.
Adjust the exhaust valve when the intake valve is at least half closed.

The reason this rule works so well has to do with the relative timing of the intake and exhaust valves. The best time to adjust any valve is when it is near the middle of the base circle. This ensures that the lifter will not be close to the lobe.

Note in the figure below that the intake valve is centered on the base circle almost exactly at the moment that the exhaust valve begins to open. The exhaust valve is centered on the base circle almost exactly at the moment that the intake valve has closed.

= Intake Valve Operation
= Exhaust Valve Operation

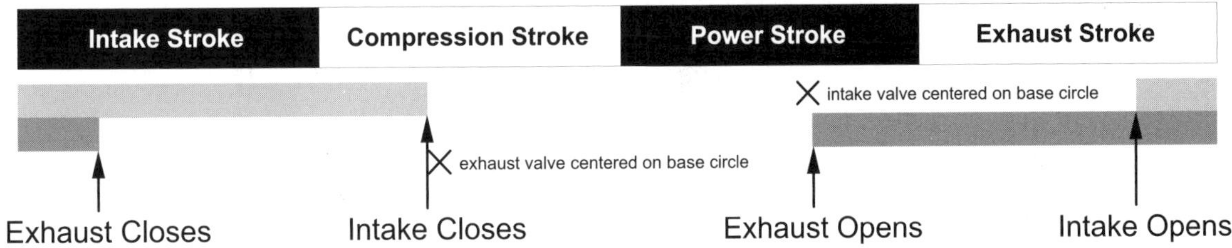

Always make your initial lash settings tight by .004" on aluminum heads. This helps compensate for the expansion of the aluminum when the head reaches operating temperature.

Set the cold valve lash .004" tighter than the cam card specs. Crank the engine over and watch the action of the valves. Set the intake lash when the exhaust valve opens. Then set the exhaust valve lash when the intake has just closed.

Step #3 - Install the Intake Manifold:

Intake manifold leaks can have a serious effect on engine performance. Test-fit the intake manifold first to be sure it has been machined correctly. Place gasket material under each side, and use a light to look down the ports or feel with a stiff wire to be sure the port alignment is correct. There must also be a small gap at the front and rear where it seals with the lifter valley of the block.

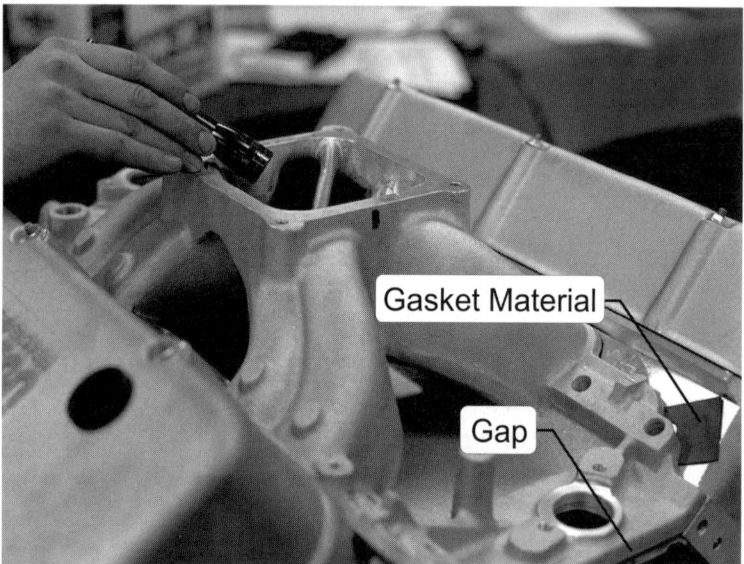

Test-fit the intake manifold to be sure it will seal correctly. Note the gasket material under the sides of the manifold and the end gap where it seals with the block. This manifold had a good fit and was ready for installation.

Several manufacturers make intake manifold gaskets that have sealant "printed" around each port (*print-seal* types). If you use this type of gasket, the sealer goes up toward the intake manifold surface. However, we prefer "cut-to-fit" gaskets that take a little more time to trim and install, but that result in a better fit.

Note that this "print-seal" gasket doesn't fit the head ports very precisely. In theory, this can disturb the intake flow characteristics of the manifold and head. We prefer "cut-to-fit' intake manifold gaskets for our engines.

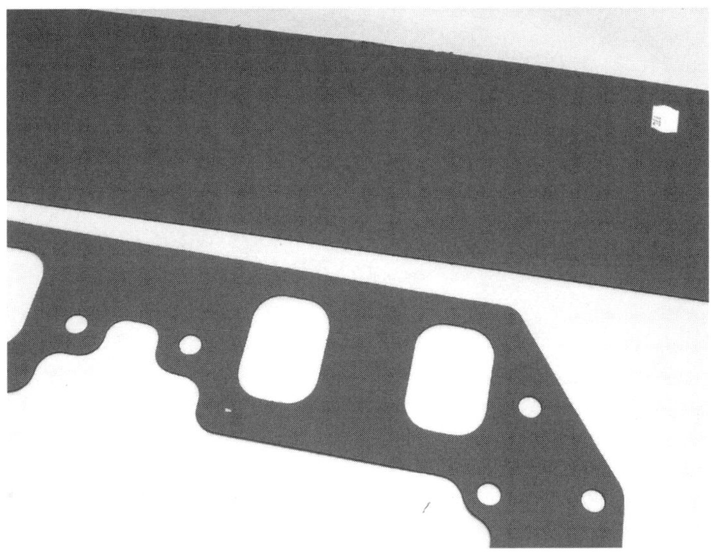

These are examples of "cut-to-fit" intake manifold gaskets. The blank style can accommodate any port size and shape. The precut version has port openings that are nearly always smaller than the heads and require minor trimming.

Follow these steps for installing cut-to-fit intake gaskets:

Step 1: Apply quick-drying contact cement to the surface of the manifold and to the manifold side of the gasket.

Step 2: Gently tap the gasket down all over the surface to spread the glue and to ensure good adhesion.

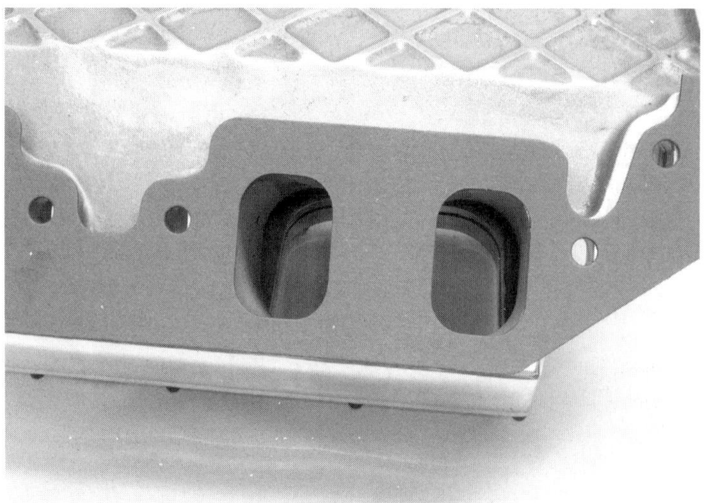

This is the installed intake gasket prior to trimming. The gasket material overhangs ports, bolt holes, and the manifold mating surfaces.

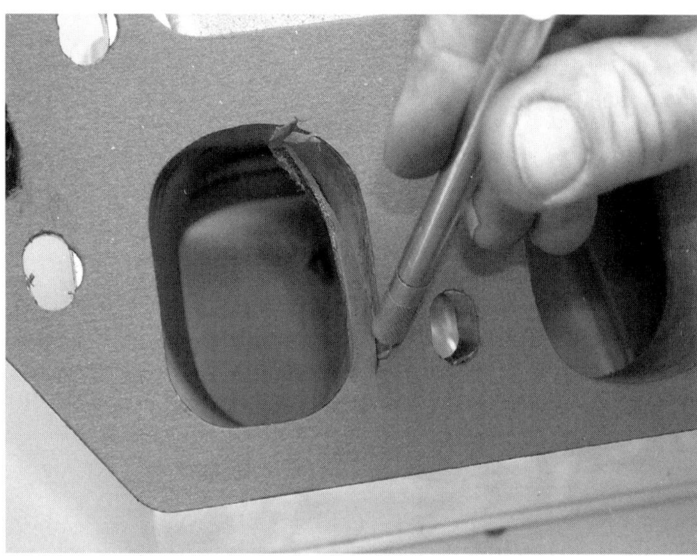

Step 3: Carefully trim the gasket to the port shape. Then trim the water jacket ports, bolt holes, end rails, and valve cover ledge. If the manifold has very large ports with very little mating surface, leave additional external gasket material around the ports so that it distorts less during installation.

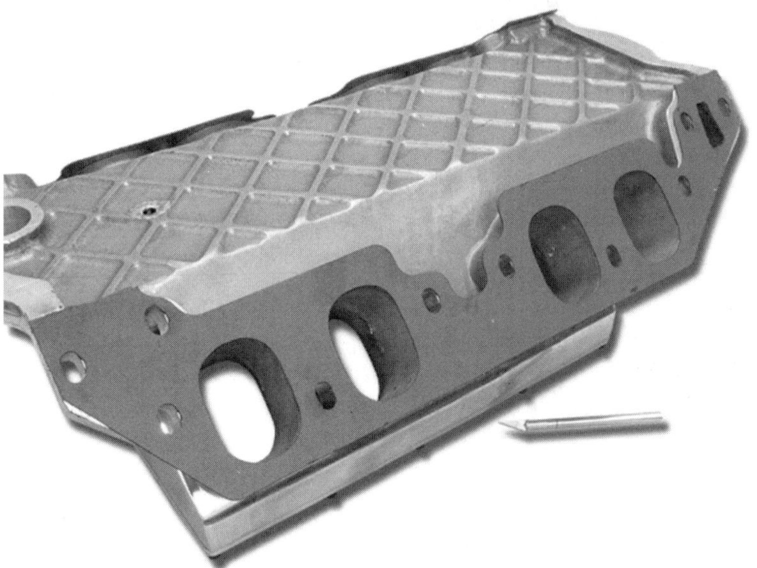

This is the completed gasket installation and trimming.

Clean the gasket mating surfaces with a solvent before you apply RTV silicone sealer. Apply a thick, consistent bead of RTV silicone sealer along the ends of the block lifter valley. If the gap is too large to seal reliably with silicone alone, we make spacers in 1/8", 3/16", and 1/4" thicknesses to take up the excess gap.

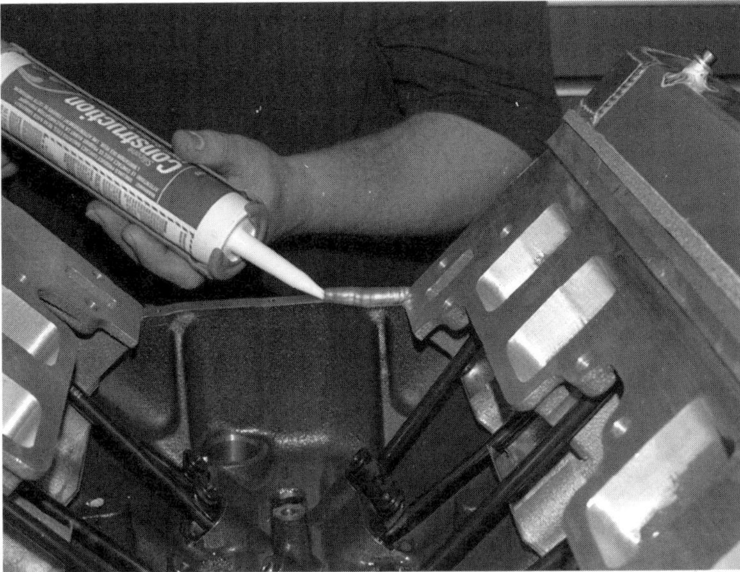

Apply a bead of RTV silicone sealer as shown here on both ends of the block lifter valley.

On drag racing applications that use a throttle stop, intake manifold vacuum can spike extremely high. This can distort the intake gasket and even pull it into the port. In these cases, it's a good idea to also put a very small bead of RTV silicone sealer around each intake port on the head. This gives the gasket adhesion to both the intake manifold and cylinder head mating surfaces.

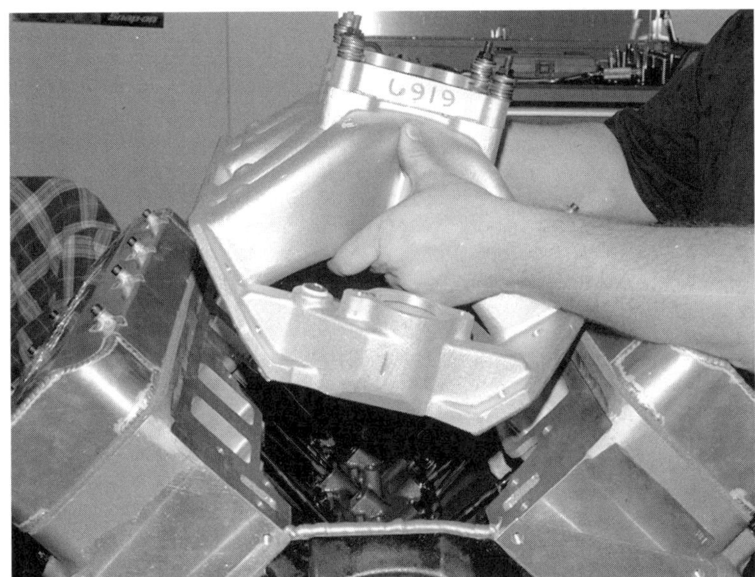

Place the manifold straight down onto the gaskets. Do not allow it to slide around.

Thread all of the bolts into the heads before you tighten any. Begin by tightening the innermost bolts on both sides, and then work toward the ends. You must repeat the tightening sequence several times before the manifold will fully compress and seal the side gaskets.

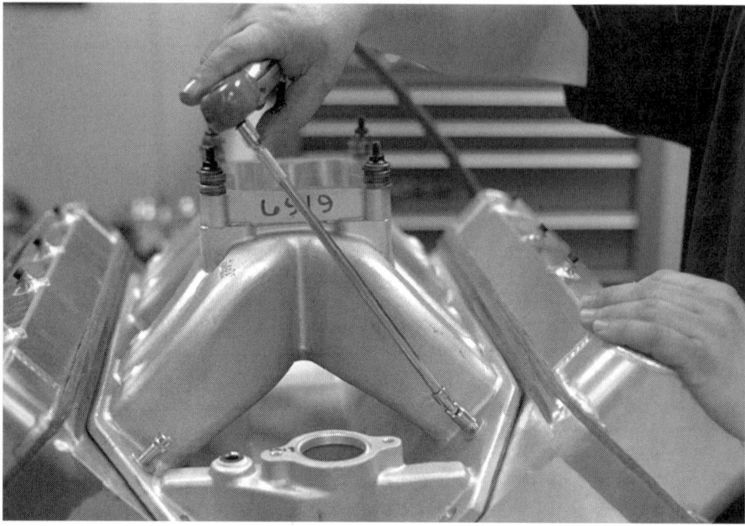

As you tighten the intake manifold bolts, work side to side from the center bolts to the ends.

Step #4 - Prime the Oil Pump (wet sump systems):

The first few moments when a racing engine starts up are the most critical. Clearances may be a little tight, and cylinder wall friction is high. An air locked oil pump will not begin to deliver oil unless the rpm's are high enough. Revving a new engine to fill the pump and passages can result in a lot of needless damage to moving engine parts.

To avoid these problems, we always prime the oil pump and oiling system. If you have a wet-sump oiling system, use a pump priming tool to spin the oil pump driveshaft. An oil pump priming tool may be purchased, or you can make your own by removing the drive gear and cutting the advance weight mechanism off the top of an old distributor.

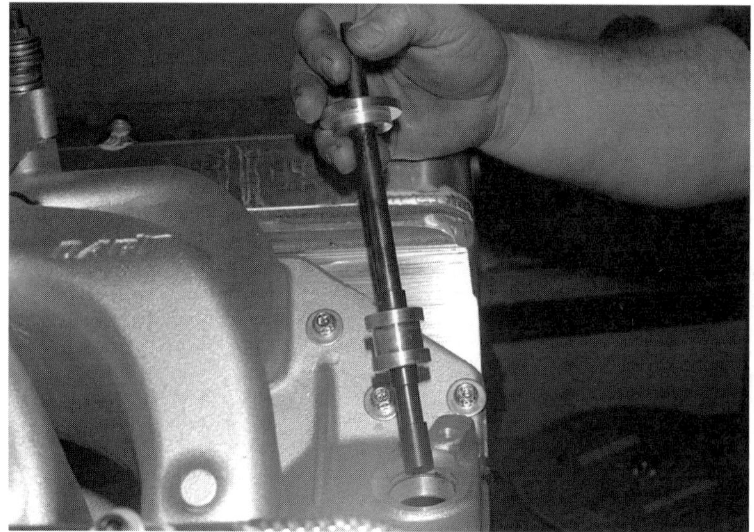

Never start a racing engine with a dry oiling system. Make or buy an oil pump priming tool that engages the oil pump driveshaft.

Attach an oil pressure gauge to a main oil gallery in the engine. This will allow you to monitor the oil pressure and detect serious problems before the engine has been started.

Locate the oil gallery plug near the back of the block. Remove the plug, and install an oil pressure gauge here.

Install the oil filter, oil pan drain plug, and racing motor oil. Refer to the oil pan manufacturer's information for the recommended oil capacity. Insert the oil pump priming tool into the distributor hole, and rotate the shaft until it engages the oil pump driveshaft.

Use an electric or pneumatic drill to spin the oil pump in a clockwise direction. Hold on tight! When the pump primes and the passages are filled with oil, the drill will try to turn suddenly.

Continue to spin the oil pump with the priming tool until you feel the resistance of the pump in the electric drill. Note the oil pressure. It should be at least 60 psi, and oil should begin to dribble from the top of the pushrods.

Monitor the engine oil pressure as you prime the oiling system. A plug that has been left out or other serious problems will show up as a lack of oil pressure.

If you have a dry sump system, you can wait until the end of the assembly procedure to install the pump and lines. The external dry sump pump can be spun with a drill before the drive belt has been installed.

With a dry-sump oiling system, the pump and lines will be installed at the end of the engine assembly procedure. Spin the pump with a drill to prime the system.

Step #5 - Install the Distributor, Plugs, & Wires:

Remove the oil pump priming tool. Rotate the crankshaft until #1 cylinder begins a compression stroke. You can identify the compression stroke by watching the action of the valves (both valves closed) or by feeling for compression at the #1 spark plug hole. Continue to rotate the crankshaft clockwise until the timing marks on the harmonic balancer indicate the correct base timing setting for your engine.

Place a gasket (and shim, if required) over the end of the distributor, and insert into the distributor hole. Choose a tower on your distributor cap that will have the #1 spark plug wire attached (usually one toward the front of the engine). Try several gear engagements until the rotor points at the #1 tower of the distributor cap and the oil pump shaft is fully engaged.

The rotor must point directly at the #1 spark plug tower when you install the distributor.

Install the distributor hold-down clamp. Leave the bolt loose enough so that the distributor body can be moved to set the spark (ignition) timing.

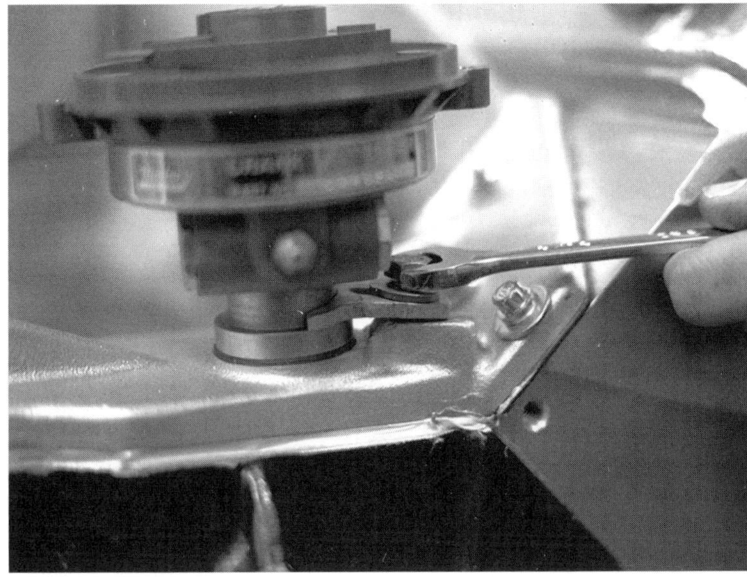

Install the distributor hold-down clamp. Leave it loose enough to allow you to set the timing.

Follow the manufacturer's recommended procedure for setting the initial spark timing. This is very important to prevent engine backfires.

Install the spark plugs, but be sure to test them all of them first. We have had customers with engine misfires that turned out to be a broken plug center electrode. Use the ohmmeter to make sure there is continuity from the terminal on top to the center electrode.

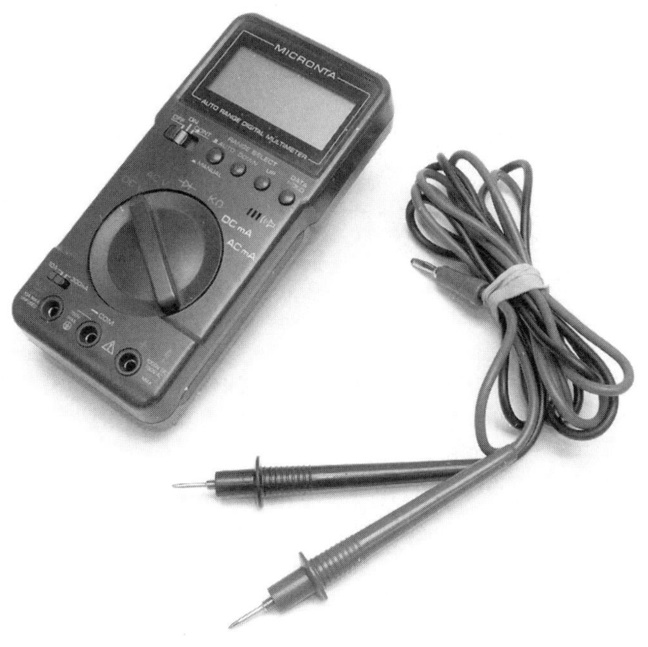

You can use an ohmmeter like this one to test spark plugs prior to installation. The same meter can be used to test the plug wires.

Replace any defective plugs, adjust the end gaps to specification, and then install them. If you have aluminum heads, it is a good idea to apply anti-seize compound to the threads. This will help discourage damage to the soft aluminum threads when they are removed. Always use a spark plug socket when installing spark plugs to avoid cracking the porcelain insulator. If you drop one on to a concrete floor, retest the center electrode to be sure it hasn't broken.

IMPORTANT! The correct torque specification for most washer-seat spark plugs is only 18-22 lb./ft. Tapered-seat plugs require only a slight snugging after they've seated. Most inexperienced racers drastically overtighten the spark plugs. This can cause damage to the threads, especially with aluminum cylinder heads.

Test and install the coil and plug wires. If you make your own wires, be sure to do a neat job to minimize ignition and electrical system problems. Use your ohmmeter to test the electrical resistance of each wire. Most spiral core racing wires should have no more than 150-1200 ohms per foot length. Make sure the wires are fully connected at both ends.

Step #6 - Install Accessory Components:

Install the remaining engine accessory components. This may include:

- Carburetor
- Crankshaft Drive Pulley
- Water Pump
- Fuel Pump
- Valve Covers
- Starter Motor
- Dry Sump Pump
- Crankcase Evacuation Pump

NOTE: The headers are not normally installed until the engine has been mounted in the race car or engine dynamometer.

The carburetor, water pump, fuel pump, and valve covers usually require gaskets. For easier installation, you can keep the gaskets in place with a small amount of a gasket adhesive, except for the carburetors.

IMPORTANT! Never apply any sealer to the base plate of a carburetor. This can cause a number of serious problems including clogged passageways and linkage binding.

We strongly recommend that you have your engine dyno tested before you install it in the car. This eliminates all the guesswork about the true horsepower output and is the best way to determine the best ignition timing and fuel mixture settings.

Congratulations! Your racing engine is fully assembled and ready for dyno testing.

Review Questions

1. Why is it so important to work in a clean shop environment when assembling a racing engine? Why is it important for your hands and tools to be clean?

2. Name some fluids & sealers that you will need when you assemble a short block.

3. Name six types of tools you will need to assemble a short block. Identify the special tools in the photo below:

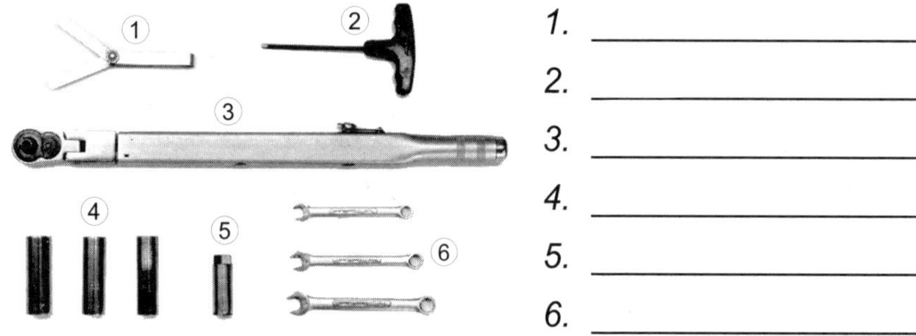

4. Why studs are better than bolts for holding down the cylinder heads? How do you keep the studs from backing out of the block when the heads are removed?

5. What type of sealer should be used on a head gasket? How can you identify which way goes up on a head gasket?

6. Describe the how to install the head bolts or nuts and washers.

7. What is the purpose of using a torque sequence when you tighten cylinder head bolts or nuts? What tools should you use to tighten the head bolts or nuts?

8. Describe the installation of the lifters and pushrods.

9. Describe the installation of the rocker arms. Describe the valve lash adjustment procedure. Why should you make the initial adjustment .006" tight?

10. How do you check the intake manifold for leaks and port alignment? What is a "print-seal" intake gasket? How do you install and trim "cut-to-fit" intake gaskets?

11. Where should you apply sealer on the intake manifold gaskets? What type of sealer should you use? What torque sequence should you use on the manifold bolts?

12. Why is it important to prime the oiling system on a racing engine? How do you determine the engine oil capacity? Why should you install an oil pressure gauge when priming the oil pump? How do you engage and spin the oil pump?

13. Describe the procedure for installing the distributor. Describe the initial timing adjustment procedure.

14. Describe how to test, gap, and install the spark plugs. Why should you use anti-seize compound on the threads if you are using aluminum heads?

15. How can you test the coil and spark plug wires? What is the normal resistance range for spiral core racing spark plug wires?

16. Name accessory components that must be installed to complete the engine assembly.

17. Why should you never use sealer on the carburetor base gaskets?

18. Explain why it is important to have your completed engine tested on a dynamometer.

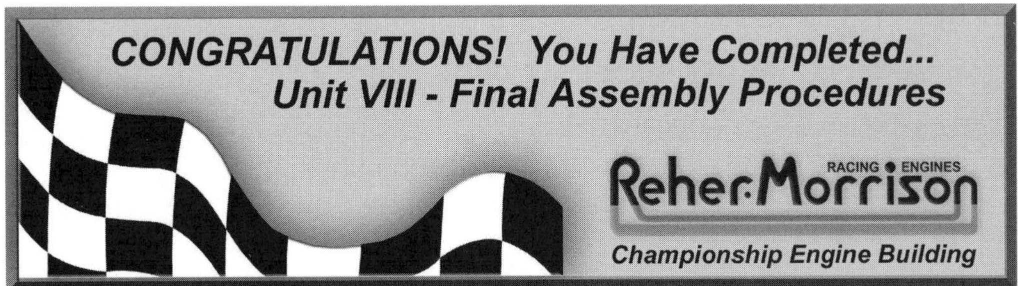

Appendix

Fractional-Decimal Conversion Chart

16ths	32nds	64ths	decimal
		1/64	.015625
	1/32	2/64	.03125
		3/64	.046875
1/16	2/32	4/64	.0625
		5/64	.078125
	3/32	6/64	.09375
		7/64	.109375
2/16	4/32	8/64	.125
		9/64	.140625
	5/32	10/64	.15625
		11/64	.171875
3/16	6/32	12/64	.1875
		13/64	.203125
	7/32	14/64	.21875
		15/64	.234375
4/16	8/32	16/64	.25
		17/64	.265625
	9/32	18//64	.28125
		19/64	.296875
5/16	10/32	20/64	.3125
		21/64	.328125
	11/32	22/64	.34375
		23/64	.359375
6/16	12/32	24/64	.375
		25/64	.390625
	13/32	26/64	.40625
		27/64	.421875
7/16	14/32	28/64	.4375
		29/64	.453125
	15/32	30/64	.46875
		31/64	.484375
8/16	16/32	32/64	.5

16ths	32nds	64ths	decimal
		33/64	.515625
	17/32	34/64	.53125
		35/64	.546875
9/16	18/32	36/64	.5625
		37/64	.578125
	19/32	38/64	.59375
		39/64	.609375
10/16	20/32	40/64	.625
		41/64	.640625
	21/32	42/64	.65625
		43/64	.671875
11/16	22/32	44/64	.6875
		45/64	.703125
	23/32	46/64	.71875
		47/64	.734375
12/16	24/32	48/64	.75
		49/64	.765625
	25/32	50/64	.78125
		51/64	.796875
13/16	26/32	52/64	.8125
		53/64	.828125
	27/32	54/64	.84375
		55/64	.859375
14/16	28/32	56/64	.875
		57/64	.890625
	29/32	58/64	.90625
		59/64	.921875
15/16	30/32	60/64	.9375
		61/64	.953125
	31/32	62/64	.96875
		63/64	.984375
16/16	32/32	64/64	1.0000

English Conversions

Volume & Weight:

1 pint(pt) = 16 fluid ounces(oz)

1 quart(qt) = 2 pints(pt)

1 quart(qt) = 32 fluid ounces(oz)

1 gallon(ga) = 4 quarts(qt)

1 gallon(ga) = 128 fluid ounces(oz)

1 gallon(ga) water = *8.4 pounds(lb)

1 gallon(ga) gasoline = *6.2 pounds(lb)

1 gallon(ga) oil = *7.0 pounds(lb)

2.77 grams of aluminum = 1 cc. volume

*approximately

Length & Area:

1 foot(ft) = 12 inches(in)

1 yard(yd) = 3 feet(ft)

1 mile(mi) = 5280 feet(ft)

1/ 8 mile(mi) = 660 feet(ft)

1/ 4 mile(mi) = 1320 feet(ft)

Other Conversions

Useful Conversions:

Length:

millimeters(mm) = inches(in) ÷ .03937

centimeters(cm) = inches(in) ÷ .3937

decimeters(dm) = inches(in) ÷ 3.937

meters(m) = inches(in) ÷ 39.37

meters(m) = feet(ft) ÷ 3.2808

meters(m) = yards(yd) ÷ 1.0936

kilometers(km) = miles(mi) ÷ .6214

Weight:

1 pound(lb) = .4536 kilograms(kg)

1 pound(lb) = 453.6 grams(gm)

1 ounce(oz) = 28.35 grams(gm)

Area & Volume:

1 fluid ounce(oz) = 29.573 milliliters(ml)

1 quart(qt) = .9461 liters(l)

1 gallon(ga) = 3.7843 liters(l)

Useful Conversions:

Length:

inches(in) = millimeters(mm) ÷ 25.4

inches(in) = centimeters(cm) ÷ 2.54

inches(in) = decimeters(dm) ÷ .254

inches(in) = meters(m) ÷ .0254

feet(ft) = millimeters(mm)) ÷ 304.8

yards(yd) = meters(m) ÷ .9144

miles(mi) = kilometers(km) ÷ 1.609

1/8 mile = .201125 kilometers(km)

1/4 mile = .40225 kilometers(km)

Weight:

ounces(oz) = grams(gm) ÷ 453.6

pounds(lb) = kilograms(kg) ÷ .4536

Area & Volume:

cubic centimeters(cc's) = cubic in. x 16.387

gallons(ga) = liters(l) × 3.7843

Formulas

Circumference:

Circle

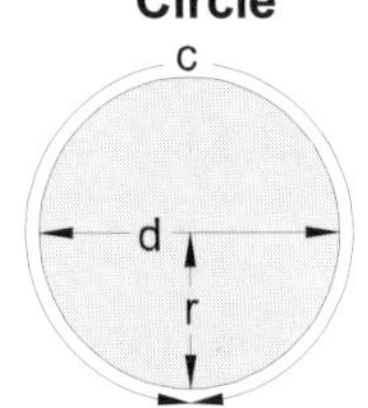

$C = \pi d \quad C = 2\pi r$

Ellipse

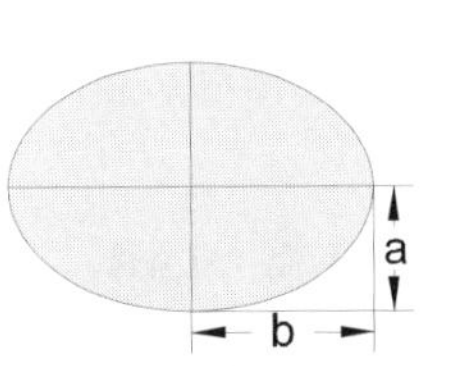

$C = \pi\sqrt{2(a^2 + b^2)}$

Area:

Circle

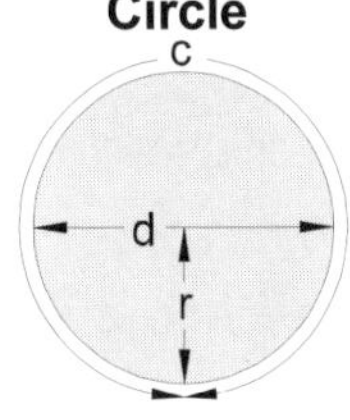

$A = \pi r^2 \quad A = \frac{\pi d^2}{4}$

Ellipse

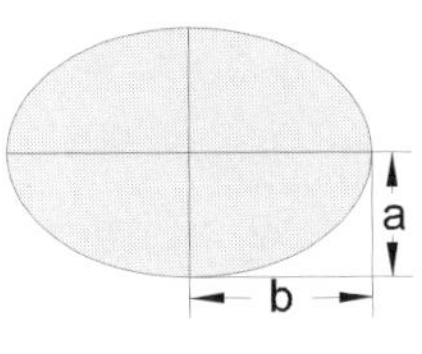

$A = \pi ab$

$\pi = 3.14159$

Area:

Triangle

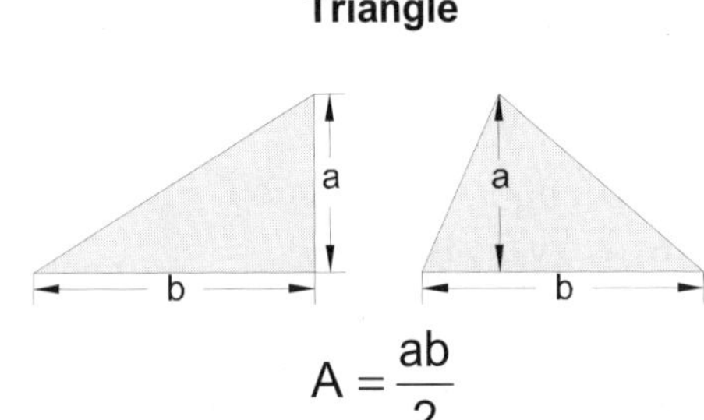

$A = \frac{ab}{2}$

Volume of Cylinder:

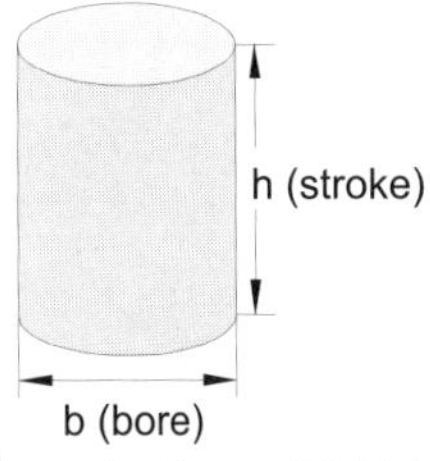

$V = bore^2 \times stroke \times .7854$

Glossary

***4-stroke cycle* -** A repeating series of these four events—intake, compression, power and exhaust.

***ABDC* -** An acronym for "after bottom dead center" (see bottom dead center).

***ATDC* -** An acronym for "after top dead center" (see top dead center).

***babbitt* -** A mixture of soft metals (usually tin, lead, and antimony) that is used as a coating for engine bearing inserts.

***BBDC* -** An acronym for "before bottom dead center" (see bottom dead center).

***BDC* -** An acronym for "bottom dead center". This is the point of crankshaft rotation when the piston is at its lowest.

***bearing crush* -** A characteristic of bearing inserts in which the bearing extends beyond the parting line of cap. When the cap is bolted in place, the bearing "crushes" into the outside diameter of the bore to prevent it from spinning.

***blow-by* -** The gases that leak past the piston rings into the crankcase on compression, power, and exhaust strokes.

***bottom dead center (BDC)* -** The point of crankshaft rotation when the piston is at its lowest.

***boundary layer* -** The thin layer of gas in contact with the port surfaces that moves much more slowly than the other gases in the port.

***breathing efficiency* -** The ease with which an engine or engine component can flow gases (see volumetric efficiency).

***BTDC* -** An acronym for "before top dead center" (see top dead center).

***cam card* -** A handy quick-reference specification card that is included with a camshaft at the time of purchase.

***cam sprocket* -** The driven sprocket on the camshaft of an engine. A belt or chain connects this sprocket to a drive sprocket on the crankshaft.

***camshaft* -** The shaft that contains all the lobes that operate the lifters and engine valves.

***canted valve (cylinder head)* -** See "splayed valve".

***carbon dioxide* -** A colorless, odorless gas that is a primary component of exhaust gas.

***carburetor* -** A device that mixes and meters air and fuel to the engine.

***centistokes* -** A sensitive measurement scale that is sometimes used to indicate the viscosity (thickness) of very thin synthetic motor oils.

***chamfer* -** An angled edge, or bevel, around the edge of an engine part.

***checking depth* –** A standard piston depth below the block deck surface that allows the builder to accurately determine TDC (Top Dead Center).

***checking height* -** A standard height of a lifter above the low point (cam base circle) that is used to accurately determine camshaft lobe centers and locations.

***CID* -** An acronym for cubic inch displacement (see engine displacement).

***companion cylinders* -** Engine cylinders with pistons that move in unison.

***compression dome* -** A raised portion of the piston deck that increases the static compression ratio of the engine.

compression ratio **-** See static compression ratio.

compression stroke **-** Part of the 4-stroke engine cycle, the stroke in which the piston moves up and increases the pressure of the air/fuel mixture.

connecting rod **-** The rod that joins the piston to the crankshaft.

core plugs **-** The plugs that seal holes left in a block or head after casting. Engine block core plugs are often called "freeze plugs".

core shift **-** A manufacturing defect in which the internal mold was shifted in relationship to the external mold. Core shift causes inconsistent interior wall thicknesses.

crank sprocket **-** The camshaft drive sprocket located on the front of the engine crankshaft.

crankcase **-** The open area in the lower part of an engine block & oil pan where the crankshaft and rods operate.

cylinder head **-** A major engine component that contains the combustion chambers, valves, and valve springs.

degree wheel **-** A wheel that is marked in single crankshaft rotational degree increments.

detonation **-** An explosive combustion process that is harmful to an engine.

dial caliper **-** A precision measuring instrument with jaws and an indicating dial that can measure inside and outside dimensions of parts or component depth. Most dial calipers have an accuracy of .001 inch.

dial indicator **-** A precision measuring instrument with an indicating dial that measures linear distance or depth.

duration (camshaft) **-** The time measured in degrees of crankshaft rotation that an engine valve is open.

dynamic compression **-** The amount of pressure in the cylinders created by a running engine on compression strokes.

dynamometer **-** A piece of equipment that is used to measure the power output of an engine.

engine displacement **-** The combined volumes of all the cylinders of an engine. Racing engine displacement is usually expressed in CID (cubic inch displacement).

exhaust stroke **-** Part of the 4-stroke engine cycle, the stroke in which the waste gases left over from the power stroke are expelled from the cylinder.

external balancing **-** A type of engine balancing in which some of the weight is outside of the engine on the flywheel and harmonic balancer.

fatigue failure **-** A type of metal breakage that occurs when the metal is flexed repeatedly.

feeler gauge **-** A measuring device that consists of multiple leafs with varying known thicknesses. A feeler gauge is often used when measuring piston ring vertical clearance and setting valve lash.

ferrous **-** Containing iron.

fillet radius **-** A rounded (radiused) corner of a part between two surfaces on different planes. Crankshaft journals have a fillet radius on both sides of the journals where they meet the throw or counterweight to discourage the formation of cracks.

firing order **-** The sequence of power strokes in an engine.

flex fan **-** A type of engine cooling fan with flexible blades that flatten at high rpm's. A flex fan improves performance by reducing the drag on a racing engine.

flow bench **-** A piece of equipment that is used to test the flow efficiency of cylinder heads, intake manifolds, exhaust headers, or other engine components.

flywheel **-** A heavy wheel bolted to the rear of the crankshaft that smoothes the motion of the crankshaft. The flywheel also provides a friction surface for a clutch system and an engagement gear for the starter motor.

forged **-** Hammered into shape under extreme pressure and/or heat.

gross valve lift **-** The calculated valve lift based on the height of the lobes and the rocker arm ratio (see net valve lift).

harmonic balancer **-** A flywheel-like device that is attached to the front of the crankshaft. The harmonic balancer smoothes crankshaft torsional vibrations and provides a mounting surface for accessory drive pulleys.

honing **-** A process of smoothing the interior surface of a cylinder or bore with abrasive stones that spin and reciprocate. Honing machines are usually set to leave a visible crosshatch pattern of fine scratches in the surface.

hot tank **-** A container with a heated chemical bath that dissolves organic materials from dirty engine parts.

hydro-dynamic wedge **-** A principle that causes lubricating oil or other fluids to flow between two surfaces to separate them and reduce friction.

imbedability **-** A property of soft (babbitted) engine bearings that allows dirt and particles to sink into the surface to reduce scratching problems.

inside micrometer **-** A precision measuring tool that can be used to determine the diameter of a bore.

intake manifold **-** The part with a group of passageways that connect the intake ports on the cylinder heads to the carburetor or other air/fuel delivery device.

intake stroke **-** Part of the 4-stroke engine cycle, the stroke in which the air/fuel mixture is drawn into the cylinder as the piston moves down.

internal balancing **-** A type of engine balancing in which all of the counterweights are contained on the crankshaft inside the engine.

ISO octane **-** A particular type of hydrocarbon chemical that is used as a standard for measuring the anti-knock characteristics of a fuel (see octane).

journals **-** The machined round bearing surfaces of a crankshaft or camshaft. The crankshaft spins on main journals and has offset rod journals.

keepers **-** The small tapered pieces that connect the valve stem to the retainer. Keepers are sometimes called "split locks".

keyway **-** A slot in a part that creates an alignment with another part that contains the woodruff or straight key.

laminar (flow) **-** The flow of gases in smooth, consistent layers (see turbulence).

lash **-** The clearance or looseness between operating engine parts. Valve lash is measured between the tip of the rocker arm and the top of the valve stem.

lean (mixture) **-** A condition in which there is too little fuel for the amount of air in the cylinder for optimal combustion (see rich mixture).

***lifter* -** A cylindrical metal part that rides on the cam lobes to operate the pushrods in an engine.

***lobes* -** The offset "lumps" that push the lifters up on a camshaft.

***Magnaflux®* -** A process using magnetism and a liquid containing iron particles that makes cracks in ferrous materials more visible.

***main journals* -** The round machined surfaces on which the crankshaft spins.

***manometer* -** A tube filled with a liquid (usually water) that is used on a flow bench to measure pressure.

***monopropellant* -** A fuel that requires no additional oxygen with which to burn completely. Under certain conditions of pressure and temperature, nitromethane is considered a monopropellant.

***naturally aspirated* -** A type of engine that draws only the outside air into the cylinders without the benefit of a supercharger or nitrous oxide injection system.

***nitrous oxide* -** An oxygen rich gas that can be injected into a racing engine along with additional fuel as a means of making more power.

***octane* -** A rating that expresses the ability of a fuel to resist knocking, detonation, and pre-ignition. Racing engines require high octane fuels to run properly.

***oil gallery* -** A passageway for oil through the engine block.

***oxygenates* -** Chemicals that contain oxygen. Oxygenates are sometimes used as fuel additives to allow more fuel to be burned in the cylinders. This increases power output.

***parasitic losses* -** Unwanted sources of drag on the engine that reduce power output.

***parting line* -** The location on a component where a cap separates to allow the installation of a bearing or shaft. The parting line is on or near the bore diameter.

***pin bore* -** The bore for the wrist pin in either a piston or connecting rod.

***piston stop* -** A metal bar that bolts across the block deck surface to create a mechanical stop for piston travel. Some builders use a piston stop when adjusting a degree wheel to TDC (Top Dead Center).

***plasma/moly* -** A very hard coating that is applied to the surface of some racing piston compression rings.

***plenum* -** An open area for gas expansion, usually in the intake manifold.

***power stroke* -** Part of the 4-stroke engine cycle, the stroke in which pressure from burning gases pushes the piston down with force.

***pre-ignition* -** An undesirable condition in an engine in which the fuel is ignited by some heat source before the spark plug has fired.

***PSI* -** Acronym for "pounds per square inch", a common English unit of pressure.

***pushrod* -** A hollow tube that delivers the motion of the lifters to the rocker arms.

***reciprocating motion* -** Up and down motion.

***retainers* -** The round parts that connect and center the valve springs.

***reversion* -** A reversal in the normal direction of the flow of gases in an engine.

***rich (mixture)* -** A condition in which there is too much fuel for the amount of air in the cylinder for optimal combustion (see lean mixture).

***ring ridge* -** An overhanging ledge at the top of a cylinder caused by the wear of sliding piston rings.

***ring seal* -** The degree to which a (piston) ring seals the piston to cylinder.

***rocker arm* -** A lever-like device that reverses the motion of the pushrod and pushes the engine valves open.

***rocker arm ratio* -** The distance from the tip of the rocker arm to the pivot divided by the distance from the pivot to the pushrod cup.

***rocker arms* -** The levers that reverse the motion of the pushrods to open the engine valves.

***rod angularity* -** An expression of the angular change that a connecting rod goes through in operation.

***rod journals* -** The round machined throws of a crankshaft to which the connecting rods attach.

***rotary motion* -** Circular motion.

***short block* -** The lower engine assembly including the engine block, crankshaft, camshaft & cam drive assembly, pistons, and connecting rods.

***sonic testing* -** A test that uses sound waves to measure the thickness of the cylinder walls in a number of locations. Sonic testing can reveal block core shift.

***splayed valve (cylinder head)* -** A cylinder head design, also called canted valve, that has the intake and exhaust valves tilted and different angles.

***split locks* -** (see keepers)

***spread* -** A characteristic of an engine bearing insert in which it is spread wider than the bore. Friction from bearing spread causes the bearing to remain in place until the cap can be attached.

***static compression ratio* -** A calculation of compression that is expressed as a ratio to one. Example 14.5:1 (fourteen point five to one).

***stoichiometric (mixture)* -** The ideal mixture of air and fuel for the most efficient combustion process.

***stress risers* -** Small surface imperfections or sharp corners from which a crack may develop.

***stroker (motor)* -** An engine with an unusually long stroke.

supercharger - A belt-driven device that increases engine horsepower by compressing the incoming air/fuel mixture.

***synthetic* -** A material that is man-made.

***TDC* -** An acronym for "top dead center". This is the point of crankshaft rotation when the piston is at its highest.

***throws (crankshaft)* -** The offset rod journals of a crankshaft.

***thrust* -** Linear (in & out) movement of a shaft along its bearings.

***thrust plate* -** A bolt-on metal plate that limits the thrust movement of a shaft.

***TIG welding* -** An acronym for "tungsten inert gas" welding. In this process, the electric arc is shielded from the atmosphere with a cloud of an inert (non-reactive) gas such as argon.

timing belt **-** A cogged rubber belt that is used on some racing engines to drive the camshaft sprocket (gear).

top dead center (TDC) **-** The point of crankshaft rotation when the piston is at its highest.

torque **-** A twisting force.

torsional vibration **-** A rapid twisting and un-twisting that can damage crankshafts, camshafts, and other engine components.

turbulence **-** Disorderly flow (see laminar flow).

vacuum **-** A pressure level that is lower than the surrounding atmosphere.

valve float **-** An unwanted condition in which the valve fails to close at the correct time.

valve job **-** A procedure in which the valve faces and seats are re-machined for a better seal. It also includes the testing and adjustment of spring height and pressure and the re-machining or installation of new valve guides and seals.

valve lash **-** The clearance between the tip of the rocker arm and the valve stem.

valve lift **-** The height to which a valve moves off the valve seat.

valve overlap **-** The time when both the intake and exhaust valves are open at the same time. Valve overlap occurs at the end of an exhaust stroke and the beginning of an intake stroke.

valve relief **-** A machined recess, usually in the top of a piston, that increases the clearance with the head of a valve.

valve seat **-** The machined surfaces of the cylinder head that seal with the valve. The valve seat in aluminum heads is always a hardened steel insert.

valve springs **-** The springs that keep the valves in a normally closed position.

valve train **-** The series of engine components that open and close the valves. The valve train consists of the valves, springs, attaching hardware, rocker arms, pushrods, lifters, camshaft, and cam drive mechanism.

velocity **-** In general terms, speed, but with a particular direction.

viscosity **-** The thickness of a fluid.

volumetric efficiency **-** The actual flow into the engine divided by the engine displacement. This provides a numerical way to express the ease with which gases flow through an engine. Engines with relatively high volumetric efficiency usually have a higher output than do engines of the same design with a lower volumetric efficiency.

vortices **-** Small, circular flow paths.

windage **-** A mixture of air, blow-by gases, and oil droplets that are whipped together as a mist in the engine crankcase.

woodruff key **-** A crescent shaped metal block that fits into a slot. The woodruff key slides through a keyway in another part to create a particular alignment or to prevent unwanted part rotation.

wrist pin **-** The hollow machined pin that connects the piston to the rod.

Zyglo® **-** A process of crack detection using a special dye and light that is commonly used on non-ferrous materials like aluminum.

Index